Everything You've
Ever Done

Dave and Amelia

Everything You've Ever Done

Amelia Marie Whalen

Ambos Books

Tucson

ISBN: 978-1-946109-92-7

Library of Congress Control Number: 2017945557

To Dave Zagorski

Thank you for being a magnificent creator and for living fearlessly. Thank you for showing me what's really going on and teaching me unconditional love. I appreciate everything you've ever done for me.

Table of Contents

Part One

Dragonfly

"He's been hanging out with me all day," Dave said with a nod to the dragonfly perched on his shoulder. He was bare-chested and his cut-off jeans hung so low on his skinny hips it was obvious he wasn't wearing underwear. The sun had gone down an hour earlier. Illumination came from red and yellow party lights dangling from the trees.

We stood in timeless silence: Dave watching the dragonfly, me watching Dave. He was deeply, evenly tanned. It was mid-August, and I figured he must have spent a lot of time outside with his shirt off that summer.

"His wings are generating light," Dave said, his eyes wide and staring at the bug as it crawled down his arm. "You're a light generator. Do you see that?"

He didn't look up from his arm and I couldn't tell if he was talking to the bug or to me. I stepped in and looked closer at the dragonfly. It stopped moving when it reached the spot on Dave's arm where the clock face would be if he were wearing a wristwatch. He slowly turned to face me and raised his arm so the bug sat between us at eye level. We stood barefoot, only inches apart, and I noticed we were almost exactly the same height. I raised my arm so my fingertips touched Dave's and my stance matched his.

For some reason, in that moment, I thought of my mom. She'd been dead thirteen years, and I'd mostly stopped thinking about her. When she did come to mind, it felt more like a visitation than a memory. When she entered my mind, it wasn't a choice I was making, more an act of her will.

So, there she was, suddenly present. I felt her standing in the party crowd Dave and I were on the edge of. My mom had been a gorgeous, outgoing, and popular girl. She was twenty-four when she died, so eternally a hipster, still just the right age to be hanging out at the house party with all the other artists and hippies and punks.

"Let's go swimming," Dave said. My thoughts interrupted, I followed him to the pool, forgetting my mom and the dragonfly. He pushed his cut-offs down his body without unbuttoning them. In the not-quite-total darkness, backlit from a yellow floodlight aimed at the water, he stood naked and facing me.

I strained to see his eyes in the shadowy darkness as I pulled off my clothes. Dave took my hand, and we stepped to the pool and jumped. As my feet left the ground, time slowed and energy swirled. With a momentary flash of concern, I pictured the dragonfly resting on Dave's skin, and then with a wash of relief I imagined it flying away. I visualized my mom, too, flying—no, swimming—through the air like it was water.

My mom and I loved to swim together. When I was small, in the summers after she died, I believed she was alive under the water in my grandparents' swimming pool. In my mind, the pool connected to the ocean that connected to the Earth's core that connected to an infinite universe. I'd dream of diving into the pool, deeper and deeper, until I found her. Together, we would swim to a radiant light above the water's surface.

In my first memories, it's clear everything is connected and beyond human understanding, like the pool to the ocean to the universe.

Dave and I smacked the cool water and our hands released. With my eyes open in the underwater darkness, I sank until my bare ass bounced on the floor of the pool and then floated back up toward the yellow light glimmering above the water's surface.

I've always had an airplane-about-to-take-a-nosedive understanding of my life and the world around me. Part of that understanding, though, is the airplane doesn't explode in a fiery crash. Instead, it rights itself just before impact and glides into the swimming pool.

Dreams and visions matter. Relationships and experiences are cosmically intertwined in a flux of time and space. Dave's dragonfly *was* generating light. And so was I. He was talking to us both.

That night was important, but there was never an official start to our relationship.

We met when I was twenty and Dave was twenty-four. We knew each other through a handful of mutual friends who met up to see live music or party. That night Dave's band, Giant Ray Soda, headlined a four-band lineup at a house party in the suburbs. He'd been chomping on psychedelic mushrooms and palling around with the dragonfly all day.

The next morning, after partying all night, he asked me, in an old-fashioned, gentlemanly way, "Would you like to rendezvous with me sometime?"

Of course I wanted to rendezvous with Dave. He was adorable and hilarious. He was charismatic and energetic, a contagious force to those around him. Dave was as cool as they come. And I sensed he was genuine and kind.

When he called me a couple weeks later, I suggested we look at the full moon from the top of Cohoes Falls.

That summer, I'd been riding my mountain bike on the trails that overlooked this enormous waterfall. I knew the water level was low enough that accessing the top of falls would be easy.

Dave picked me up in his twelve-year-old Toyota Corolla. The car was sexy and cool. It was a red five-speed sport model, and it was beat up.

I tried not to step or sit on cassette tapes, pictures, unopened mail, and guitar effects pedals as I maneuvered into the passenger seat.

Dave sped up the highway, with the sunroof and windows open and the music cranked at high volume.

Dave reached over to the pile of stuff at my feet. While he kept his eyes on the road, he fingered through the mess until he grabbed hold of an envelope stuffed with photographs. He pulled the stack of photos from the envelope, and using both hands, held the pictures up one-by-one. He used his knee to steer the car.

"This is Richard and me busking on the Charles Bridge in Prague," Dave said. "It was crazy. We made more money than doctors do there."

I looked between the pictures and the road. Dave focused on the pictures as he recapped the short time he lived in Prague. I was interested, but also concerned about staying on the highway we were blasting over at seventy mph.

"This is the bar around the corner from Richard's place," Dave said. "The beer's so good there. Czech pilsners are my favorite. A bottle was only thirty cents!"

"Wow. That's cool. Um, hey, this is our exit," I offered, hoping Dave would ditch the pictures and return to driving.

I directed Dave through the desolate city of Cohoes. Cohoes once bustled as an industrial mill town. Its heyday was in the early 1900s.

As Dave drove, I looked around at the Dutch style row houses and factories, mostly abandoned. Cohoes was a ghost town.

We parked on a city street, next to a barbed-wire-topped chain link fence that held back a tangle of thick brush. We squeezed through a cut in the fence and followed an overgrown trail through weeds and bushes.

Stepping from the grass to the rocky riverbed was like stepping onto the moon. The smooth black rock was studded with deep water-filled potholes. As the sun set, shadows fell eerily across the uneven rock.

"It's cool to jump in some of these deeper potholes," I said. "Some of the holes are so deep, you can't touch the bottom."

Dave surveyed the waterfall's rock bed. Every spring, a massive amount of shooting water covers it. Now, only a few streams trickled over it.

"Do we know for sure the water won't start up?" he asked.

"We're fine unless they open the dam," I said. "And they blow a whistle if they do that. Well, they almost always remember to."

Dave looked upstream, considering, then looked at me.

"OK. I'm following you."

We headed out onto the falls.

"Dave, I was only teasing you about the dam. The water's low because it's been so dry."

"Really?" Dave said. "Well, it seemed worth it!"

We stopped at the exact center of the falls. There was just enough light left in the evening sky to get a clear view across the 1,000-foot span of the falls and ninety feet down to the base.

Abandoned brick mills loomed just downstream. The Erie Canal branched off to the right, a black gouge surrounded by ancient houses.

Deep green trees crowded the left bank. It looked cool and dark and mysterious, probably exactly how it looked when the first people arrived here.

"They found a mastodon skeleton underneath the falls," I said. "They think he waded into the water up here, then got sucked over."

"Must've been a wild ride while it lasted," Dave said.

We sat until only the moon glow lit the sky. I was psyched to be with such a gorgeous and vivacious boy. Dave had classic rocker boy looks: wild, shaggy hair, chiseled features, and a wiry physique. His lips were full and luscious. His eyes danced with life. They changed color, reflecting his shirt or his surroundings. Now, they glimmered silvery-grey in the moonlight.

A shadow beneath his left eye caught my attention. I reached out and ran my fingertip over it. He had a deep scar there, on his cheekbone, a groove that punctuated his eye with a sharp underline.

"A gift from my brother," he said. "He pushed me into the coffee table when I was six."

"That's the day you became a rocker, Dave," I said. "After that, you had no choice. That scar is pure rock-n-roll!"

We lost the path on the walk back to Dave's car, and he used his pocketknife to cut through thorny vines as we bushwhacked. It impressed me that supercool, world traveling, artistic Dave carried a knife and was ready for adventure.

Days later, he invited me to go with him to Manhattan to buy a used sixteen-track reel-to-reel analog tape recorder for Analog Underground, his recording studio.

Dave drove us south to the city—sunroof open, music blasting. Instead of paying to park near the music store, Dave found a free spot on a side street, several long city blocks away.

Eyes wide, I stood back as Dave paid for the complicated and fragile looking recorder, hoping it wasn't as heavy as it looked. It was. It was easily a hundred pounds. Together, we carried the unwieldy machine back to Dave's car. It was too cumbersome to set down, so we shifted its weight between us as we waited in tight crowds of New-York-City-diverse people to cross intersections. Horns blasted, people shouted, smells from hot dog and gyro carts wafted. My arms burned and my knees wobbled. Each time my grip slipped or my balance wavered, I looked at smiling, unfazed Dave and carried on.

Most of my suggestions for ways to spend our time together were adventure-based. I wanted to hike, rock climb, and camp. Most of Dave's ideas for a good time were art-based. He wanted to play his music for me, or he'd encourage me to help with projects like upholstering a recording gear rack with furry cow-spotted fabric.

When Dave and I first started dating, he'd study my bookcases, browsing as if he was in a library.

"Can I borrow this one?" Dave asked while paging through Charles Bukowski's novel *Women*.

"Sure. You like Bukowski too?" I replied.

"I do now! This is some dark shit. And funny."

As we got to know each other, Dave and I traded books and music. So much of what we loved overlapped, but every once in a while we introduced one another to what would become a new favorite. I gave him Bukowski; he gave me Che Guevara. He gave me *Juxtapoz Art & Culture Magazine*; I gave him indie comics by James Kochalka and Craig Thompson. I gave him Fugazi; he gave me Pavement.

Our friends merged and overlapped, too. In this pre-Facebook era, we found ourselves at the center of connected circles of people with similar passions and interests.

Dave and I both loved living in Albany, New York's capital. A small brick city on the banks of the Hudson River, Albany made a great home base. It's less than a hundred miles from world-class rock climbing—the Adirondacks to the north and the Gunks to the south. New York City, Montreal, and Boston are all less than a day's drive away.

Because of its location at the crossroads of these big cities, and because it's full of college kids, it's a great town for music. Many bands stopped here on their way to somewhere else. Our nights were full of good music, and the streets were full of cafes, bookstores, movie houses, and ethnic eateries that stayed open late, spilling warm light onto the gritty sidewalks.

Watching over it all was Nipper, Albany's icon, a black and white dog thirty feet tall and perched on a four-story building. RCA abandoned this fiberglass mascot decades ago when they moved out of downtown, but we all adopted him as our own. His head tilted as he gazed down on us, as if he was forever trying to understand our antics.

Dave loved to take off to Manhattan to party with friends and check out live music. I made frequent trips to the Adirondacks or the Gunks to climb. We were both on the move. We were both passionate about—almost obsessed with—our favorite pastimes. Dave reworked songs the way I reworked rock climbing routes.

I went rock climbing for the first time with my dad the year I was thirteen and he was thirty-two. He had been mostly absent from my life since around the time my mom died, but moved back to Albany when I was twelve. He returned as an untamed adventurer instead of a wild partier. My dad liked to pursue adventures that held greater and greater intensity. Hiking and skiing weren't always exciting enough for him, so he tried skydiving, white water rafting, and rock climbing.

We spent time together on the weekends, and during these visits he'd take me on wild adventures. I thought my dad was so cool. I admired his know-how and adventurous spirit. I was so glad to have him back in my life, I didn't hesitate to follow him on hard and scary expeditions.

Rock climbing came naturally to me. I immediately understood and trusted the safety system—the web of rope, harness, and hardware that keeps you from plummeting to earth if you fall. I became fascinated with the intricacies of rock, how climbable the thin seams and tiny edges that were invisible from the ground could be. On Mondays after adventures with my dad, back at junior high school, I entertained my rapt friends with tales of scaling rock faces deep in the woods. I was a thirteen-year-old badass. While my peers were going to the mall, I was defying death in the wilderness.

By the time I met Dave, climbing was a defining part of my life. It was a way of being: I connected deeply to nature and rock. My spirit grew from the mind-body connection rock climbing granted me. My life goals were inspired by the hedonistic allure of adventure. I planned my life to allow more and more time to explore rock, which challenged my mind and body and enhanced my connection with Earth.

Dave and I made our own schedules. We were each raised by entrepreneurs and came from nontraditional families that lived just outside of normal. We were both college dropouts, making money in creative ways without full-time jobs.

Dave recorded local bands at Analog Underground. He heard subtleties of sound with a superhuman sense, and he was a master of recording and sound equipment.

He committed to each of the bands he recorded. He asked for payment on a sliding scale, and if a band was broke but talented, that meant he worked for free.

I operated my own graphic design and screen printing company. I made t-shirts for bands, schools, and local businesses with equipment I'd set up in a room at my dad's auto repair shop.

Dave convinced his older brother and dad to back him in starting a candle company. Besides his keen ear, Dave's other senses were optimally tuned. He loved smells. He took "stop and smell the roses" to a new level.

One day, I visited Dave at his candle shop. Soon after I arrived, an elderly lady entered the shop, looking hesitant. Dave made her feel at home. He took her hand as he guided her through shelves of colorful scented candles.

After listening to what she wanted, he selected a jar candle. He removed the cover, closed his eyes, and inhaled. With a huge grin, he handed the candle to the lady.

"It's lilac. *Our best seller.* Go ahead, give it a good whiff!" Dave urged. "Here, let's light it up! I really want you to smell this." He was a proud, confident businessman. He made the best candles, and he knew it.

Dave didn't do anything he couldn't stand behind. He didn't have a job just to make money. He chose jobs because he believed in the work. Building candles was art to Dave. Once, after he mixed scented oils into an original blend he called "rain," he sat with his eyes closed, breathing in the new candle smell.

"This smells blue. Light blue. But *bright* light blue. I see it; now can I create it with the dyes I have? I may have to order some new dye..." he pondered. Dave's "rain"—with its clean scent and perfectly suited blue coloring—became a best seller too.

Dave relished making art tangible. As he captured scent in a jar, he captured sound on tape.

In these early days, we made only occasional confessions about our feelings.

"Sheila told me I'd need to lace up my running shoes to keep up with you," Dave confided in me.

Sheila was like a second mother to Dave. Since junior high, he'd spent more time at her house than at his own. Her youngest son, Mark, was Dave's best friend. Her older boys, Richard and Dan, were like brothers to Dave. Sheila's mother, Granny, lived with the family and loved Dave along with her grandsons.

Sheila knew Dave well. I was surprised—and pleased—that she thought Dave would have to keep up with *me*. I had assumed it was the other way around. Dave ran a million miles an hour, had a million friends, a million talents and ideas. The matriarch he most loved and respected thought I could outrun him? That was a true honor.

One night, I slept beside Dave in his twin bed and had a vivid dream. We were on the beach at Cape Cod. In the distance, we saw giant waves rising. The waves were thirty or forty feet high; they shrunk before crashing on the shore, but they were still frighteningly huge. I was screaming, backing away from the ocean. Dave grabbed my hand, and we walked even closer to the water. The waves were crashing and getting bigger at the point they broke on shore.

"We should've gone to a different beach!" I said.

"No way! The waves are cool here!" Dave said.

The current was pulling us out, but we fought it and stayed on shore. Our feet were sinking in the soft sand.

I woke with a racing heart and Dave's arms around me, our bodies pushed together in his tiny bed.

I rolled over and studied his face in the early dawn glow. I wondered if Dave and I were destined to ride crazy metaphorical waves. The dream had seemed real. Was it an awareness of danger and chaos to come? Was this wild boy going to take my hand and drag me, screaming, closer to the big waves?

After dating for nine months, Dave and I had an argument and didn't speak for a week. In the local free paper, I read about a musician— Cat Power—who was signed to Matador, one of our favorite record labels. She'd be playing at a small club ninety minutes away from Albany. Impulsively, I called Dave to tell him about the show.

The conversation was terse.

I reported what I'd read.

"OK," Dave answered, "let's go. I'll pick you up tomorrow at seven."

Half an hour into the set, Dave and I abandoned our stance in front of the stage to go downstairs to the quieter lounge.

We sat on a red leather bench in the dimly lit hallway. Dave put his hand on my cheek, shifting my head to meet his eyes.

"I missed you?" he offered as a question.

"I missed you too?" I asked back.

After some silence, I confessed, "If I wasn't going to see you again, I would've regretted never telling you I love you."

He pulled my face to his shoulder and whispered in my ear, "I love you too."

In nine months, that was our big relationship talk. That was our style; it worked.

Dave and I were headstrong individuals. We were both wild and passionate and impulsive. Part of what drew us together is exactly what forced us apart—we both survived difficult and unusual childhoods.

We were a little less tame, a little more raw, than most people our age.

Dave may have grown up in suburbia, but his home seethed with drugs, guns, schemes, and violence. In the upper middle class world he grew up in, Dave was an entertaining anomaly. He prided himself on his sordid past. He prided himself on living through a childhood and young adulthood that included buying drugs in South America, smoking crack in Belize, and his parents' drug use. In contrast to what most children are taught, his father had taught him to be a nonconformist, a rebel, and a lawbreaker. His family had lived outside the law in many ways, and he relished that outlaw life.

He also used it in his art. The lyrics in his songs referenced the hard times, but also captured his deep appreciation of being alive. In "Son of May," a song he wrote about his life, he sang:

> *I was born on a combat zone*
> *Far from myself, even farther from home...*
> *I was born a child in vain*
> *A long time coming but I'm glad I came*

Despite the questionable integrity of some of the adults in his life, Dave seemed to have his own finely tuned moral compass. Despite the sordidness of his past, he had upbeat stories and memories. One of my favorites was from when Dave was seven years old and on a bowling league. One weekend, his team was playing in a tournament. Dave couldn't find either of his parents to give him a ride, so he walked—carrying his bowling ball—to the bowling alley, miles away. He arrived just in time for his team's turn to play. He bowled a perfect zero. Then he walked back home—all by himself—carrying his bowling ball. He did what he decidedly thought was the right thing; he did his best.

I appreciated Dave's upbeat stories, but the more dicey aspects of his background didn't disturb me. I had experienced darkness, too. My parents were unmarried teenagers when I was born. We spent my early years moving between trailers and apartments in slums.

One of my earliest memories is in a rundown apartment with my too-young parents. My mother is holding me and crying. My father is yelling and thrashing. The refrigerator door is open and a soft light is pouring from it into the otherwise dark room, lighting our scared faces. We're all scared because our lives seem beyond our control. I'm the only quiet one. At two or three years old I recognize this is beyond me. This isn't about me. The best thing for me to do is be quiet and be love and wait out their storm.

As a kid, I was comforted by the knowledge that forward motion is inevitable. I sensed I'd be carried through whatever pain or hardship I encountered.

My own needs seemed so minimal. It was clear the adults around me needed much more than I did, so I shouldn't add to their overwhelmed, stressed-out state. I learned to not ask for help.

These memories come with a soundtrack. I remember toddling around our apartment with The Who playing. My mom had *Who's Next* in heavy rotation.

My parents fought a lot in that apartment, and my dad often disappeared for days or weeks at a time. I remember thinking, when he wasn't there, that it was him singing "Behind Blue Eyes." Roger Daltrey's voice was my father's, lamenting about being a sad man and a bad man.

Somehow, I was wise enough to know those words were apropos, but I was too young to understand where music came from. It seemed logical that it was my dad's voice coming through the speakers with a message for me when I was missing him.

I could manage missing my dad. When he wasn't around, things were quieter and my mom seemed almost relieved because it was one less thing she had to take care of.

I couldn't manage without my mom though. When I was three, she almost died. A months-long strep infection spread to her heart. She had a heart attack and underwent emergency heart surgery.

While doctors worked on repairing her heart, my mom suffered a stroke. The heart surgery was halted so they could perform a procedure to relieve the pressure in her brain. Many hours after the brain surgery, when she was a bit more stable, my mom's doctors decided that they had to risk another surgery to make the cardiac repair. The doctors told my family (including my mom's college-age sisters, Patti and Barb) that they should pray a lot.

She survived the third surgery, but my mom's condition was critical for days afterwards.

After the hospital, she was sent to a rehabilitation facility. She had brain damage and her left side was paralyzed. Her recovery took over three months. I wasn't allowed to visit, and that time without her was agonizing. I would talk to her on the phone and beg her to come home. I would cry inconsolably.

During this time, I moved in with my mom's parents. My dad started a relationship with a different woman.

When my mom was finally released, we stayed with my grandparents until she was strong enough to tackle her new life as a single mother.

Eventually, the two of us got our own apartment. I understood my mom was proud and happy to be independent, but I missed the luxuries of my grandparents' home. I never let her know I noticed the difference between Grandma's home cooked macaroni and cheese and the boxed kind she served or how her one pink highlighter along with red and black office pens didn't entertain me like Grandma's full set of fruit-scented markers did. I was so grateful my mom was back at my side; I didn't want to question any of the details of our life.

I didn't question why I saw less of my dad, either. I visited him at his new home, with his new girlfriend, a couple times each month. When I was six, my mom told me those visits would end because my dad was moving away. She said I might not see him for a long time.

I remember thinking I was OK with just about anything—subpar living conditions, absent dad—as long as I had my mom.

Three weeks after I turned seven, my mom's heart stopped while she slept.

At my mom's funeral, I was acutely aware of how much I had missed her while she was in the hospital. I couldn't imagine how I'd survive without her for *the rest of my life*. Three months had been an eternity.

I spent the following spring and summer imagining my own heart stopping, thinking I knew what it felt like to die. I'd lie in bed and feel what it was to be dead. It was lonely. I was scared. I used to tape pictures of my mom facing out the windows of my grandparent's house where I lived. Somehow this connected us; she was still there, looking out at the world.

The more times I felt my own heart stop, the more connected I felt to my mom. Fantasizing my death brought me to a place that was terrifying and vast, but worth braving because being in that place was being with her.

Surviving our pasts gave Dave and me fierce independence. We were proud and determined, acting with single-minded ferocity. We had our own agendas that sometimes didn't include time and energy for cultivating a relationship.

After almost a year of dating, I started an argument that broke us up. We were out on a Friday night, listening to live music at a coffee house downtown. We sat near the back and talked over the music.

"It's nice to see you," I said. "It's been a busy week. I'm glad we got time to hang out."

"I know! I was too busy mixing those new songs to have band practice this week," Dave said.

"Well, the weekend is here and we get to relax. I felt like all I did was drive this week. I climbed in the Adirondacks on Tuesday and then was down in the Gunks on Thursday," I said. "It'll be nice to lie low with you tomorrow."

"Tomorrow?" Dave said after a long pause.

"Yeah. We're hanging out tomorrow, right?"

"I want to meet up with Jay to lay drum tracks tomorrow," Dave said. "I thought you were climbing."

"No. I told you I wouldn't climb this weekend so we can hang out."

"Oh. You should just go climbing. I have too much to do," Dave said. He was suddenly intent on watching the stage we'd been ignoring.

"What the fuck, Dave," I raised my voice. "When are we ever gonna spend time together? You're always so freaking busy."

"I don't know. You could come by the studio if you want."

"So I can stand there and watch you? So I can be your tag-along girlfriend? No, thanks."

"All right. Then I guess you won't see me."

"It'd be nice if I felt like you wanted to spend time with me, Dave. If I felt like you wanted to make time for me."

"You're busy too! You just said you were climbing all week."

"Yeah, and I said I wouldn't climb tomorrow so we can hang out. I made time for you."

We listened to the music for a few minutes. I was disappointed Dave had made other plans, but I decided not to ruin the time we had together by arguing.

When we left the show, we went to my place. Dave collapsed on the bed with a gigantic sigh.

"I'm so tired. I could sleep a hundred hours," Dave said more to himself than to me.

I sat on the floor across the room from the bed and thumbed through my records. I pulled Pavement's double-album *Wowee Zowee* from the crate. I'd bought the record after Dave introduced me to the band's music a few months earlier. I was still trying to figure out if I liked it.

"Which side is best?" I asked as I held the record up for Dave to see.

He didn't reply. I turned to see him sleeping in my bed. I blindly took one of the records from its sleeve and set it on the turntable.

I crawled into bed with Dave and gently kissed his ear. He rolled on his side away from me. I pressed up against his back and lifted his hair so I could kiss his neck. He slid his hand between my face and his neck.

"I'm sleeping," he said.

"I'm waking you up," I said. I wanted to make love. I was wildly attracted to Dave. His sexy body in my bed was a temptation I couldn't ignore.

"I'm tired," Dave said without turning to face me.

"Are you serious? We left the show early. It's not that late," I said with a voice full of disappointment.

Dave didn't reply.

"You're just going to sleep?" I said as I sat up. "I can't believe this. You won't make time to hang out this weekend and now you're just going to pass out?"

"What do you want from me?" Dave groaned.

"I brought you home so we could sleep together," I softened my voice, trying not to sound angry.

"Yeah. And I'm sleeping."

"You know that's not what I meant. I want you to fuck me," I said bluntly.

"Well, then, let's fuck," Dave said as he rolled onto his back with an exasperated sigh.

"Oh, my God," I hissed through gritted teeth. "Not like that! Not if you act like you don't want to."

"Amelia, I've told you a million times: I always want you. I'll always fuck you. I just don't think about it all the time like you do. I just don't want sex like you do."

It was true. He'd said it before. And I knew my insatiable sex drive shadowed his. We had great chemistry and great sex, just not enough. He was always willing, but rarely initiated.

"Forget it. I'm tired of throwing myself at you," I said.

That did it. Dave sat up.

"I can't please you. I don't spend enough time with you. I screw up our plans. I don't give you what you want. I'm tired of this," Dave announced.

"I'm tired of it, too," I answered. "I wouldn't want so much from you if I wasn't so crazy about you."

"I'm crazy about you, too," Dave agreed. "But we can't seem to make it work. It's like that Wilco song." He sang a line from "Sunken Treasure," about a couple being completely out of tune with each other.

"Yup. I don't know, Dave. Maybe you're right. It's not working for us," I said. "We *are* pretty out of tune."

We were both sad. We wanted it to work, but it didn't. Dave crept from my bed in slow motion. He kept his eyes down and focused on dressing himself, slowly and carefully getting the job done. When he finished tying his shoes, Dave looked at me.

"I'm going," he said.

I nodded. I stood and followed Dave from my bedroom, down the stairs, and out the back door.

Barefoot, I followed him across the driveway to his car. Before Dave opened the car door, he stood to face me. We hugged in the dark, holding on to one another, not wanting to be the first to let the other go.

The Horses Are Going to Kiss Me

Weeks passed and Dave and I didn't talk. I pined over him constantly. I wanted him back but was too stubborn to reach out.

While we were separated, I discovered a six-song EP that one of our favorite bands—Modest Mouse—had released the previous year. I loved the songs and played the album over and over. It made me miss Dave. I wanted to share it with him; I knew he'd love it as much as I did.

The other album in heavy rotation on my stereo was *Bundle of Joy* by Land of the Loops. One of the songs, "Multi-Family Garage Sale," became a soundtrack for my missing-Dave emotional state. Its slow beats and vocal samples were repetitive and melancholy. A little girl's lost and desperate squeak eerily overlaps a woman whispering goodbye to her lover. The song was pretty and sad.

I recorded it on a cassette tape, followed by the new Modest Mouse songs. I wrote on the jacket, "The first song sounds how I feel." I took it to the post office, put it in a manila envelope, and mailed it to Dave.

Two days later, I came home to a manila envelope in my mailbox. My heart sank when I thought I recognized the envelope as the one I mailed to Dave. Was he so over me he returned my package? I turned it over. The envelope was the exact type I mailed—but it was *from* Dave.

I tore it open and found a cassette tape. It baffled me. There hadn't been enough time for Dave to repack my tape and mail it back.

As I examined the tape, I realized it wasn't the one I sent to Dave. Dave's handwriting was on the A-side sticker: "To Amelia" and he'd scrawled a few lines on a sheet of notepaper announcing that he wrote and recorded the song for me.

I held the tape and note, and the room spun. Really? After a month with no communication, Dave and I sent each other identical packages? Our mixtapes passed in the mail. Despite our headstrong ways and relationship strife, Dave and I were cosmically right on.

We had music to help us communicate when we were too proud or too inarticulate to confess our feelings. Music was a huge part of both of our lives. We each loved bands and songs on an almost spiritual level.

For me, the bands I loved and records I played at particular times created a soundtrack to my life. That had been happening for as long as I could remember. My mom and I watched music videos on MTV together when I was four and she was twenty-one. She took me to see live music in parks and bars when I was thigh-high. On car rides, she let me plug the cassettes I chose from her eclectic punk, new wave, and rock collection into the tape deck.

Once, when I was old enough to play on my own, maybe five years old, my mom was in her bedroom with the music cranked up loud. She must have been listening to The Clash's *Combat Rock*. I remember hearing the song "Should I Stay or Should I Go." I loved it! It rocked. I also remember hearing the song "Straight to Hell" and loving it. I got up from my toys to look in the room at my mom, wanting to get closer to the sound.

I wasn't old enough to wonder what band we were listening to. I only knew I liked the sound.

Years later, after my mom died, and I was seven or eight, I discovered an unlabeled cassette tape at my grandparents' house. I stuck it in my boom box and the sound of *Combat Rock* poured out. Memories and emotions flooded in as soon as I heard it. I didn't know what it was, I only knew I recognized it as the music my mom blasted years prior and knew we both loved it. Those songs brought my mother back to life.

I felt the same deep connection appreciating music with Dave. The Modest Mouse and Land of the Loops songs united us the way The Clash had united me with my mom.

When Dave and I had been living together almost two years, we adopted a cat. I was waiting tables at Quintessence, the historic silver trailer restaurant near our apartment in downtown Albany. I juggled dinner plates between the kitchen door and the front patio.

On one of my patio circuits, Dave yelled from down the block. He'd come to say goodbye before he left to spend the weekend in New York City. I jogged down the sidewalk to meet Dave.

"I'll miss ya, Davey!" I said as I reached him.

I forgot my restaurant duties as I cozied into Dave's arms. A persistent meow interrupted our embrace.

The meows were coming from an orange striped kitten. She came to a stop in front of us and continued to meow as she stared up at us.

"Oooohhh, who are *you*?" I asked as I bent down to pet the kitten.

"She's adorable! So lovable," I said to Dave.

"Yup. She's as cute as they come," he confirmed.

Just then, as if on cue, one of the neighborhood regulars appeared.

"That cat needs a home. It's the last one from the litter born in the community garden down the block. All the others were adopted," he said.

Dave and I looked at each other. We didn't want a cat. We had a future packed with travel plans.

The kitten meowed as she twined around our legs in a figure eight. She looked up intently at Dave and me.

"I think she wants us to take her home," I said.

"Yeah, I think you're right," Dave agreed. He bent to scratch the cat's head. She purred and leaned into him.

"We don't want a cat," I said.

"Nope. We sure don't want a cat," Dave said as he stood to face me.

"We might have to take her home anyway," I said.

"*You* might. I'm going to New York," Dave said. "Bye!"

He kissed me and jumped in his car.

I rushed back to the restaurant. The kitten followed. She followed me all night, between the patio and kitchen door. She shadowed me as I served the patio customers.

That Sunday night, when Dave came home from New York, he walked into the apartment with wide, scanning eyes.

"Where's the kitten?" he asked.

We named the cat Abby. The home we brought her into wasn't always peaceful. Dave and I were passionate and headstrong twenty-somethings. The issue of our uneven sex drives resurfaced every few months. The previous fall, after barhopping and beer drinking, Dave and I stumbled home together. Inside the entranceway, I leaned into Dave and we kissed sloppily.

"Let's go lay down," I whispered between long kisses. "I want you."

"Me too," Dave said and slowly backed me toward our bedroom.

With my hands on his ass, I felt his phone vibrate in his back pocket.

Dave stopped kissing me and reached for his phone.

"It's Mark. I gotta answer," he said.

Mark, Dave's best friend, was living in Queens, 150 miles to the south. The two boys talked on the phone daily. I thought sex with me should trump a late night call from Mark, but I wordlessly headed to the bedroom to wait while Dave took the call. I sat patiently for at least three minutes before I drunkenly decided enough was enough. I changed into a tight, lacy lingerie top and sexy panties before slinking out to the living room to entice Dave into the bedroom.

As Dave sat talking into the phone on our couch, I swiveled my hips and ran my hands over my ass. I tried to look as irresistible as possible. Dave ignored me.

"C'mon, Davey," I said sweetly. "Come to bed."

He ignored me.

Smacked with rejection, my sweetness dissolved and I reached forward to grab the edge of the heavy wooden coffee table that sat in front of the couch. With one adrenaline-fueled lift, I launched the table, flipping it bottom to top. A crash of shattering glass accompanied the loud sound of cracking wood. The coffee table and the framed picture of Dave and his brother displayed on it were both destroyed.

Dave stood with a tremendous growl. He threw his phone with one hand and picked up his guitar with the other.

"What the fuck!" he shouted as he bashed the guitar over the broken table at his feet.

I backed away, aware that I'd created a cataclysm.

In slow motion, Dave stomped toward me and I inched away. I reached up and swept a vase from the top of a rack of shelves so it smashed on the floor between us. Dave one-upped me by pushing the entire rack to the floor. Books and picture frames and knickknacks broke into pieces and scattered.

This time I growled, and lunged at Dave. My foot caught on the fallen bookcase and I tumbled forward. Dave retreated to our bedroom. I lay in the rubble for a silent minute before sitting up and assessing the damage. Our living room was a disaster zone and blood dripped from my arm. A chunk of the ceramic vase I toppled was embedded in my forearm.

Slowly, I became aware of a tiny voice calling from the wreckage.

I crawled across the room and picked up Dave's phone.

"Hello?" I said hesitantly.

"Holy shit," Mark said. "Are you OK?"

"No. I'm bleeding," I said and started a tearless theatrical whiny cry.

"Holy shit," Mark said again. "You guys are fucking crazy."

"Dave knocked over the shelves and I fell in all the broken glass. I'm bleeding," I reported through gasping breaths.

"Don't call the police," Mark said. "I hope your neighbors didn't call the police."

"Why would I call the police?" I asked.

Mark was silent.

"Oh. Because we had a domestic dispute," I answered myself.

The next morning we woke up in our bed with our clothes on and hung over.

"Did what I think happened last night really happen?" Dave asked me.

"I'd have to look at the living room to be sure, but I think so," I said.

"What happened to your arm?" Dave reached out and touched my bandaged forearm.

"I fell in the mess," I said.

"That's bad. We fucked up," Dave said.

"I know. Do we get to have make-up sex now?"

I never could figure out Dave's low sex drive. He was gorgeous; he was sexy. He was the singer in a band! He could've had any girl he wanted.

More than once, I stopped to see him while he was working at his candle store in the mall and found a flirty girl leaning on the counter trying to pique his interest. After his band played a show, there would inevitably be a bunch of adoring female fans waiting to talk to him. At parties, if I wasn't by his side, other women would cozy up to him.

Dave was charming. He exuberantly described his artistic endeavors and creative interests to whoever would listen. So, he engaged his admirers, but never in a way that threatened me. He was outgoing without flirting. I could see his intentions in his body language and on his face. Dave wasn't a player; he didn't seek flings or affairs.

When we first got together, his shyness shocked me. He was a puritan about sex. I was pleasantly surprised that the handsome, charismatic rocker with a million friends and fans didn't tomcat around or have a long roster of one-night stands.

After months of intimacy with Dave, I realized it just wasn't in his nature to seek sex. He was irresistible and great in bed, but he just didn't get horny.

In contrast, I lived by the principle that food, sleep, and sex were all we humans really needed. I justified any irritability I had by claiming a lack of one of those three things.

Living with Dave, I learned to put vanity and pride aside and be the sexual initiator in our relationship.

Despite our over the top alcohol-fueled arguments, we found peaceful resolutions to our differences. In our own rowdy punk rock way, we built a strong, meaningful partnership and a life together.

Later that spring, doctors diagnosed my maternal grandmother with terminal lung cancer. They predicted she wouldn't live a year. She was in rehab at a nursing home, recovering from a broken femur. She wanted to go home, but wasn't fit to live on her own.

My grandparents raised me with unconditional love. They were generous and selfless people.

Grandpa died in a hospital after a surgery. I drove my grandparents to the hospital for the surgery and Grandpa was adamant about not wanting to go; he was only following doctors (and Grandma's) orders. After the surgery, when he wasn't getting better, Grandpa only wanted to go home. Before the family could facilitate his release, he died.

I didn't want Grandma to suffer the same fate; I didn't want her to die in a hospital. I couldn't let her live her last time on Earth unhappy and away from her home.

One night as Dave dozed in bed next to me, I agonized over the next step in my life. Grandma was dying. She was the strongest person I knew; she never relied on anyone and now she couldn't care for herself. Dave opened his eyes and asked why I wasn't sleeping. Suddenly, I knew the plan.

"When our lease ends, Dave, I'm going to move into Grandma's house so she can come home."

"OK," he said, "I'll do that with you."

Though I expected Dave to take time to digest what I said, to decide what role—if any—he wanted to have in my decision, his immediate response didn't floor me. Dave knew what he wanted and what was right. He didn't deliberate much.

He'd always gotten along with Grandma, appreciating her frank, sharp wit. He didn't hesitate to go along with my plan. I was impressed; I felt loved.

The next eight months were intense. Grandma's health declined. She hired aides to come to the house to bathe her and dress her. An aide was at the house whenever Dave or I couldn't be there.

Dave learned to cook a steak the way Grandma liked it ("mooing") after disappointing her only once by cooking it to his liking ("burnt to hell"). He sat with her to chat or watch TV when I wasn't there. When she needed a late night bedding change, he called me home from a friend's house. He would've done it for her, but she refused to let him.

I knew I loved Dave before we moved in with my Grandma. I knew he was kind and helpful. I knew he had committed himself and was devoted to me. But the way he stood by me and Grandma in those months amazed me. Dave was, after all, a twenty-nine-year-old party-loving stoner musician. He was a boy: self-absorbed and stubborn. But he was also a selfless caregiver who was more attentive to Grandma than most of her blood relatives.

During that time, we lost privacy and freedom. We witnessed or joined all kinds of family arguments and meltdowns. Our space was shared with a handful of aides and visiting family, many of whom we didn't like. Grandma's failing health was an unavoidable daily strain.

It was hard, but it always felt right. Our relationship transformed in ways I couldn't have predicted. We moved in with Grandma so she could live her last months in peace at home. Neither of us could've foreseen the effect it would have on us: we started to feel like a family. Our bond and intentional living allowed Grandma to die at home. That felt profound to Dave and me.

After Grandma died, Dave and I were back on our own. We moved into a new apartment. Dave was working in construction, and I was freelancing as a technical writer. We both moonlighted at a microbrewery concert hall: Dave as a sound engineer, me as a cocktail waitress.

One night in April, we couldn't take our eyes off each other. For hours, Dave sat behind his huge mixing boards on the side of the stage. He stared intently at the band whose sound he was mixing, watching for facial expressions and hand gestures from the performers and adjusting the hundreds of dials and knobs before him.

I carried drinks precariously through the raucous crowd and strained to hear shouted orders over the pounding music. I ran up and down the long industrial staircase between the customers and the bar. From the balcony where I was serving drinks, I had a bird's-eye view of my sexy, talented boyfriend.

We'd been working at the club together for months. Usually an entire night passed with us too absorbed in our duties to look up to find one another. On that spring night, we were even busier than usual. People packed in shoulder to shoulder to see a national act rock our local stage. Despite the club's pulsing urgency and fervor, I couldn't keep my eyes off Dave. An intense beam of light connected us, like we were each shooting out light and it was meeting between us. Every time I rounded the corner where I had the best view of my love, I looked his way and our eyes would meet.

Now, back home, our eyes stayed locked. I unlocked the front door, then pushed it open with my back so I could keep my eyes on Dave as we stepped over the threshold. The light beam between us revved up to white-hot. We weren't talking, only smiling and gig-gling. My chest and stomach ached pleasantly; I yearned for Dave. I felt love, love, love pouring from both of us.

I dropped my jacket on the floor just inside the front door.

"I gotta pee," I said as I rushed to the bathroom, watching over my shoulder as Dave followed me down the hall. As I sat on the toilet, he leaned with an arm up on the doorframe, staring at me with his twinkly eyes.

"What are you thinking? Right now. What have you been think-ing all night?" Dave asked me with his most serious voice.

The words came out before I even thought about them: "I want to marry you."

"I know," Dave whispered.

Then louder, he almost shouted: "Me too! I want to marry you."

The only talk of marriage Dave and I had up to that point was to say we weren't the marrying types.

We had been contentedly committed to each other for six years. We'd been to eleven weddings in that time. Weddings, marriage, and convention were boring and unnecessary to us.

Together, we appreciated the sentiment expressed in the Pave-ment song "Rattled by the Rush," that you didn't need an official to make your relationship real.

We didn't do much planning for our wedding. Dave and I had been throwing rockin' parties together for six years; we knew how it should be done. And, although we were acting more like tame grownups, we'd always be DIY punks at the core.

Many of our friends suffered through stressful weddings. We decided not to plan out of obligation. Invitations would only go out to the people we absolutely wanted there, and we wouldn't invite anyone who would cause stress or create drama.

Many of our friends acquired debt hosting their weddings. We'd do it cheap, keep it simple.

We were unceremonious about telling our friends and family. A few days after the bathroom chat, when Dave and I confessed our desire to get married, my dad and his girlfriend came to Quintessence. After I took their dinner order, I said something like: "Hey! Big news! Dave and I are gonna get married."

Two days before the wedding, I went rock climbing. After finishing a difficult 200-foot climb, my partner and I sat on a ledge to admire the view. One strap of my loose fitting tank top slid from my shoulder.

"Dude! You have a serious tan! It looks like you're wearing a white shirt where your strap should be," my partner said.

"I guess you're right. I've been out climbing a lot this summer. And I always wear this shirt," I said as I looked down to examine my skin. "Oh, well."

My mind flashed two days forward to my wedding. I pictured myself standing beside Dave dressed in the lacy, white gown I'd picked to wear.

"Oh shit!" I said. "My wedding dress is strapless!"

I pulled the other strap down so both shoulders were exposed.

"Maybe if I keep the straps off for the rest of the day, the tan lines will fade?" I asked hopefully.

"Oh, man," my shocked partner replied, "*you're* wearing a *dress?!*"

The day before our wedding, I drove Dave and myself—adventure-girl tan lines and all—to the 18th century farm where we'd host the love fest. It was late September, and sunny. Only a few leaves on the trees had changed color.

Almost everyone we invited was coming to the big party at the farm in the woods. Most of our guests were staying for the whole weekend.

We unloaded Dave's gear from my over-packed Honda. We set up a sound system under the huge tent erected in the field and filled with tables, chairs, and a dance floor. Together we hoisted two half-kegs of beer from the trunk and onto the lawn.

The rooms in the main house, barns, and farmhouse were ready to receive our guests. I ran around putting nametags on the doors, assigning bedrooms according to proximity to other guests and personal tastes. Our older, mellower friends were in the main house. The rock climbers were on airbeds in the huge wide-open loft in one of the barns. The hard partying, sure-to-be-up-all-night crew would crash, dormitory style, in a few bedrooms on one side of the farmhouse.

In the afternoon, our friends rolled in. Glenn, the farm's proprietor, saddled his horses for our guests to ride the trails through the surrounding woods. Some friends took off on the bikes they brought to explore the backcountry roads. Others started day-drinking on the porch.

Dana, our chef friend, bought a bunch of fresh ingredients from the farm stands she passed driving up from New York City. Impromptu, she recruited a team to back her up as she prepared a meal for the thirty of us. We ate in the converted tack room just before midnight.

Saturday was more of the same. Glenn served breakfast. The late risers ate Dana's leftovers. Our guests ran around the grounds partying or adventuring.

In the afternoon, Dave and I exchanged vows. A good friend officiated over a traditional civil ceremony. The fall day was warm and clear. Everything was perfect; everyone was happy.

I noticed Dave was missing within ten minutes after we were married.

"Have you seen Dave?" I asked as I wandered from guest to guest.

After a while, I saw Dave walking arm and arm with Susanne. They were heading back to the party from the horse barn. Susanne's unwieldy fancy camera hung from her neck; she'd fallen into the unofficial role of wedding photographer.

Dave answered my curious gaze as soon as I was within earshot, "We had to go visit the horses!"

"Yup, they were waiting for Davey," Susanne said. "They wanted to give him a kiss."

With my groom back in grabbing distance, I wrapped my arms around Dave. He was always on a mission and often wandered away. I was determined to hang on to Dave in those moments: he was mine, my husband.

Dave pulled Susanne into our embrace.

"Show her!" he urged.

I rested my head on Dave's shoulder to look at Susanne's digital camera screen.

Inside the frame, Dave stood in front of the horses' pen. Two enormous horses towered over Dave, looking in opposite directions away from him.

"When I shot this one Dave said, 'No, wait, the horses are about to kiss me,'" Susanne said.

She let the camera rest around her neck and looked at me dramatically, with tears in her eyes.

I wrinkled my brow, confused.

Susanne held the camera up and advanced to the next frame. In it, the horses' heads framed either side of Dave's face. Their noses were resting on his cheeks. A window-shaped sunbeam shone on Dave's face and the horses' noses. All three were staring into the camera. Dave's smile was huge, illuminated and glowing.

Susanne's eyes watered as she showed me the pictures because sometimes just being around Dave was overwhelming. He connected with people and animals deeply and intensely.

Oh yeah: Dave wasn't just mine. He belonged to Susanne, and to the horses. Dave belonged to us all; he was too good to keep to myself. And sometimes, he just had to go on a mission for a horse kiss.

I married Dave because I loved him unconditionally. That New Year's Eve, almost ten months before, Dave and I had seen the reggae band John Brown's Body play a live show. When the clock struck midnight, the singer announced, "This is the year of unconditional love."

That declaration stuck with us. In our world, this really was the year of unconditional love. Through the years together, Dave and I had always chosen to stick with one another. We were both self-righteous and stubborn and both had a "love it or leave it" attitude. We fought and struggled, and sometimes we wondered if the relationship was worth the work. In the six years leading up to our marriage, we almost gave it up a handful of times. We held on because something deep and fundamental bound us. The words "unconditional love" articulated that bond.

I was the DJ for our all-night wedding dance party. On the down low, after the grandparents left, I distributed psychedelic mushrooms from a colorful canvas purse slung over my shoulder to the friends I knew would want to trip out at our joyful event.

The mushrooms enhanced, and made visual, the powerful energy and love that pulsed through me, Dave, our guests, and the land.

Late in the night, with the party roaring around us, Dave and I locked eyes. We grinned at each other. Without a word, we took each other's hand and slipped out into the darkness beyond the dance tent. Stars whirled through the huge black sky. The breeze smelled like wildflowers and balsam. It gently rocked the trees, and us.

Holding on to each other in the cool country night, we looked back at the glowing dance floor. It looked like a lit stage that had been magically lowered into the immense dark field. The spectacle of our friends on it, dancing and laughing, was endearing.

We were beyond words. I knew Dave and I were feeling the same thing, without having to say it; I knew we felt different. The ceremony had changed something. We had become a family that day. I felt surprised, and pleasantly overwhelmed.

There was something else, too. I could feel how long it had been since either of us had been in a golden, intimate, core family. Now I was experiencing it—now I could feel it as a tangible true thing—I could see it had been almost our whole lives since we experienced it last. We each had only a few happy years with our parents before reality intervened, before the drugs and the struggling and the ugliness cratered our birth families.

Now, latched onto each other on our wedding night, we were in a family again. We felt the infiniteness of unconditional love. I saw myself wedged in a fraction of time and space, with the expansiveness of the universe spilling out in every direction. I saw Dave there with me and knew we had created something. We were linked through time and space as the universe pulsed around us and lifetimes swirled by.

Dragged out to Sea

I'm a climber/adventure chick. I camp out and hike and road trip alone. I hang out with a crew of boys who are like brothers to me. I have a lot of male insight into how crazy women can appear to men, how irrational and demanding wives can seem. I didn't want to be that kind of girl: worried, angry, controlling, needy.

In the months after our second wedding anniversary, when Dave started coming home late, short-tempered and aloof, I was careful not to take it personally.

We had a routine. We woke up early and ate waffles or eggs. I worked, writing at home or waiting tables at The Ginger Man restaurant, while Dave went off to his nine-to-five construction job. I cooked dinner each evening, so it was ready just after Dave got home.

We relished the normalcy of our life together. We got a kick out of acting out such a typical husband and wife routine. Our DIY punk rock approach to life was tempered by these mainstream habits.

In the two years since we married, Dave and I had mellowed out. We were acting the part of maturing adults instead of wild early twenty-somethings. Still, to me, it seemed that Dave took his maturity to the extreme. He was suddenly acting much older. He came home from work exhausted and would sometimes go straight to bed after our early dinner.

Dave had always been a late-night creator. He'd always worked hard at multiple jobs and still had time and energy to make art. So this was unusual.

He was grumpy, too. He complained about his job, about being worn-out, about being bored.

It was all out of character. Dave was engaged in the mainstream aspects of life he'd always avoided: a regular job, a regular sleep schedule, moneymaking, watching TV.

He was too tired or concerned about money to make plans on the weekend. His lack of energy seemed strange for someone who was only thirty-two.

We'd always partially maintained separate lives. We had different interests and friends. Dave was distancing himself from these other aspects of his life, too. When I spent the weekend in the Adirondacks rock climbing with my favorite partners, he stayed home instead of visiting his friends in Manhattan as I would've expected him to.

The more aloof and distracted Dave became, the more often I took off on adventures. I diverted my concerned mind and occupied myself by climbing harder than ever. I'd grown bored with the usual Adirondack crags and scoured the guidebook to find routes off the beaten path. My dad was intrigued by my quest to climb these routes, and he eagerly partnered with me on these adventures.

Meanwhile, a pair of local climbers were compiling a new Adirondack guidebook. There was fervor among the climbing community to establish new routes so they would be published in the book. When a person is the first to climb a route from the ground to the top without falling or resting, it's called a "first ascent." The climber is rewarded with the privilege of naming and grading the route, and her name is printed in the guidebook along with the route information.

My dad and I weren't seeking first ascents; we were only looking for novel adventures. The crew I climbed with was disinterested in first ascents and fame. We climbed for personal gratification and fun. We were a hard, loud, dirty bunch.

One day, my dad belayed me as I struggled up a difficult route. The route was a mystery; we couldn't find a record of it in the existing guidebook.

"Fuck! Fuck! Fuck! This shit is hard!" I exclaimed as I took a rest on the rope.

"You can do it, Sweetie!" my dad encouraged from the ground. "Give it another try!"

After the rest, I barely managed to scramble over the steepest section of rock. As I blindly threw for overhead holds, I groaned and growled. When I finally made it, I hollered with joy.

"Motherfucker!" I squealed. "Hey, Dad! That was some serious shit!"

The next day, one of my climbing partners called me. He was on the end of a phone chain that originated with the guidebook authors.

"They think you got a first ascent. Someone saw—or heard—you and your dad yesterday. You were on a route some of the locals have been trying to climb as a first ascent," my friend said.

"How do they know who I am?" I asked. I was baffled.

"You're the only one who meets the description: cute young girl with the foulest mouth imaginable climbing with her dad. It didn't take too many calls to track you down," he explained.

I didn't really care about scoring the first ascent, but I was entertained by the thought my reputation as a badass, albeit raucously unladylike, climber was growing.

When he wasn't working, Dave closed the door to his music room in our apartment. I could hear him play the same bits of songs over and over. He was fixated beyond his usual artistic drive for perfection.

He began writing a screenplay. He obsessed over that too. He asked me to show him how to use a word processing program on our computer so he could transcribe his pages of notes, but he was too frustrated to follow through on learning to use the simple program.

Dave was acting weird. He was distant. He would get stuck obsessing on ideas, but not follow through.

None of these things led me to believe anything was truly wrong. Dave had lived hard and fast up to that point. He'd been rolling with an off-the-beaten-path lifestyle for a long time. Maybe he needed time to be introverted and slow down.

I tried giving him space to do what he needed to do and sort through whatever he needed to sort through. I had a hunch he was dealing with difficult childhood memories and realizations.

Over our years together, Dave had told me a little about his parents' rocky marriage and hard-partying lifestyle.

One night, around the time he started acting strange, Dave sighed and shifted in bed.

"Can't sleep?" I said.

"Oh, I don't know," Dave said. "I guess not."

"What's up?"

"I'm not sure I want to tell you," Dave answered.

My heart raced. What was Dave hesitant to tell me? He'd always been uncensored.

"It's about my dad," Dave said.

I was relieved Dave's secret wasn't about us, wasn't an admission of doubt about our relationship.

"You can talk to me about anything, Dave," I encouraged.

"It's pretty bad," Dave said and stayed silent for several minutes.

"I guess you'll find out anyway," Dave sighed. "There's a book about it."

My heart raced again. Dave was more serious than I'd ever seen him.

"The reason my dad didn't go to jail when I was a kid is because he set someone else up," Dave said.

I knew his dad had sold drugs. Dave had never volunteered many details, and I never asked, so it was shocking to hear this confession.

"The woman he set up had kids. She had a really hard life. My dad got caught and he rolled over on her instead of manning up. She went to jail and lost everything, and he got to keep his life," Dave explained. "Now she's out of jail and someone wrote a book about her. It says my dad's name in the book and it's on the new release shelf at Barnes & Noble."

I didn't know what to say.

"I don't blame you if you're upset with me," Dave said.

"Dave, I'd never be upset with you about stuff your parents did," I said, "just like I know you'd never be upset with me about anything my family did."

I tried to console him. "I'm sorry you had to go through that," I said, "and I'm sorry you have to deal with those memories now."

This talk was unusual for us. Dave's admission he was hurt by his past was a first. After that night, I cut him even more slack. I knew it was difficult for him to talk about that stuff, so I tried to be supportive by hanging back and not confronting him about his behavior.

We were a strong couple, in love, who had worked through years of relationship evolution. We had been happily married for two years. I felt confident we were on the brink of working through some big marriage stuff. I felt like I just had to be patient.

I knew the value of patience. At eighteen, my life derailed, and it took years to recover. After graduating from high school, I moved in with my mom's sister, Barb, and her family. It was a golden time in my life. I was in college, studying art and writing, and drawing comics and taking photographs in my free time.

Midway through my second semester, Barb died when she lost control of her car and crashed into a tree.

In the spring and summer that followed, I'd visualize my own body crashing through windows. I'd see myself bloody, my skin almost gone it was so mangled from broken glass.

These fantasies differed from the ones I had after my mom died. I wasn't connecting with Barb; I wasn't drawing comfort from dwelling in a place in my consciousness that brought us together. I only felt lost and disconnected. I was suffering a fate worse than death, stuck on Planet Earth feeling mutilated and alone, separated from my mothers.

After Barb died, I didn't regain focus at school and wasn't motivated to write or make art. I dropped out of college. I only wanted to move and travel. I worked part-time jobs just long enough to make enough money to take the next trip.

A few months before I turned nineteen, my friend, Jeremy, and I set out to drive across the country and ski in Utah. After stopping to visit friends in Tempe, Arizona, I was driving us to see the Grand Canyon before heading to snow country.

According to Jeremy, I was more focused on selecting the next cassette tape to play than on driving when the wheels dropped off the pavement. He describes the crash as happening in slow motion, with what must have been seconds dragging on for what felt like minutes. The car swerved back and forth across both lanes and I held on to the steering wheel with both hands, looking confident and unfazed, like I'd somehow regain control. Then stillness and silence.

Jeremy was unharmed. The driver's side of the car was crushed against a massive tree. I didn't move, my body eerily slack and displaced by the tree, my head gushing and mouth dripping blood.

A helicopter brought me to Flagstaff Medical Center. When I arrived in the ER, I wasn't breathing and had zero blood pressure. My skull was smashed. My brain was swollen. My neck was broken. I had fractured my C1 vertebrate, the one where the spinal column attaches to the skull.

When the hospital staff called my family back in New York, they weren't sure I would live through the night or regain consciousness. If I did wake up, the doctors said there was a good possibility I'd be brain damaged or paralyzed.

When I woke up, after four days in a coma, I was still far away.

Each morning of the following weeks I needed to be reminded where I was and what had happened. I had to be reminded that Barb was dead. I kept asking why I wasn't in school. My injured brain was missing memories; it had reset time to when I was happily living with my family and psyched to be in college.

I never regained some lost memories. The time around the crash will forever be foggy in my mind. The few surreal memories I have of the weeks after the crash are like remembering a dream. I remember giving the answers I knew my family members and doctors wanted to hear in response to their quizzes.

"Do you know who you are?" would be the inevitable first question of the nurse waking me.

"Amelia Whalen," I'd say with confidence.

"Do you know where you are," would come next.

"Flagstaff, Arizona. The hospital," I'd say as part of the routine, only because I knew it was the answer they wanted to hear. I thought I was dreaming or had slipped into some sort of twisted alternate reality.

"Do you know what happened to you? Why are you here?"

This is where it really got weird. I definitely didn't believe the answer I'd give next.

"I crashed my car and broke my neck."

Didn't you die when you broke your neck? Was I dead? Was I alive? I wasn't completely sure.

Slowly, I came out of the dream state. I only recall fragments from the month I spent being rehabilitated at Flagstaff Medical Center. I remember random moments: slipping from a big inflated rubber balance ball, fitting pegs in holes on a game board using my wooden-feeling fingers, clinging to a walker to travel the cement path in the hospital's courtyard.

I spent almost five months bolted into a halo neck brace. Four bolts were drilled into my skull, and rods ran from the bolts to a hard plastic vest which I couldn't take off. After that, I spent five more months wearing step-down neck braces.

Friends later told me I was like a glitchy holographic version of myself. I seemed less than substantial, more like a collection of molecules impersonating me. I'd blink in and out, scratchily. Though I don't remember much from that time, I do recall the sensation I was simulating myself. I was piecing together who I was and how I should act.

I couldn't drive and needed help dressing and showering. I saw occupational and speech therapists to rebuild my mental capacity. It took over a year to come all the way back.

A year is a long time when you're nineteen. I was forced to practice a depth of patience I'd never known. My faith deepened and my appreciation for life grew. I saw firsthand how thin the veil between the living and the dead was. Aunt Barb and my mom were in my dreams often and the dreams often felt more real than my waking moments. I could relate more with the dead than the living.

I had died, and nothing happened. I lived the Buddhist analogy: the bottle broke, but the air inside the bottle was the same. Without the bottle, the air inside just merged with the air outside.

My body broke; my spirit did not.

Time and patience didn't seem to help Dave as I'd hoped. As the months passed, scenes in our day-to-day life became surreal flashes I couldn't understand or quite believe were actually happening. Was Dave really this weird? Were our lives truly abnormal? These flashes made my brain blurry. I doubted myself. As time went on, I sensed something other than typical marital unrest was going on.

When winter turned the corner into the new year, he went from being aloof and unconcerned about time to seeming to lose giant chunks of it.

He went from being a few minutes late every once in a while to having an unpredictable schedule.

Instead of coming straight home at the 5 p.m. quitting time to eat dinner with me, he'd wander in sometimes earlier than 5 p.m. and sometimes as late as 7 p.m. When he was late, he didn't answer my calls to his cell phone.

When I asked Dave about it, his answers were vague.

"Dave! Why are you so late?" I'd ask. "What have you been doing?"

"Oh, just this, that, and the other thing," he'd reply.

One morning late in a week when he hadn't been coming home on time, I tried talking to Dave about his plans for the evening.

"Are you going to come home and have dinner with me tonight?" I asked.

"Of course. What are you gonna make?" he asked sweetly.

"If you'll show up on time, I'll make you whatever you want," I answered, half sincere and half antagonistic.

"Will you make that seafood stuff? The recipe from your mom's cookbook that's not very healthy?" Dave requested.

In a time when Dave was withdrawn and hard to drag an answer out of, I was pleased he had an opinion.

"You got it," I said. "So, I'll see you 5:30ish?"

5:30 p.m. came and went. The seafood stuff from my mom's cookbook sat on the table until it got cold. It was after 7 p.m. when Dave did come in.

I stood angrily beside the neatly set table.

"What?" Dave asked. "What's the matter with you?"

"Are you kidding me?" I said. "Don't you remember your dinner request? You told me you wouldn't be late."

"I'm not," Dave said. "I'm not late. What'd you make?"

"Dave! What the fuck?" I shouted. "Where have you been? What's going on with you?"

"I don't know what you're talking about, Amelia."

I started working dinner shifts at The Ginger Man because I was tired of being stood up by my husband night after night. All of Albany seemed to dine at The Ginger Man, with its inspired menus and deep wine list. It looked like a little slice of Paris on Albany's scruffy streets, with inviting windows and a bright, coppery wine bar. The atmosphere seemed to put people in high spirits. It became a bright spot for me, too, and I found friendship and support there.

One thing that made gauging Dave's state of mind difficult was that he was a complete character. He prided himself on doing things the *wrong* way, on being a troublemaker and an instigator. He was a talented and moody artist, a Gemini. As long as I'd known Dave he'd had a short attention span and would interrupt. He didn't put stock in social niceties or protocols. But these qualities were intensifying ever so slowly.

I trusted Dave. I didn't believe he was lying or deceiving me. Dave was faithful and committed. Throughout our time together, he expressed his disgust for his father's infidelity. Dave would confront his friends if he ever suspected they weren't faithful or respectful to their girlfriends or wives.

I couldn't figure out what was causing him to be so inconsiderate. I was growing more and more discontent and concerned. I started countless discussions and fights trying to get to the root of Dave's strange behavior. He was either completely baffled, like when he missed the seafood dinner, or irritated by my constant complaints.

He continued obsessing over his screenplay and music, but he wasn't producing any finished artwork.

Then came Dave's birdhouse obsession. He was keeping notebooks with measurements and diagrams about building birdhouses. He explained his craft to almost everyone, and offered to build birdhouses for many friends and family members. Sometimes he wanted to start a birdhouse business; sometimes he wanted to do it just for fun.

As a carpenter, he always had wood around. He had a shop on our back porch, and he'd go out there to cut and measure scraps of wood.

He left pieces of paper with scribbled measurements around the house and in the car. However, in three years of birdhouse talk, Dave only actually constructed three birdhouses.

Dave was always bringing up his birdhouses and it frustrated me. I wrote poetry about it, lines like "He's measuring straight lines and angles because he's broken and can't fix himself," and "Building a warm house for a bird while girl's out in the cold."

I felt the irony of Dave's obsession. He was investing so much energy and thought into these little houses while our already-built life was breaking apart.

After Dave carried on about his birdhouses to some friends one night, they shared my frustration and concern. None of us knew what to make of his behavior or what could—or should—be done about it.

Our best guess was that stubborn Dave was having a meltdown because of repressed childhood traumas. He was pouring himself into his art to escape, or to work through, emotional distress.

Dave had always relished his outlaw, outsider background. Now, I realized it must have taken an enormous will to spin those dark years into a positive. I wondered if some of the negative was catching up to him. I asked Dave to consider seeing a therapist or counselor. He refused and insisted everything was fine.

Things continued to unravel for Dave and me through the year. By the end of the summer, we were officially on the rocks. I thought Dave was being a selfish, thoughtless jerk. He was aloof and scatter-brained. I was still hoping he was just going through a bad time; I was still hoping he'd get his shit together.

As our wedding anniversary approached, I thought a romantic getaway in Cape Cod would help us. Early in September, I booked a night at a B&B on Martha's Vineyard followed by two nights in Provincetown. We planned to leave the weekend after our anniversary date, September 27.

In mid-September, Dave's grandmother went into the hospital. After a few days, she moved to the hospice suite. Dave was remote and unemotional regarding his dying grandmother. He'd always been close with her; he grew up next door to her, and we spent holidays at her home. It was out of character for Dave to be unmoved by his grandmother's condition.

Dave's grandmother died on our anniversary. His mom and family planned her wake and funeral to be on the weekend. I was confused when Dave told me he wanted to go to the Cape instead of staying home to be with his family and honor his grandmother.

We kept our plan and went away. The dark cloud we were in got darker and thicker as we drove east. We were mourning a close family member's death, and we were skipping town instead of staying with our grieving family.

It felt wrong to leave under the circumstances, but we did. I was desperate to mend our relationship.

I wanted our anniversary to be special. Our wedding was awesome; our one- and two-year anniversaries had been great. Somewhere in that third year of marriage, things had started to go wrong.

After a long drive, we put the car on a ferry to Martha's Vineyard. On the ferry ride, I felt impending doom. Dave and I were disconnected. He was far away and apathetic, unwilling to help me make plans or decisions.

We parked the car near the ferry dock on Martha's Vineyard. We'd brought our bikes and planned to ride all over the island during our two-day stay. First, we needed to ride our luggage to the B&B and settle in.

The bikes were intertwined in the folded-down back seat and trunk space. Dave tugged the top bike from the open trunk while I tried to free it from the other bike in the backseat. Suddenly, Dave got frustrated and yanked the bike at full force.

"No! Wait!" I screeched. My hand was stuck between the bikes. "Stop! My hand!"

He kept pulling and my hand got hung up on the chain ring. My skin tore open in a bloody gash.

"Look what you did!" I whined and held up my injured hand to Dave.

He grunted a response, maybe a "sorry" under his breath, before jumping on his bike and riding away. He left me to finish unloading my bike, and our overnight bags, from the car. Fighting back tears, I gathered as much of our stuff as I could and pedaled off after Dave.

When I caught up, Dave was standing next to his bike. The chain was off and the tires were flat. The bike was in need of a serious tune-up; it was unrideable.

"What's going on with your bike?" I asked as I rolled up to him.

"This bike is a piece of shit. This bike sucks. I can't ride it," he answered.

"How come you didn't tune it up before we went on a bike-riding vacation? Did you know it was like this?" I asked, exasperated.

"Oh yeah. This thing's been beat for a while," he shrugged.

Wow. I was mad and shocked. We walked our bikes back to the car and reloaded Dave's into the back. There was a bike shop just off the ferry, so we rented a bike there.

We rode to our B&B, stashed our bikes in the alleyway, and checked in. Dave was so oblivious to the problem of his not having brought a working bike on the trip that it was impossible for me to stay mad. He just didn't get it.

He didn't have a plan; there was nothing in particular he wanted to do on Martha's Vineyard. Usually, Dave ate new places up. He'd want to explore and feast and drink and talk to locals. This trip, he was sedate and content to follow along to wherever I pointed. Very un-Dave.

Our two days on Martha's Vineyard were memorable, but not much fun. On our bike tour, I was often pedaling as hard as I could to catch up to Dave on my bike. He furiously pedaled ahead and seemed to forget I was behind him.

Much of his behavior should've made me mad, but I was desperately sad. I didn't understand what was wrong. Whenever I asked, Dave was surprised I thought something was amiss. I tried to bring up his grandmother and find out if he wanted to go home to be with his family, but he didn't want to talk about it.

His lack of emotional response to his grandmother's death was out of character. I'd known Dave for nine years. We'd supported each other through the deaths of many friends and family members. We'd taken many trips together. I knew Dave well. I knew he wasn't himself.

He didn't want to go home. But I did. I realized that the vacation wasn't going to cure our relationship trouble as I'd hoped it would. I felt lost and lonely with the man I married acting like a cold stranger.

We stuck it out. We pressed on to Provincetown on our third vacation day. The hotel we booked was totally cool: very close to the ocean and richly distinctive. A great bunch of super-friendly people ran it. All the rooms had a theme, and the decoration was extravagant. It was exactly the kind of place Dave and I loved and felt comfortable in.

After checking in, we walked around the cool neighborhood streets near the hotel. We found a great wine shop and a great cheese shop. We bought wine and snacks to bring back to the hotel. For a few hours, Dave seemed himself. He played guitar in our room while I fixed us sliced cheese and bread and fruit.

Before I realized Dave was making a call, he was talking into his cell phone.

"Hi, Mom," I heard him say. "Good. We're good. I called to see how you are."

Dave listened while his mother was speaking. He sat at the edge of the bed and looked down at the rose printed carpet between his feet, tracing his toe over the flower pattern.

"Yeah, Mom, I think you're right. Amelia thinks we should've stayed home," Dave said.

When Dave hung up, he tossed his phone on the bed and picked up his guitar. He worked on tuning it.

"Does your mom think we should go home?" I asked.

"No. She said she's happy we're having a good time. She thinks it's what my grandmother would want the most," Dave said.

I felt a wash of relief. It was good Dave had the wherewithal to call his mom. It made me feel better to know she thought we were doing the right thing, and it was comforting to think his grandmother would want us to be having fun on our anniversary.

"*Are* we having a good time?" I asked Dave. I said it without thinking, not meaning to start the inevitable argument.

Dave sighed long and hard.

"You tell me, Amelia. Are *you* having a good time?"

I sighed long and hard.

"I feel like something's wrong. You aren't yourself. Are you unhappy?" I asked.

"No, Amelia, I'm not unhappy. Everything's fine. We're in Provincetown, right?" Dave answered.

"Yeah, I guess. Something doesn't feel right," I said.

Dave ignored me. He didn't move from his spot at the end of the bed. He stayed focused on tuning his guitar.

I lay down on the huge, elaborately made-up bed. Once I allowed myself to acknowledge the strain I was feeling, I couldn't let it go.

"It's just that, I don't know, things just feel weird," I said.

"You always say that," Dave said.

"I've been saying it lately because things *are* weird," I answered. "Don't you see? You don't talk. You forget stuff. You act like you don't care about me. Or anything else."

"Maybe something's wrong with *you*. Are *you* happy? This is the way I've always been. You know I don't do things the 'right' way—never have, never will."

This was our usual almost-argument about how things were going between us. We had a routine. Dave usually got the last word. He had a valid point. I was the only one of us who thought something was wrong. Maybe it was my problem. As he said, we were in Provincetown. We were doing exactly what I wanted to do for our anniversary. I was married to the man I loved. I decided I'd stop being critical and start enjoying my anniversary.

"All right, Dave, you're right. I'm happy to be here with you. Let's go have some fun," I said. I sat up and hugged him from behind, causing the guitar to blurt an out of tune chord.

We spent the rest of the day walking around, stopping in bars, and having a lobster dinner. I was content. Dave wasn't completely acting himself, but as time passed and we drank more beer, he was mellower and easier to be with.

The next day we went whale watching. It was absolutely amazing. The whales came right up against the boat. They played with each other, jumping and splashing impressively. Dave and I were happy and excited. During the time on the boat, everything was OK with us.

Times like the whale watching adventure could erase days of tension and worry. But times like that were happening less and less often. Mostly things were tense, and I was worried.

The night after the whale watch, I was frustrated at our fancy dinner. Dave asked our server all kinds of weird questions about the menu. He was genuinely confused about very simple things. I was embarrassed.

Back at the B&B, I questioned Dave. I was concerned for him; I was concerned for us. I tried to decipher the root of our problems.

Dave was always sure of himself. He never went backwards; he never decided he was wrong. Dave's characteristic self-righteous, stubborn state was normal.

Though everything about our anniversary trip felt off, I still couldn't be sure if I was taking things too personally, if I was overreacting.

Loving Dave was an adventure from the start. What he said was true: He didn't do things the "right" way. He did things however he wanted. He was an artist. He was passionate and driven—a force to be reckoned with.

Dave liked making a scene. He liked confusing people. He liked entertaining people.

Dave did not yield. Dave did not bend.

When I signed on to be his girl, I knew I was getting into something BIG. I knew I was partnering with a one-of-a-kind character. I knew our life together would be a wild ride.

During that melancholy time in Cape Cod, I remembered the dream I'd had years before, about the giant waves in Cape Cod. I left the Cape with a sense of foreboding. Was I about to be dragged out to sea?

White Quartz

When the new year came, I inventoried Dave's behavior. He'd been acting weird for over a year: forgetful, angry, disconnected. I had desperately tried to think what might be wrong with him. Now, at this time of fresh starts and resolutions, all I could think about was breaking up.

I had waking dreams of a distorted, shadowy, reptilian version of Dave slithering on the floor of our apartment towards the music room. Our home felt haunted. Had a bad spirit attached itself to Dave? Had we cursed ourselves somehow?

I thought about writing a story and calling it "The Boy who Built a Birdhouse." The story would be about a boy who is twisted. He looks broken. Or put together wrong. He's building a birdhouse with perfect lines and right angles in an effort to make himself straight. He's working day and night.

I couldn't forget I'd hit a big age milestone this year: thirty. I started the year with an acute knowing I couldn't slow time down; it only speeds up. As the years passed, faster and faster, I was trying to figure out what mattered in life. I wondered what was important to learn as a human being: math, medicine, music? I knew success measured worth. Yet, I wasn't sure what was worth succeeding at. What was important?

Late in January, a Rob Brezsny horoscope printed in the local free paper moved me. It read: "When will you finally be old enough to figure out what you want to do when you grow up? When will it be the right time to reveal your secret superpowers to the world? How long are you going to wait before you get around to being completely committed to what you were born to do?"

I liked the idea that I was born to do something. It was exciting and beautiful. It made me feel connected: connected to the past and future, connected to heaven and earth. I was a part of something. It was a new idea, but a familiar concept and feeling.

I had a sense that big things were happening in my world. During the same time I was coping with my husband's destructive personality changes, I was feeling spiritually whole and generally positive. Maybe this year would mark the undoing of my stable, comfortable life, but it was also the right time to dedicate myself to a huge purpose. It wasn't clear what this exact purpose was, but I was committed and thus motivated and inspired.

After everything I had been through in life, I felt resilient and self-sufficient. It was time to stop feeling cursed and start discovering my superpowers.

I spent a lot of time in the previous year doubting myself and questioning my spirituality. I was hard on myself for letting time slip by without accomplishing much. New Year's Day gave me a jolt; I was ready for action.

Dave and I went to Hawaii in February. After taking the previous two winter vacations to third-world countries, we were ready for the relaxation and safety of an island paradise.

The dream vacation was a nightmare. It started with us renting a Jeep to tour the Big Island. When the car rental attendant asked Dave for his driver's license, he shrugged.

"Lost it in Peru," he said.

"Peru?!" I said. "That was a year ago!"

Dave nodded matter-of-factly.

"You never replaced it?"

"It's OK," he said. "I showed them my passport to get on the plane."

"Sir, you'll need to show a valid driver's license for me to add you to the rental contract," the attendant said.

"David!" I burst out. "Now you can't help me drive! We have weeks of driving to do!"

He shrugged again.

"Good. I didn't want to drive anyway."

I was confused and angry. I didn't understand how Dave could go without a driver's license for a year. He didn't understand why I was mad at having to do all the driving and at his general lack of responsibility.

Dave was alarmingly unconcerned by his mistake and my displeasure. It hurt me he hadn't been looking out for me—or even himself—when he didn't renew his license before we left home. What was worse, he didn't seem to care I was upset.

It was weird. He was weird. Dave's behavior was beyond normal boy oversight and poor planning. He was lukewarm about everything. He didn't care what we did, where we went, whether I had to do all the driving.

I couldn't understand it because Dave had always been our tour guide on adventure vacations. He had an excellent sense of direction. He could find his way around in a new place. Dave was a gentleman, too. He always looked out for me.

Like the time in Prague, a few years after we started living together. I got mad at Dave and stormed out of a bar late at night. I quickly got lost trying to find my way back to our hostel. The narrow, cobblestone streets all looked the same to me and wound circuitously instead of being laid out on an easy grid. The street names were foreign and meaningless. I was worried, but I tried to look casual as I attempted to get my bearings. Just about the time I was figuring out I was in trouble, lost in a foreign land, Dave rescued me.

"Hey!" Dave shouted from a block back. "You ready to go back to the hostel?"

He'd settled our bar tab and hurried after me without my knowing. He trailed me to make sure I was OK while I blew off steam. He easily navigated us home while I sulked beside him—grateful but embarrassed.

That was the travel partner I expected. Dave looked out for me, he got us unlost, he discovered the coolest spots. He was passionate and energized in new places. He loved exploring and adventure.

Through years of traveling together, Dave was our adventure leader. He was great at picking up foreign languages and was charming enough to communicate when he couldn't figure out the language. He was outgoing and fearless where I was shy and reserved. He had plans for us: places we had to go and things we had to do. He helped me without my having to ask.

That Dave seemed to be gone. This new Dave was distant and disinterested in our Hawaii adventure.

We did sprinkle in good times. We hiked and camped and swam in the huge ocean. We made friends with a local couple who invited us into their home for food, a place to crash when we had nowhere else, and some fabulous music jams.

Playing music with Dave in that home was perfect. We looked deeply into each other's eyes as we played. I loved him so much; we loved each other. At one point, when a dozen people were jamming in the garage, Dave and I went into the house together. Standing in the kitchen, I drummed and Dave played mandolin. We wore big, silly smiles and played in perfect rhythm with each other. I thought, "We are so right-on. I don't care about our troubles; if we have *this*, we'll be OK together."

On one of the days we spent with our Hawaiian friends, we took a hike to an awesome waterfall and swimming hole deep in the woods behind their house. The cold water was clear and invigorating. We splashed and played. We stuck our heads under the rushing waterfall and squealed with exhilaration.

After we walked back home, I realized I'd lost two of the semi-precious stones that Dave had bought for me at a gem store a few days earlier. He and I went back to the waterfall alone and found the stones where we'd taken our clothes off to swim.

These stones had become very important to me. They felt strong and protective. I prayed a lot during those Hawaii days. I prayed to the stones, the island, the volcano. The earth-as-my-protector-and-home concept was soothing to me while I was feeling alienated from my usual protector and home: Dave.

On the walk back from retrieving the stones, we stopped, sat, and took in the peacefulness of the tropical woods. There, on a bed of huge green leaves, we made amazing, soul-connected love.

Things were so off for us. I knew something was wrong, and it was breaking us up. On a day-to-day, practical level, Dave and I weren't getting along. Yet, on a primal and spiritual level, we were as connected and as much in love as ever. When it came to playing music or making love, when we lost ourselves, things were still perfect.

The uncomfortable and uneasy times were outweighing the primal connected ones. I didn't feel as if Dave could take care of himself. He was unable or unwilling to decide on places to go, where to stay, even what to order from a dinner menu.

He hadn't brought swim shorts for our tropical island vacation. He brought a wool hat, though. On eighty-plus degree days, he was wearing his wool hat and lounging on the beach in his underwear. He didn't see a problem with his beach outfit, even as it embarrassed and irritated me.

I wished the Hawaii days would end. I wished for escape from my wool hat and underpants on the beach husband. I thought: "Oh shit, how did I get here?"

Back home, I had to figure out what to do with my life. Dave was unwilling to admit we had problems. I was tired of hearing "If you're unhappy, you need to fix it" when I tried to discuss it. There was only one time I remember Dave admitting something may have been wrong.

We were sitting together on the couch on a hot summer day, letting the fan wash over us.

"You're just not yourself, Dave," I said. "And you're not happy."

He looked at me hard. Instead of his usual immediate dismissal of my concerns, he was thinking. His face strained; he looked confused.

"You're right," he said. "I think something *is* wrong with me."

"What do you think it is?" I said. This was the first time I ever heard him admit something was wrong, or that his behavior didn't match his intentions. I was glad, but I was a little scared, too.

"It's like I don't always know what I'm doing," he said. "I don't mean to upset you. I don't plan to upset you."

"Then why *do* you?" I asked.

"Things just happen, it's like I can't control it. Sometimes I feel like I'm losing my mind."

"I don't know what to make of that, Dave," I said. He seemed vulnerable and confused, and my heart went out to him. But I was also annoyed that he was avoiding responsibility. Instead of admitting to a mistake or shortcoming, he was claiming things were out of his control.

"Can you try harder to control it?" I asked. "Maybe you could try being more aware of your actions?"

"Yes," he said. "I will. I promise I will."

"And I'll try hard to communicate problems as they come up, instead of bottling things up and then getting mad and throwing fits," I offered.

"There's nothing I want more than to make this work," he said.

"We love each other. There's no reason we *can't* make it work."

But our endless fights and talks weren't productive, and our attempts at changing or improving our relationship were futile. In March, I knew things were bad enough for me to leave Dave.

He told me his boss and coworkers complained about his short temper and unpredictability. He couldn't seem to understand why people were concerned about him or irritated by him.

I talked to Dan, one of Dave's best friends since childhood.

"I'm uncomfortable being around Dave," he admitted. "He's so off-the-wall and unpredictable."

"I feel the same way," I said.

"Especially in public," Dan said. "It's embarrassing. The last time Dave came down to New York, we stayed in."

"Stayed in?!" I said. They had been going out and partying together since they were kids.

"Yeah, it felt too risky to leave the apartment," he said. "Odds were just too great Dave would embarrass me, or start a fight, or get into trouble."

At New Year's, I had recognized this year as a time for change. At first, I wasn't so sure I was committed to leaving Dave and our home. As the weeks passed, I felt more and more that I should.

We'd had lots of rough patches in our time together. It was a constant battle to work through our stubborn, opposed personalities to find peaceful solutions to disagreements. We were a passionate, dramatic young couple.

But now, something new had entered the relationship, something I thought of as the Big Trouble. The Big Trouble was in full swing by spring, but I wasn't sure if I was just approaching the old problems with less tolerance. I was doing my best to work through things, keep a level head, not take things personally, and not make rash decisions I'd regret. I loved my husband and was committed to my marriage.

I was also supremely bothered by Dave's brattiness. His negativity and constant complaining exasperated and depressed me. I thought the problem was that Dave was toxic. Or maybe I was too sensitive. Maybe it was both.

I established early in the year that this would be a year of positivity and discovery for me. I wanted to be free of the heavy drama. Leaving Dave seemed essential for that. He wouldn't compromise because he didn't see a problem. He didn't see a problem despite his friends and coworkers being put off by his aggressive, negative behavior. I decided that if he chose to stay the way he was, I'd choose to leave him.

I was deciding to leave my comfortable life and once-lovable husband. I was stressed and sad, but I wasn't panicking. I was calm about what was unfolding. I didn't like it, I wanted to change it, but I also felt an innate acceptance.

I was taking solace in my past. I had faith I'd survive heartbreak because I'd done it before. In losing Dave, I was remembering my strength. I was experiencing being by myself, being alone and OK with it.

I'd felt destroyed at times in my life before I met Dave. I lived through the devastating and untimely deaths of my mom and Barb. I lived through breaking my neck and injuring my brain in a car crash. Feeling the pain of losing Dave was flashing me back to the pain of those earlier tragedies. The solace came from knowing I overcame pain and loss when it felt as if I couldn't lift my head from my pillow. And each time, I came out stronger.

The other comfort I had was the knowledge I was a strong, independent adventure girl. I was happy and content in the woods, camping, hiking, and rock climbing. I wasn't afraid to do things by myself, and I had a crew of great adventure partners.

In the spring, I went on more adventures than ever. I went rock climbing whenever I wasn't working and could find a partner. When I couldn't find a partner, I hiked. I spent a lot of my time in the Adirondack High Peaks.

In early June, I received a message that helped me make up my mind. I was climbing at Deadwater Cliff with my favorite partner, Sugar Shack Mike. As I was walking along the approach trail, taking in the lush late spring scenery, I looked down to see a beautiful piece of white quartz. I stopped to pick up the stone. Its weight felt comfortable in my hand; I really liked it. I wanted it as a souvenir.

I asked God—the earth, the cliffs, the air surrounding, the rock itself—if it was OK to take the rock. This is my standard procedure when taking souvenirs from the woods, and I had always received a quiet "yes." This day was different. I got a "no" and a message. The message was something like, "You don't have a home right now. You're in transition. You shouldn't take. This is the best you have for a home now; leave the rock here."

The message was heavy. And sad. But also reassuring. My awareness of my surroundings brought me to an awareness of myself. I knew I was losing my home with Dave. I took comfort in knowing I'd always have a home among my adventure partners in the woods or at the cliff.

I was content and peaceful when I was on adventures. My time at Deadwater Cliff gave me comfort and insight. On the two-hour drive back to Albany, I thought a lot about how not having a home with Dave would feel. The closer I got to our apartment, the worse I felt.

I was torn between a perfect spiritual awareness and a sense that everything was OK, and complete confusion and dread about my life and relationship. I was living and grateful. I felt connected and aware, yet I couldn't fix Dave and me.

Going home to Dave over the course of our almost ten-year relationship had always been exciting and wonderful. That night, going home to Dave was hard. What used to make me happy now just made me anxious. There was no telling how Dave would act.

A few days before I met Mike at Deadwater, Dave and I were at home, hanging out in the music room. Everything was cool; we were in a good place, a place Dave loved. I was drumming. Dave had set up his digital recorder with microphones to my drums and his vocals. He started playing harmonica, but it was out of tune. It was out of tune, so Dave threw it against the wall. I recoiled and gasped.

Dave always handled his musical instruments and recording equipment with the utmost care. Time spent making music or recording was the most precious to him. Seeing him throw the harmonica was as shocking to me as watching him strike a child. It was so out of character it terrified me. Dave was peace and comfort to me. He was family. Marriage is never a perfect union, but it was one we had pledged to honor.

Now, driving home from Deadwater Cliff, my peace and comfort were broken. I was dreading going home to my family of one harmonica-throwing, changed man.

Along with outdoor adventures, music was soothing my aching, on-the-brink-of-broken heart. I drove around blasting music. In my sensitive state, certain songs were hitting me deep. The new Built to Spill album *You in Reverse* became my soundtrack. The songs fit what I was feeling—a combination of melancholy and resigned contentment.

In July, I planned a trip to Burlington, Vermont, to see Built to Spill play a live show. The High Peaks were halfway to Burlington, so I planned to meet my dad for a day of climbing before the show. Then I'd stay at Sugar Shack Mike's place in Burlington and climb with him the next day.

On the night before my adventure, I left work at the Ginger Man as early as possible. I was in bed and asleep by midnight. Dave came home in the middle of the night, turning on lights and making noise. He was drunk.

I asked him to turn off the bedroom light.

"Nah," he said. Shocked, I sat up.

"You know I'm getting up early tomorrow," I said.

"I don't really give a fuck," he said.

"You're totally screwing up my sleep," I said.

"Fuck you."

All the time I knew Dave, he could be mean or antagonistic—especially when drunk. But this night was different. He was never mean to me out of the blue. He was generally very considerate and would tiptoe around if I was sleeping. This off-the-wall angry behavior was part of New Dave, part of the Big Trouble.

The next morning, I took off for my rock 'n' roll via Adirondack rock climbing adventure. I was exhausted from the dramatic middle-of-the-night encounter with Dave. I left for the weekend with his last words to me being "fuck you." I felt as if I was escaping, leaving behind stress and discontentment.

I met up with my dad, and we had a good day of climbing in Keene Valley. Despite my lack of sleep, I was energized in the Adirondacks. From there, I pushed on to Burlington. I arrived at the club to find an almost-full parking lot. I found a spot in the back corner and noticed a bunch of indie rock boys drinking cans of PBR next to their Subaru. I headed over with a freshly rolled joint.

They passed me a beer, and I passed them a joint. They were playing with a child's toy voice distorter, saying creepy lines from *The Silence of the Lambs*. I started my night right, left the boys with the joint, and headed into the show. Inside, I bought a Long Trail Ale and pushed into the crowd to see the opening act's last song.

As Built to Spill set up, I moved up near the front of the stage. They started the set with "Liar"—one of my favorites from the new album. The sound was perfect. They were tight and rockin'. I was dizzy with a flood of emotion. I felt the paradox of living: complete peace simultaneous with agony.

"Liar" seemed to be speaking about Dave. It described someone lost in his plans and dreams while life relentlessly chews him up.

The song also described a girl, a girl like me, who sees what's happening. In the end, she finds peace. It's melancholy and real. It's peace in sadness, peace in knowing pain. Peace in living in a clear reality.

The Built to Spill show was magic. The music was cosmic, mathematical. While listening, I felt waves and saw strings. Everything was connected by these songs. Time and space disappeared. I was seven, taping my dead mother's picture facing out the living room window. I was eighteen, driving across the salt flats of Utah and allowing the magic, foreign landscape to relieve the grief of losing Aunt Barb. I was thirty, rock climbing and feeling spiritually whole.

At the show, inspired by the perfect music, I knew: if you don't love somebody right now, then you never did. I felt what it was like to be married and in a family. To be married and alone. I lost track of past and future.

While the band played, images projected on the wall behind the stage. The art was by Mike Scheer, who created the artwork for the *You in Reverse* album. I was captivated and inspired. The lead guitarist had a tattoo across his fingers: F.R.E.E. It took me a while to read it clearly. When I did, I felt awed. He is free. He wears permanent ink across his fingers for everyone to see. He's free to be judged and not care.

I plotted my own new tattoo, one that would capture the perfection of that Built to Spill show. A tribute to my spirit and my discoveries. A tribute to my freedom. And love. And the connectedness of all things. And God.

After the show, I drove to the restaurant where Mike worked. I walked in with the glow of the music cushioning me. The bartender was Mike's friend and was expecting me. He set a half circle of beer samples in front of me. The crowd at the bar was welcoming and buzzing with engaging conversations.

When Mike finished work, we sat to talk about his new love interest. She was moving to California to go to school. Mike wondered if he should follow her. I was reminded of how, after I met Dave, I decided not to move to New Mexico for school. I wondered if Dave would've followed me if I'd chosen to move west.

The next day, Mike and I hiked near Lake Champlain to check out a cliff to climb. It was wet, dirty, and uninspiring. We bailed on our planned day of climbing. The weather was questionable, and we were both tired from our lives and the busy days preceding.

I drove south late that morning. By the time I reached Crown Point, after an hour of driving, I wanted a coffee and a snack. I walked into the only open shop for miles: the Crown Point Bakery. The deep-eyed man behind the counter welcomed me with a warm smile and glowing aura.

He offered me a salad he threw together with greens and vegetables from friends' gardens. I asked for a cup of coffee, which he gave me in his personal, handmade mug. We sat together eating salad, and it felt like a meaningful, deeply friendly encounter. We talked about changing consciousness, organic food, and small self-sufficient communities.

We talked about the project I was working on, goal-setting web-based software. We talked about manifesting goals, motivation, and allowing things to unfold and happen. He called me a wizard.

I went home feeling blessed by two days of perfect, cosmic living. I felt connected with my world and the people in it. I felt the opposite of lonely!

Back at home, I was charged and motivated by my travels. I felt strong and independent. The Built to Spill show reminded me I'm the same strong person who had overcome loss and trauma in the past. It reminded me I'm connected to and supported by an infinite spiritual universe. Taking a road trip and meeting a variety of fun people to connect with reminded me that loneliness can be lifted.

I was ready to leave Dave. I had to leave Dave to save my sanity and my heart. I was ready for freedom from a sour and negative relationship and for the freedom to rediscover myself. In the months leading up to July, there had been a lot of me talking about breaking up, and a lot of Dave saying, "Whatever you think is best." All that talking hadn't added up to any action.

I couldn't bear another month in the apartment with Dave. I was ready to go. I saw my jump off point, and I had to take it. I told our landlord we'd move out at the end of the month.

I moved my stuff a little at a time into a storage unit. Dave wasn't preparing to move out at all. It was as if he didn't grasp what was happening. I made plans with my dad to move into his apartment until I figured out a new living situation. Dave made no plan about where he would live.

The last day of July finally came. I packed the last of my random things into my car. Dave had a truck and was haphazardly loading his stuff while I cleaned the apartment. The last thing I put in my car was our cat, Abby. Dave and I stood on the porch together, and I cried. We hugged. He told me everything would be OK. He told me I was right, things hadn't been working out. He told me I was being strong and doing the right thing, and I had to keep doing the right thing.

Abby and I went to my dad's. I held it together. I had a wide open future. I was lost from my husband and alone in my life, but had a protected spot where I could regroup and find my path again.

That first night away from Dave and our home, sleeping on a futon in my dad's living room, I dreamed of driving north along the Pacific coast. The ocean was close to the road with beautiful dark rock rising from it and creating sea inlets. There were pieces of white quartz along the shore. I thought of stopping to take a bit home, but remembered how the Gods in the Adirondacks told me I wasn't allowed to take rocks because I didn't have a home to take them to.

The next day I noticed a poster leaning against the wall in the cluttered spare bedroom. It was a photograph of a spectacular waterfall. We looked up the location of the waterfall in the picture and found out it was near the Pacific coast in Oregon.

I was remarkably comforted by this synchronicity. Even though I was in transition and feeling loss, I felt right in my world. I was where I was supposed to be. I was open to being cared for and loved by my family and friends. I was open to messages in my dreams and the details in the world around me. I was open to receiving help and guidance from the universe and from God.

This is the Place Our Love Built

After Dave and I stopped living together, I started living like a college kid in a college neighborhood. I moved into a one-bedroom apartment next door to The Ginger Man, in the heart of Albany's student ghetto. I worked late nights there, then went out with my coworkers. I stayed out late, drank a lot, and smoked pot. I developed a crush on a twenty-two-year-old boy cook. We went dancing at the gay clubs. My friend Tracey had taught me, "A man dances like he fucks." After I danced with the boy cook, I was determined to have sex with him.

I was still seeing Dave. We were getting together once every week or two. I was sure Dave and I would get back together. That's why I picked such a young boy as the object of my desire. I knew nothing serious would come from it, so it was a safe way to pass the time while Dave and I sorted through a rough patch.

When Dave would stop by my apartment, I could never relax. I always wanted him to acknowledge our separation and trouble, and he always seemed oblivious.

One evening he met me at my apartment so we could go to a marriage counselor. Though it was well after quitting time, he showed up wearing paint stained, dirty work clothes. He was skinny and scruffy.

I drove us to the suburbs to meet with the social worker a friend had recommended to me as a good relationship counselor. It was nighttime, and the building was mostly dark, as if everyone had gone home.

Sandra met us in the lobby and ushered us down a long corridor to a small room. The light was low. Bright art hung on the walls. Besides an office chair where Sandra sat, there was a love seat and a recliner. I took the recliner, and Dave sat on the love seat.

"Amelia, you initiated the breakup, so can you explain the problem?" Sandra asked.

"It's like Dave's been going through a transformation," I started. "A gradual transformation. Over the months, he started working more," I said. "He was short-tempered and apathetic. He doesn't have much interest in planning travel and fun anymore. And that used to be central in our lives."

Sandra listened attentively. Dave shifted between looking distracted and exasperated.

"He hardly plays guitar or writes songs," I continued. "He used to do that all the time. He's obsessed with writing a screenplay and building birdhouses, but I don't see any tangible evidence of those goals coming to fruition.

"He's always late when he's expected somewhere, and he…" I paused, and when I spoke again, my voice sounded funny, a register too high. "He doesn't seem to care we're breaking up."

"Dave, what do you think about the things Amelia said?" Sandra asked.

"It's accurate," he said and shrugged. "But I don't know how to fix it."

Dave was slouched and defeated-looking. He was lost in the counselor's love seat; he looked small.

"Do you want to fix it?" Sandra asked.

"Yes. I want things to be different," he said. "I want Amelia in my life." He sounded detached and resigned. He didn't look at either of us.

"How might things be different, Dave?" Sandra asked. "How could they change in a positive way?"

"I don't know." He shrugged again.

"Can you tell me what you want?" Sandra asked. "What do you want from life, from your relationship?"

"I don't know," he said again. His voice seemed to come from miles away.

Sandra looked down at her notes. She flipped back a few pages, re-reading.

"I'm concerned that you're living apart," she said. "Why didn't you seek help before you separated?"

"I couldn't get Dave to admit there was a problem until we stopped living together," I said. "I was never ambitious enough to seek help when I was the only one with a problem or desire to fix things."

She looked at Dave for his response, but he was silent. She waited a beat or two. I could feel the entire dark, deserted building around us. The bright art on the wall looked out of place.

"Dave, I recommend you come see me independently," she said at last. "It seems like Amelia knows what she wants, and she's taking action to take care of herself and get what she needs."

I felt validated, yet disappointed. I didn't want the problem all in Dave's hands, because I feared it wouldn't get fixed that way.

We wrapped up the session and drove back to my apartment, barely speaking.

"Can I come in?" Dave asked in the driveway.

"Will you see the counselor again?" I asked. "Like she recommended?"

"I don't see a reason to!" he said.

"Then I can't let you come in," I said. "I'm sorry. But if you're not taking action to help us fix our crumbling marriage, I can't perpetuate a false hope we'll get back together."

In September, on my fourth wedding anniversary, my good friend Kristen called to wish me a happy anniversary. She was living in Chicago with her husband and young son. We hadn't been in close touch for a few months.

When I moved out, I had kept the phone number Dave and I shared at our apartment together. Kristen had no idea she was calling my new apartment. I was too sad and ashamed to tell her I was living alone, separated from Dave. I was still hoping Dave and I would patch things up before I had to tell everyone our marriage had failed.

A few weeks later, Dave came over for dinner. Sometime after dinner, I thought we'd go to bed. I went to the bedroom and encouraged Dave to follow. I ended up falling asleep before he joined me. When I woke up alone hours later, I could see Dave, through the cracked bedroom door, kneeling on my living room floor measuring pieces of wood—presumably for a birdhouse—and writing the measurements on a piece of notebook paper.

I groggily walked out of the bedroom and stood behind him.

"David, what are you doing?" I asked, confused and annoyed.

"I don't want to go to bed. I need to do this." He spoke quickly, his sentences running together. "I need to get this done."

"What? What are you getting done?" I asked. I was sad and tired. I was letting Dave stay at my place so we could spend time together, so we could be intimate. I longed for my husband to go to bed with me, and my husband wanted to stay up all night measuring scraps of wood.

"You're being weird," I declared. "You're obsessing. I think you have OCD or something."

It was scary seeing him like that. He was crouched on hands and knees, wide-eyed, like a mad scientist. We were in my tiny apartment, our home together gone, and our futures eerily undecided.

I sent him home. I was sick with loving him and losing him. I couldn't bear his disconnect, his dwindling sanity.

In October, my paternal grandfather died. Dave had respected and gotten along with Grandpa, who was deaf and nearly impossible to communicate with. I called Dave to tell him the news.

He showed up at the ceremony—a formal event at the college where Grandpa worked as a professor and research scientist—dressed in dirty work clothes. He was loud and disruptive. He didn't seem to know what was proper attire or behavior. He sat beside me in the front row, a complete foil to my somber disposition and fancy outfit.

Dave's home was a third-floor studio apartment four blocks from mine. The building was an old brownstone. The original wood trim and railings were finely polished. The long, narrow stairways were covered with 1960s-era paisley patterned carpet. The hallway outside Dave's apartment smelled of Indian spice. Inside his apartment, the smell was so strong it could've been an Indian restaurant.

Around Christmastime, I visited Dave. Every inch of the tiny room was filled with Dave's stuff. In one corner, he had a table with two chairs. In another, he'd set up his recording gear and instruments. His four-track mixer was set up to record. There was a microphone on a stand, a small drum kit I'd never seen, and two guitars. His assortment of scavenged Salvation Army kids' musical toys was piled on a shelf. Crowded as it was, his small living space was organized and well kept.

Dave pulled the two chairs out, so they were facing each other at the foot of his bed. He instructed me to sit and handed me a tambourine, a kids' xylophone, and a hand drum.

"I wrote a new song," he explained as he sat across from me with his guitar. "I'll play it and you play along with me."

He did. I did. We made music together. It was great. We were peaceful and connected. These rare times kept me hanging on. That night everything was good. Dave and I were together and things felt right.

I was hopeful that his neat apartment and songwriting were signs that Dave's mental state was improving.

When January came, I moved to a new apartment with Mary. It was a two-bedroom in a converted warehouse. The building felt like a college dorm: hip and filled with young people. The ceilings were high and the windows were big. Everything was remodeled, the trim painted bright white and the railings painted red.

Mary and I both worked at The Ginger Man. We were both trying to cope with breakups from relationships gone bad. We were both close to thirty and happy to stay out late with kids ten years younger.

Dave had always gotten along with Mary. He respected and admired her: she was beautiful, funny, smart, and a good friend. Mary thought Dave was hilarious.

I liked watching the two of them together. When he stopped by our place, Dave and Mary would chat about her goals. She was finishing her master's degree in education. Dave told Mary he liked the idea of working with kids. It was refreshing to hear Dave talk about the future and possible goals.

On one of Dave's visits, I asked him to help me build a table for our kitchen. There was a nook between the refrigerator and the wall, and not much counter space. He agreed, and we went to the hardware store to buy supplies.

Dave built the table in our living room. Normally, he was precise and diligent as a carpenter. He was an artisan. When building things in the past, he told me the importance of using screws—so you could tighten, adjust, or disassemble later. He used nails to put my table together.

"I thought you said it was best to use screws, Dave," I inquired. "Why the nails?"

He stopped and looked at me, puzzled. It was as if I'd reminded him of something he didn't quite understand. He went back to work. The job he did was slow—as if he was agonizing over making it perfect, but the finished table looked sloppy, like it was rushed. Very un-Dave.

When he finished, he seemed relieved, as if he was surprised that he'd gotten it done. Instead of helping me paint it, he watched TV. Normally, Dave saw a project through to the end, making sure it was done perfectly.

It felt strange that he watched TV as I continued working. It felt strange that he did what seemed like a half-assed job. It seemed as if he didn't care. He didn't care about me, and he didn't care about his art.

In February, I was feeling desperate and sad. I missed Dave urgently, but shied away from seeing him because all our encounters were disastrous. Dave was aloof, angry, or nonsensical when we met. My hopes were dashed repeatedly. Yet I was still completely hung up on him. Until he gave me an indication he'd stopped loving me, I still hoped to reunite.

I wasn't in contact with Dave by mid-February, but our mutual friends told me he was pining over me.

"He's a broken record," Adam said to me one day. "All he wants to talk about is you."

Then why wasn't he attempting to win me back? Why wasn't he professing his love to me? Why wasn't he making art and music? Why wasn't he writing an Amelia Breakup Song like he did during our past rough patches?

I was making broken-heart art. I was writing poetry and songs. I was trying to teach myself guitar so I could make my own breakup song.

I was struck by photographs of war-torn, blown out buildings in *Smithsonian* magazine. The half-standing, destroyed buildings still maintained their beauty and elegance. They were artfully and solidly built.

The photographs illustrated my feelings for Dave. I cut the pictures out and used them to make a Valentine. I wrote, "This is the place our love built." In that card, I told Dave that despite our physical separation, we were in the same place. We were dwelling in the tragically beautiful ruins of our love. Love was still the basis for our experience together. We were devastated and imperfect, but our strong, loving foundation was still partly standing and we were still lingering in that broken place. I mailed the card to Dave.

Around the same time, I left a note under his windshield wiper. I often passed his car parked near his apartment and seeing it always make my heart ache. One day I pulled over and scribbled "I love you forever" on a scrap of paper and left it under the windshield wiper for Dave to find. I couldn't bear seeing Dave, but I was still reaching out to him, trying to let him know he was in my heart and on my mind.

One night I called to check in on him. Work had slowed so much he couldn't afford his apartment. He'd moved in with his mother and brother.

"My brother and I hang out in the basement smoking pot and watching movies," he told me. "It's great."

After I hung up, I stood dumbfounded. I felt desperately alone. I'd been hopeful that our time apart, in separate apartments, with separate lives, would bring Dave and me back together. I'd been thinking the best, allowing optimism to build during the time Dave and I didn't speak.

I fought the urge to crawl into bed and cry. I called our mutual friend, Katie.

"I think something might really be wrong with Dave," I said. I explained what he'd just told me. "How could he think this new lifestyle is an improvement over our life together?"

"Let me call him," Katie said. "I'll find out what's going through his mind."

I waited by the phone until she called back.

"OK, I don't think you have anything to worry about," Katie reassured me. "I think Dave is just getting some bad behavior out of his system. And he says he's crazy about you."

"He's not acting like it," I said.

"He has only positive things to say about you; he wants to be with you."

"Why can't he ever tell *me* that?!"

"I encouraged him to tell you himself," Katie said. "Hold on, Aim. I'm convinced he's coming back to you when he gets his head straight."

I didn't know what to do. One part of me knew Dave had to make his own choices. One part of me wanted to intervene on the bad choices. I wanted to help my love, save my husband, and bring my partner home.

I did a tarot card reading that February. I meditated on what my role should be in Dave's self-destruction. Should I hold on to our relationship? How much effort I should put into influencing Dave and getting him back?

My interpretation of the cards I drew was positive. The message I got was to stay back and have faith. I should let Dave find his own way, and he'd come out of darkness as a new and better man. The cards representing our relationship said everything would be OK.

I hung back. I made a choice to let go. I resigned myself to have faith things would be OK, and there was nothing I could do to change the outcome.

I spent more time with a guy I'd met at the climbing gym and had been dating since January. We had real dates and lots of fun together. Neil knew I was married and hoping to get back together with Dave. He was a graduate student, uncertain of his own future, so we were happy to have companionship with no long-term commitment.

While I was hanging out with Neil, Dave went traveling.

In March, Dave called me to say he'd just gotten home from a road trip to North Carolina. He'd driven to Charlotte to visit his old friend Murph for a few days. He'd also stopped in Raleigh-Durham to see another old friend, Frank.

Since our breakup, Dave had been talking about visiting Murph, or maybe even moving in with him. I thought moving there was a bad idea because Dave seemed out of control. I knew Murph was a heavy drinker and a hard partier, so I worried Dave would be swept further down a self-destructive path.

"Baby, all I did was think of you while I was away," Dave said sweetly. "I missed you so much. I know now I could never move away from you."

I was guarded, but this was music to my ears.

"I fixed Frank's porch," Dave explained. "He was so happy. I saved him a bunch of money. He and his girl are so happy together. Seeing them made me miss you."

Not only was Dave expressing his feelings for me, but he was traveling and fixing things. We had a great conversation. He told me about his adventures, his partying with Murph, and making music with Frank.

He asked if he could see me. I couldn't resist. We made plans for the following day.

That night, I met up with Neil. I told him about Dave's trip and his apparent clarity. I told him I couldn't see him anymore because I was ready to give Dave another chance. Neil was happy for me. In our time together, he saw how deeply I cared for Dave.

"I was hoping this would happen," Neil said with a smile. "I know you guys are meant to be."

Dave's clarity didn't last. When he came to see me that next day, it was as if our great phone conversation hadn't happened. He was considering moving to North Carolina. He didn't have money and was hardly working. He was pissed at his mom; she was nagging him too much.

He didn't ask any questions about my life.

"I thought you missed me. I thought we were going to try again," I whined.

"Huh? Oh, yeah, I did miss you. I do want to try. You're my girl," Dave answered, confused, as if he didn't know why I'd think any differently.

"Dave, you're going to have to do some things differently if we're going to be together," I explained.

Then I heard myself and stopped. I realized I was hearing myself say those words for the umpteenth time. I realized I didn't want to hear those words again. I knew what I had to do.

"You aren't making an effort to change, so we aren't getting back together," I said. "Mary's mom gave me the number of a divorce lawyer. I'll make an appointment this week."

"Whatever you think is best," Dave said.

"If you come with me, and we agree about the terms of our separation, it will be cheap and smooth," I explained.

"OK, I'll do whatever you want."

So, we met up later that week and drove together to our new lawyer's office. We signed a separation agreement. In New York State, a couple had to go through a one-year separation to be divorced without a lawsuit. That was the cheapest way to do it.

Otherwise, for a faster divorce, one party had to sue the other for adultery, abandonment, or abuse.

Though we wouldn't be divorced right away, taking an official step to show Dave things weren't improving felt productive. I hoped it would motivate him to take our breakup seriously.

Dave faded away again. We spoke occasionally. Once, I called him to tell him we were invited to our friend Michelle's wedding in California that May. Dave loved Michelle and he loved Los Angeles. I expected him to jump at the opportunity to travel west. Instead, he was apathetic.

I was hurt and confused. Again. Dave was passing up a chance to spend time with me—the woman he claimed to want to be with. He was also passing up a chance to go to one of his favorite places to party with a group of his best friends. Me, friends, parties, travel… these were Dave's favorite things. Why wasn't he interested in celebrating them all at once on a cool adventure?

I backed off again. The next time I heard from him was in April.

The phone rang.

"I'm so happy to be back in the U.S. It's good to hear your voice," Dave sighed.

"Back in the U.S.? Where were you?" I asked.

"My brother and I went to Mexico. I got stuck there. My brother went home yesterday. I'm at JFK waiting for a connection," he explained.

"Huh? How'd you get stuck in Mexico?" I interrupted.

"I got arrested. My brother left without me."

"WHAT? You were arrested!? In Mexico?"

"Twice!" Dave joyfully exclaimed and broke into his characteristic cackle.

I was silent, shocked. I thought this was more evidence that Dave's problems were extending beyond me and marital unrest. He was out of control.

"I can't wait to see you. I missed you," Dave confessed, his tone softening. "Can I see you when I get home?"

"Of course you can, Dave. Call me when you're back in town."

We hung up.

I didn't hear from him for another few days. In those few days, I started using my head over my heart. I'd moved out of my home with Dave because his erratic behavior was hurting and stressing me. We weren't living together, but he was still hurting and stressing me. I decided I had to make a stronger statement to Dave and take better care of myself.

After he was home for a week, he came to my apartment. The details of his Mexico trip were foggy for him. I assumed he'd been drinking and using drugs on his vacation. He was arrested for sleeping in a public park. He was detained at the airport for acting intoxicated before getting on the plane home.

"Oh, David," I sighed. "You're supposed to be getting your shit straight. Getting arrested in Mexico isn't helping."

He shrugged. "I was on vacation with my bro. I was having fun."

"You've had eight months to show me you wanted to be healthy and work on our relationship. Things have only gotten worse. You're unemployed, living with your mother, getting arrested, drinking too much..." I was tired of hearing myself complain.

We were stuck in an exhausting, unproductive cycle. We were holding onto each other through discontent and frustration. Neither of us knew how to get on without the other.

Well, if Dave was having fun on a Mexican vacation, and plowing forward with no concern for his future, maybe I should try a similar approach. I accepted the invitation to Michelle's wedding in May. I convinced Sugar Shack Mike to meet me in Red Rocks, Nevada, to climb for a week before I headed to Los Angeles for the wedding.

I flew to Las Vegas and rented a convertible. We stayed at the climber campground and met people from all over the world. Mike and I climbed hard every day and partied at the campground at night.

The place was crawling with cute young climber boys. I was one of very few girls and the only one there without a boyfriend. I soaked up all the boy attention, letting it soothe my lonely heart. By the end of the week, I was smitten with Luke, a ski/climber bum from Aspen, Colorado.

There's nothing like spending a few nights with a twenty-two-year-old athlete to ease the pain of a filed-for-legal-separation thirty-year-old woman. I left Vegas in my convertible and felt high from my Nevada vacation. I drove the three hours across the desert with my music blasting a soundtrack to the first feeling of contentment I'd had in months.

I arrived in L.A. and was greeted by a group of my oldest and best friends. Reunited from around the world, we were thrilled to be to-gether. We went out to eat and then to the local dive bar to drink beer and play Ms. Pac-Man.

That first night, the thrill of being with my old crew was enough to overshadow Dave's absence. No one asked about him, but everyone listened raptly as I described my short but thrilling affair with Luke and my Red Rocks climbing adventures.

The next morning, I woke up on the couch in Michelle's apart-ment and was painfully aware that I was surrounded by four couples. And I'd be going to a wedding the next day—the first since my mar-riage breakup. I felt heavy. I missed Dave.

While the bride- and groom-to-be spent the day making last mi-nute wedding preparations, the rest of us went to the beach. We walked, swam, and rode the Ferris wheel at Santa Monica Pier. Throughout the day, I couldn't help but cheer up. I was having fun with my friends.

In the evening, we moved from Michelle's apartment to a hotel room. I'd be sleeping on the floor while Jeremy and Shiho took one bed and Katie and Charlie took the other. Settling in to the room, I was again aware of Dave's absence. He should've been there to make me a couple like the rest of my friends.

Shiho noticed my sad face and put her arm around me.

"We all miss Dave," she consoled, "but we'll make you happy!"

Tears squirted down my face and everyone gathered around me as I sat on the edge of Shiho's hotel bed. I reported on Dave's crazy behavior and my exasperation. I admitted I felt alone in a room full of well-matched couples.

"Oh, Aim, I know it's hard. Remember, Dave is a wacky guy. He's always been wacky. You guys will sort it out," Jeremy assured me.

"Yeah, we know he loves you. He'll come around," Katie consoled me through her own tears.

We reminisced together, laughing and crying over the past, until we felt better.

Everyone was emotional. These friends had been witnesses to Dave's and my long relationship road. They had been at our amazing weekend-long wedding. They empathized with my loss. We all loved Dave and were confused by his choices.

Climber-Bum

I came home from California feeling vastly different from my friends. They were married, pregnant, buying houses, planning international moves. I opened my mailbox to find a packet from my lawyer. As of May 15, Dave and I were legally separated.

I decided since I was so far off from my peers, I'd embrace my lifestyle and live an extreme no-strings-attached summer. The lease for our apartment was up at the end of June, so Mary and I went our separate ways. Mary found a one-bedroom apartment, but I decided not to look for a new apartment.

In June, I loaded my car with camping and climbing gear. I stuffed everything else into a storage unit. I activated the pay-by-the-minute cell phone my aunt had given me for Christmas and gave up the land-line number Dave and I had since we moved in together eight years before. I rented the cabin on Lake George in the Adirondacks that my paternal grandparents had been staying in for decades. Without my grandfather, my grandmother didn't feel up to the usual June getaway.

I stayed in the cabin for the last two weeks of June. I always loved time spent at the lake. It was peaceful and quiet. I cherished the solitude. I made a lot of art. I sketched birdhouses and guitars. I wrote poetry inspired by lines from Shakespeare: *And I will die a hundred thousand deaths, Ere break the smallest parcel of this vow.*

About Dave, I wrote, "Not having you turned into having nothing." I felt truly alone, but not lonely. I felt as if I was making choices to be strong away from Dave. I felt independent. Shedding my partner, my home, and my stuff felt liberating. I was existing in a simple, peaceful way. I was starting from nothing, instead of holding onto broken pieces of my married life. I was committed to living, but also not breaking my vow to Dave.

I was still his wife, but I was taking a new approach. I was adapting to our changes instead of holding desperately to the past.

After the two weeks at the cabin by the lake, I headed to the Adirondack High Peaks. I camped or stayed at the hostel in Keene Valley for most of July. I spent my days climbing when I could find a partner or hiking when I was alone. I used wireless Internet signals to check in with work.

On rainy nights or when I worked at the Ginger Man, I slept on couches back in Albany. I didn't hesitate to tell people I didn't have a home. I felt liberated embracing my life's lack of direction or structure. Instead of wallowing in what I'd lost, I was basking in my freedom.

Sometime in mid-July, Dave called. I was camped on the south end of Lake George near a cliff my rock climber friends were developing. I was surprised when my phone vibrated that night; I thought I was too deep in the woods to get service. I was even more surprised when I saw Dave's number on the caller ID.

I answered with the usual combination of reluctance and hopefulness I had when taking calls from Dave.

"Where are you?" he asked.

"Camping near Lake George. I don't have a home, you know," I said, showing off my newfound cavalier life approach.

"Yeah, I know. You're a climber-bum. I miss you. When are you coming back?" he asked, sounding defeated.

"I dunno. I'm not making any plans," I replied cautiously. "Why?"

"Why? Because I want to see you. I don't think you should be camping by yourself. Are you safe?"

Oh boy, here's where my hard heart softens in a New York minute.

"Of course I'm safe, David. Nobody's around; I'm in the peaceful Adirondack woods," I assured him.

"I should come there," Dave replied decidedly.

"What?!" I was shocked. I was pleased despite my best judgment based on our recent past.

"I want to be with you. You're my wife. You shouldn't be alone in the woods. How do I get there?"

Oh boy, here's where my head turns to confused mush.

This is the concern I'd been longing for and expecting from Dave for months. This is the Dave I knew. In our relationship, Dave was always a gentleman and a protector. He watched out for me. The Dave I'd known for ten years, who had been morphing into a stranger over the past one year, was showing himself to me again.

That's what made me take him back again and again. I knew Dave as a protective, caring, loving partner so much longer, so many more years, than I knew him as an out-of-control and unpredictable heart-breaker.

These glimpses of the Dave I knew blanketed me with familiar comfort. He was the person I trusted and loved most in the world. All I needed to welcome him back into my life was for him to be himself.

"It's real easy to get here," I started. I gave him the simple directions and estimated it would take him forty-five minutes to get to me from his mother's house.

I hung up. I surveyed my camp. While I was talking to Dave, the sun had set. I still needed to make a trip to my car to put my food away. I picked through the pockets in my tent until I found my headlamp. I walked the five-minute trail to my car. The woods were quiet and still.

I'd been camping and playing in the Adirondack woods since I was a baby. I always felt at ease without the comforts of home. I wasn't afraid of the dark; I wasn't afraid of being alone. I liked it.

When I got to my car parked on the edge of the dirt road, I was overcome with an uneasy feeling. I suddenly felt vulnerable. I hadn't heard anything, but I sensed I wasn't alone. I shivered in the seventy-degree night. I tucked my food bag away in my trunk and scurried back to my tent. I couldn't lose my sense of unease.

I wanted Dave to arrive and ease my lonely, vulnerable feeling. I sat on a rock at the lake's edge and watched the moonlight reflect over the water's ripples, and tried to be patient.

As the minutes passed, I became more anxious. Every sound—a snapping branch or rustle in the grass—made me jump.

That night waiting for Dave was unlike any other time I've ever spent in the woods. Instead of the usual peaceful feeling, I felt scared. I wasn't afraid of anything in particular; I was just ill at ease.

I got up and walked back to my tent. The moon was bright enough I didn't need to use my headlamp. I looked at my phone to see how much time had passed since I hung up with Dave. Thirty minutes. It felt like a lifetime.

I paced back to the rock. I lay there looking up at the moon and stars, listening to the water, and trying not to listen to the sounds in the surrounding trees.

"I'm home," I tried convincing myself in a whisper. "I picked this place; I like it here. Everything's cool. I'm safe."

My heart was pounding. I forced myself to hold my lakeside post. I was waiting for Dave. Again.

I managed to relax for a while. If I hadn't been waiting for Dave, I'd be in my tent reading a book and waiting for sleep to come. I got up and wandered back to the tent to get my book and check the time. It had been well over an hour since I'd talked to Dave.

I was overcome by Dave's absence. I couldn't stay there without him! Where was he? A warm breeze rustled the trees and made me shiver again. I jogged the path back to my car and jumped in the driver side. Something had spooked me. I locked the car door.

Once I knew he was coming to find me, I couldn't get comfortable without Dave. I tried calling his phone, but got no answer. I feared I was being stood up. Again.

I felt weak and fearful. Dave's abandonment manifested as a terror of the woods. My loneliness and loss became a monster lurking in the darkness. I decided to drive to town. I'd sleep in my car in a parking lot.

I headed out on the dirt road. After a couple of miles, headlights were bouncing on the rutted road toward me. I stopped, knowing it must be Dave. He stopped next to me and opened his window.

"I've been lost! I've been searching for you!" he screeched, exasperated.

I was confused. Dave never got lost. He had a great sense of direction. He was familiar with the area. The dirt road I was camping off was three turns from the highway and was well marked.

I was relieved. Exhausted, I led Dave back to the pull off for my camp. He followed me into the woods.

The spot at the lake was beautiful and innocuous with Dave at my side.

We sat looking at the lake. Dave put his arm around me.

"I don't know how you expected me to find you here," Dave stated, sounding annoyed.

"Dave, it's easy. I don't know how you got lost," I replied defensively.

"Easy! We're in the middle of nowhere!" he gasped.

"It's only three turns. We've been hiking along this road before. I think you've even been in here before you met me," I argued.

"No way. I have no idea where we are," Dave sighed.

"If you say so," I conceded.

He'd been as stressed by trying to find me as I was waiting for him. This was the story of our breakup: wanting to be together, but held apart and threatened by unseen forces. What should've been easy was hard. What was hard exhausted us both.

We held hands as we walked over to my tent. We lay down inside but left the door open to allow air to circulate and keep us from over-heating. We held onto each other. We didn't talk, but lay awake for a long time. We were both beyond tired, but didn't want to waste the rare time together by sleeping.

The next morning, we woke to a steady rain. Dave helped me carry my wet gear to my car.

After my car was packed, we stood facing each other in the rain. We held hands and looked at each other's faces, but we didn't say much. We hugged. We agreed that seeing one another was comforting and stressful all at once. We were both afraid to talk, painfully aware that we were likely to miscommunicate and argue.

"OK. So. So, I'll see you around?" I said, trying to be casual.

"Uh huh. Glad I found you last night," Dave answered. He kissed me and said, "Sweet baby."

My heart ached as I got in my car, smelly and wet. Dave sped off down the muddy road. I let him get a good head start before I pulled onto the road behind him. I headed to Grandma Whalen's house to regroup.

The rain that started the night Dave and I slept together in my tent didn't stop. My plans to be homeless were washed away. The bed at Grandma's house was warm and her company was therapeutic.

I was as happy to be in a home as I'd been to start the adventure of homelessness one short month earlier. With a regular shower, I picked up more shifts at the Ginger Man to supplement my regular technical writing gig. I'd been socking money away since before I broke up with Dave.

I figured out I wanted a home. After losing mine with Dave, I had fun being a free spirit. From dorm-style living to adventurer home-lessness, I maximized my experience. With that behind me, I was ready to rebuild a home for myself. I started house hunting.

Dave and I looked at houses before our marital problems began. We wanted the same things: a two-family with rental income to supplement the mortgage, a driveway, a working basement, a finished attic.

I found my house right away. I felt as if it was waiting for me. The name of my new street was Latin for "old friend." Slim as the odds were becoming, I hoped Dave would come home to me and this house would be waiting when he did.

After our night camping, Dave and I stayed in touch. We'd talk on the phone a couple of nights a week. I kept him informed about my house search. He was interested, but oddly not inquisitive. His reaction wasn't one of apathy as much as misunderstanding. When we spoke, it was as if he was missing pieces of our past. He couldn't figure out why we weren't buying a house together. He was so stumped on that part of the equation, he neglected to ask me the details that carpenter, construction worker Dave would have been curious about.

One night after talking for a while on the phone, we agreed to meet for coffee at a bookstore between his mom's house and Grandma's house. When I got there, the lights were off and the store was closed. Dave was sitting in his car in the dark parking lot. I pulled into the spot next to him and moved into the passenger seat of his car.

This was one of the rare times Dave admitted something was wrong. He was sad.

"I hate living at my mom's house," he said, "but I feel like I have nowhere else to go."

"That's why I'm buying a house," I empathized. "I'm tired of not having my own place to go to."

"You always know the right thing to do. You always know where you're going," Dave sighed.

I remembered the first song he wrote for me during a rough patch about a year into our relationship.

In it, Dave sings:

> *Get where you're going to*
> *I'd like to get there too*
> *But I just don't know the way*

This was a recurring theme for us, but Dave brought it up as if it was a new idea.

"I'm no good for you. I fuck everything up. You're better off without me," Dave said to his lap.

"Oh, David," I scolded, "stop it. You know that's not true. You're the raddest boy I've ever known. Look at me."

He glanced at me for a few seconds before looking down again, depleted.

"You just gotta get your shit straight, Dave! Please! I know you can do it," I encouraged.

"Nah. I can't. You're better off without me. In your new house. I'm happy for you. I can't give you what you need," Dave said definitively.

I was shocked to hear this coming from Dave. Feeling and fearing the things he was saying were true caused me to leave him, but I didn't *want* them to be true and I didn't want him to surrender to these ideas.

Hearing these words coming from him delivered a new pain. He was defeated and depressed—a rare state for confident, energetic Dave. He was acknowledging the reality of our situation for the first time. This was new pain in a new emotional place. It may have taken a year and my buying a house without him, but it seemed that Dave was coming to terms with our separation.

We somberly said goodbye without a hug or kiss.

The ten-minute drive back to my Grandma's house was enough time for me to feel Dave's words sink in and have panic strike. I felt a rush of loss. I didn't want Dave to give up!

As soon as I got home, I called him.

Pterodactyl Screech

"I'm *not* better off without you, David," I said when he answered. My sentences tumbled out. "I don't like this, it's not easy for me. I'm just trying to survive, and I'd rather do it *with* you. Maybe now you see there *is* a problem, you can figure out how to fix it."

My call to Dave was the first time since we separated that I poured my heart out to him. I gave up trying to be tough. I gave up trying to do what I thought was logical or had the best chance of repairing our relationship.

We were approaching the one-year mark of our physical separation. My heart didn't feel any better or different. Despite dates, one-night stands, and badass adventures, I was still in love with my husband. I was still sick from things not working for us. I wanted Dave!

Our breakup wasn't changing things as I had hoped. My first wish was for Dave to be himself and for us to have a fairy-tale reunion. If I didn't get that, my second choice was I'd figure out that I was OK—if not better off—without him. Neither wish was coming true.

I still wanted to be with Dave. All the living and planning I was doing without him wasn't curing my heartache.

I confessed all this to Dave that night on the phone. He was glad—as always—to hear I wanted to be with him. He was willing to go along with whatever plan of action I thought was best. He told me again that he loved me and wanted to be with me more than anything.

For the rest of the summer, I was resigned to the fact I was letting go of my husband and dating the weirdo who had taken his place. Knowing I wasn't happy without Dave, I was trying to be happy with Dave—no matter how strangely he was acting.

In August, I moved into my new house. In September, Jeremy moved in with me. One of my best friends, Jeremy had returned from two years of living in Japan and needed a place to stay while his wife, Shiho, lived on-campus to complete an intense graduate program. I was happy to have company and help to pay my mortgage.

Jeremy's presence gave me more insight about Dave's behavior.

Dave would stop by unannounced. If I wasn't home, he'd settle for hanging out with Jeremy. Jeremy had known Dave as long as I had, and he noticed a big difference in Dave's personality from the time before he moved to Japan.

One night I returned home after work to find Jeremy very stressed out.

"Dave was here today. He was totally weird." Jeremy explained. "He kept making pterodactyl noises."

"I told you!" I'd been describing Dave's weird noises to my friends for weeks. I was relieved to know someone else had noticed; I wasn't just being critical or sensitive.

"I'm not sure I'm comfortable with him stopping by here. It's too weird," Jeremy said.

"Don't let him in if you don't want to deal with him," I told him.

As crazy as Dave was getting, I still wanted to let him in. I didn't want to tell him he couldn't stop by. I was starting to think something was really wrong with him. He could be having a serious breakdown. I loved him too much to shut him out when he may need help.

As September wound on, Dave and I saw each other mostly when he stopped by. These unplanned visits were strained. Dave showed up super-amped, as if he'd drunk a six-pack of energy drinks. He wouldn't sit still and babbled excitedly.

Dave could party hard and had experimented with all kinds of drugs, but he wasn't a habitual hard drug user. He'd lost friends to addiction because they stole from him, disappeared, or died. He was open-minded and fun-loving, but self-preserving and smart.

I didn't think Dave had a drug problem, but—with his drastic personality changes—I considered all possibilities. He acted as if he were high on some kind of serious stimulant.

"Dave! Are you on drugs?" I asked him on one of his visits. I was exasperated. He was a wild man. "Are you smoking crack, or what?"

He replied with the screech that had become a regular part of his vocabulary and sounded like a pterodactyl call.

"Haaa! Ha ha ha, argh!" he laughed; then serious, with his head cocked condescendingly, "I'm *not* on drugs, Amelia."

Near the end of September, I asked Dave if he wanted to celebrate our fifth wedding anniversary together.

"Well, of course I do, baby. You *are* my wife," Dave answered with certainty.

Those days, I had two heads and two hearts. One side of me was reassured hearing the words "baby" and "wife" slip so casually and lovingly from Dave's lips. The other side of me was annoyed, distraught, and confused. How could he be so aloof? Was our marriage not in ruins? Did he not see how hurt and stressed I was?

We made anniversary plans. September 27 fell on a Saturday. I was scheduled to work at the Ginger Man, but my manager, Julie, promised I'd finish work early enough to go out with Dave after my shift.

On the morning of our anniversary, Dave and I spoke on the phone. We had one of our then-rare heart-to-hearts. I told him I was worried about him and us. I felt so far removed from the time in our lives when we'd decided to get married. Dave assured me he understood how I felt. He'd been thinking a lot about the state of his life and our life together. He was ready to shape up.

"I know I act crazy," he sighed. "I know I need help. I can't fix it all myself."

I was surprised to hear Dave's admission. I was relieved and reassured.

"It means a lot to hear you say that, Dave. That's an awesome anniversary gift. Thank you," I said.

I set it up with Dave that I'd call him when I was close to being done so he could meet me at the Ginger Man. I told him to expect me to be done by nine. I brought a change of clothes so we could go straight to dinner.

That night, the restaurant was busy. At 7 p.m. I was surprised and flustered when the hostess told me I had a phone call. I went behind the bar to take the call in the quietest spot.

"Hello?" I answered, not knowing whom to expect on the other end of the line.

It was Dave. He was calling hours before I was expected to be done with work.

"I can't come pick you up," he said with a cackle.

"What? Why not?" I asked, my heart sinking.

"Because I'm in jail!" Dave sounded jovial.

"WHAT?! Jail? Why? Where?" I blurted.

"They got me for drunk driving. But I'm not drunk! They're going to have to let me go!" he giggled and sounded quite drunk.

"Oh my God. I can't fucking believe this is happening. *David, it's our anniversary!*" I sighed.

"I know! I told them! That's why they let me call you. From jail! These cops are actually pretty cool. They're gonna let me go. I think they're keeping the car though. I don't know!" he babbled. He sounded entertained by the situation.

"I gotta get back to work," I whispered and hung up. Shocked and defeated, I maneuvered out from behind the bar.

Julie caught me before I could go check on my tables.

"Amelia, what's going on? Are you OK?" She was concerned.

"No," I squeaked, my eyes close to squirting tears.

"Oh, honey, what happened?" she asked through the chaotic buzz of the busy restaurant.

"Dave got arrested. He isn't picking me up," I told her.

"Oh, my God," she said. She couldn't hide her astonishment.

My coworkers were dear friends who had been following the ups and downs of my separation. Julie knew what the anniversary plan had meant to me; her eyes shone teary with concern and sympathy.

"Oh, my God," she said again. "What can I do for you? Do you need to go?"

"No. I need to pretend this isn't happening and go take care of my tables," I announced, switching off my brain and potential tears.

I finished my shift.

When I was done working, I went home. Jeremy wasn't around. The house was empty and dark. I sat at the piano and played a sad tune. I cried. My broken heart was oozing through my tears and fingertips. I made sad music and sobbed until I was exhausted.

I dug through the closet to find a box of photo albums. I sat on the floor and turned page after page of photos of Dave and me adventuring and happy together. I looked at our trips to Europe and South America. I looked at our wedding and honeymoon. I looked at out early days together, at rock concerts and parties.

I picked out a handful of my favorite shots and arranged them on the piano. I built a shrine to Dave. I sat a long time staring at the pictures. I felt absolutely alone. I missed my love; I missed our life together. I wanted Dave.

The next few days moved by slowly and painfully. I thought about Dave constantly, but ignored his calls. I couldn't bear talking to him. I couldn't bear listening to him talk crazy or make excuses and empty promises. I was broken. I was defeated. Pushing Dave away didn't work and letting him back in had failed miserably.

My heart was aching; I'd been hurt in so many different ways, yet I still couldn't let him go. I knew talking wasn't working, so I tried writing. I wrote Dave a definitive one-page letter.

I wrote about how sorry I was that we hadn't spent our anniversary together. I wrote about how disappointed I was that he wasn't following through on getting the help he admitted he needed on the morning of our anniversary. I wrote, "I will not stand by your destructive choices. I want a husband who is consistent and in-control."

I put exactly what I needed on paper as a guide to Dave and as a reminder to myself. "Take control of your life and bring yourself back to me," I wrote, and I listed the ways for him to do that: "Get a car, get your own place, resolve your unsettling issues, be creative, make music, get help from your friends and a professional guide."

My letter concluded: "That's what needs to happen before you can be my husband again. When that happens, we are free to have a peaceful family and move forward to cool vacations, babies, co-homeownership, and a wide-open future. If it doesn't happen, we're done. I won't settle for less than the rock star boy I fell in love with and the creative, talented, driven man I married. Please start making positive choices to be healthy, happy, open, and constructive. I love you. I'm yours. Fix yourself up and c'mon back to me."

I mailed the letter and took off to West Virginia. I needed to get away and convalesce. I climbed rocks for a week with Sugar Shack Mike. The climber campground was crawling with cute boys. My heartache wouldn't let me relax, and I wasn't my usual flirty self.

"I'm surprised you aren't out there chasing one of those Canadian boys. Are you OK?" Mike asked on our rest day at camp. I was sitting at our picnic table, watching the campground's goings-on from a distance.

"Nah," I said. "I miss Dave. I want to be committed to him, but we can't get our shit straight to be together." I felt tired. I felt old.

Mike and I had an unspoken policy to be climbing partners, and nothing more. We didn't want to mess up our climbing flow talking about anything too serious. So, it was out of character for me to confide in Mike. He was sympathetic; he listened. Our climbing flow *was* interrupted. My life was a mess; I was so hurt, even rock climbing couldn't soothe me.

While I was in West Virginia, Dave stopped by my house. The night I came home, Jeremy gave me a full report.

"He's got a brand new car! A Toyota," he said.

"Oh my God! That's great!" I said happily.

"And he acted pretty normal," Jeremy said. "He was disappointed when I told him you were in West Virginia and he couldn't see you. He told me he misses you, and..."

Jeremy paged through some papers on the table and pulled out a CD.

"He wrote you a song," Jeremy said. "Just like you wanted him to."

"WHAT?! A song?" I screeched happily.

Jeremy handed me the CD. It was labeled "To Melie" in Dave's writing. I tossed all my gear on the floor and rushed to the stereo to play the disc.

I recognized the music. Dave sang:

> *I broke myself*
> *I'm bad for my health*
> *I lost myself*
> *Somewhere else*

Dave had written the song "Broken Bones" several years before and had recorded countless variations. It sounded the same.

"But this is an old song!" I whined. I was confused. Why would he give me an old song?

"It sounds really good. Dave *is* talented," Jeremy mused.

"But it's an old song!" I sighed.

I tried to override my disappointment with Jeremy's good news. If Dave had bought a car, it meant he was attempting to improve his life and was responding to my letter.

The next day, I called him to thank him for the CD.

"Where have you been?" Dave asked.

"I was climbing in West Virginia," I said, "I thought Jeremy told you."

"I didn't know where you were," he said. He seemed confused.

We made a date to take a day trip to Williamstown, Massachusetts.

On the appointed day, Dave showed up at my house in his new Toyota Camry. He was calm and seemed relieved when I hugged him inside my front door.

"Ready for an adventure?" I asked playfully.

"Yeah, I guess," Dave shrugged. He was distracted and distant. "I'm not sure what's wrong with my car though. I don't know if we can take it to Massachusetts."

Together, we went to his car. He sat in the driver's seat and I sat in the passenger's seat. He put the key in the ignition, but it wouldn't turn.

"I think the car is broken. Sometimes it won't start," Dave said as he put his hands on the steering wheel and tried to move it.

The wheel was locked. I reached over, held the wheel to one side, and turned the ignition key to start the car.

"How'd you do that?" Dave exclaimed.

"The wheel was locked, Dave," I sighed, totally confused. "That happens all the time. You know that."

"Huh," he replied.

I leaned over to turn the car off and lock the wheel. I showed Dave how to unlock it.

"Huh," he said again. He looked at the wheel, puzzled.

I was amazed, annoyed, and perplexed.

Why was he so weird? Why was he so out of it? He must be on drugs. Or having a complete breakdown. He was crazy.

"Dave! What's up with you? Something is wrong!" I whined.

"You always say that!" he said, annoyed. "What's wrong with *you*? You're the one who thinks something is wrong. This is just the way I've always been. I don't do things like I should."

I'd heard it all before. Dave was a bad boy. He partied hard, stayed out all night, tried drugs, drove drunk, got in fights. He'd traveled a lot, and he was never shy about new people or places. He didn't care what people thought of him.

So his "This is the way I've always been; I don't do things the 'right' way" line was Dave's standard disclaimer. He used it to shut down many of our arguments over the years.

Once I got the car started for Dave, he drove the forty miles of back roads to Williamstown. The drive was scary. Dave had little regard for lanes or speed limits. The car would glide over the double yellow line and then almost off the side of the road. He went at least ten miles per hour below posted limits and crawled up hills—unaware he needed to downshift or push harder on the gas.

Dave had always been a very competent driver. He drove fast and attentively. On the trip to Massachusetts, he was out of it. I was concerned for our safety, but shy about starting a potential disagreement over his driving.

When we arrived in Williamstown, Dave attempted to parallel park on the main street. He hit both of the cars he was trying to maneuver between. He was bumping back and forth between the two cars.

"David! What are you doing? You can't just hit cars!" I exclaimed.

"Aw, it's fine. Fuck it," Dave casually replied.

"It's not fine!" I screeched back at him. "Stop! Stop the car!"

He obeyed. His car's back bumper pressed against the car behind us and his front end was hanging out awkwardly in the busy street.

"I'll park the car. Let's switch."

I moved into the driver's seat and eased Dave's car into the generous parking spot.

Dave was one of the most competent people I knew. He was smart, mechanically inclined, artistic, and talented. He had a great sense of direction. He could use tools and understood how things worked.

I didn't understand Dave's awful driving. I'd cut him a lot of slack because of his characteristic competency. I trusted him; I believed in him. He so doggedly did not see a problem with his behavior that I was confused: I doubted myself instead of doubting him.

Once the car was parked, we strolled around the small downtown. We window-shopped and walked to admire the Williams College buildings.

We settled in for lunch at a Thai restaurant. Dave had always liked Thai food, but today he was bewildered as he looked over the menu.

"I don't know what any of this stuff is," he loudly announced. All of his sentences were punctuated with loud tongue clicks or hard knuckle taps on the table.

I was uncomfortable as Dave drew attention to us in the quiet, upscale restaurant.

This was the new normal. This was my crazy husband, all wound up and acting inappropriately. This was me, alienated and embarrassed.

I ordered for Dave because he seemed too flustered to do it himself. He ate sloppily, sometimes putting his fingers in his soup dish, sometimes slurping and smacking his lips.

We didn't talk. He seemed disinterested and distracted, and I was too angry to try to make conversation.

After we finished eating, I suggested I drive us home. Instead of telling him I was scared to let him drive again, I told him I wanted to check out his new car. He was happy to let me drive. He even seemed relieved.

"You're a way better driver than me. It'll be safer if you drive. And you know where we're going," Dave sighed.

During the drive home, my mind raced with the usual confusion. I couldn't get through to aloof Dave. He was convinced nothing was wrong, but his mental state was worse than ever.

At home, I pulled into my driveway and left the car running. I didn't want Dave to come in. I knew nothing I said would get through to him, and if we continued to hang out, we'd argue.

I asked Dave to wait while I got something from the house. I'd made a mix CD with music that illustrated how I felt about him. I'd been playing it constantly. I thought the emotive tunes and longing lyrics might get through to him since my voiced complaints and concerns had failed.

The songs were mostly about lost love and heartache. The last song was smooth and slow: "Love is Stronger than Pride." Sade's powerful, beautiful voice reveals that, despite the problems in a relationship, she's still really, really in love. That was the ultimate message I wanted to give Dave.

I brought the CD out to him. I told him to listen to it and take the words as a message from me to him. We said goodbye, and he moved into the driver's seat. I went in the house.

I expected to hear from Dave soon after our Massachusetts trip. I expected him to call and say, "I still really, really love you too." I didn't hear from him right away, and when I did, it wasn't in a way I wanted.

"I'm teetering on a ladder thirty feet in the air!" he said when I answered his call. "This is crazy! I could totally fall! I could be dead in seconds." He laughed and screeched like a mad man.

"What?! Dave, you shouldn't be on the phone! What's wrong with you? Why are you calling me right now?"

"I wanted to hear your voice! It's like how you go rock climbing! Only I'm not wearing a harness! I don't have a rope! This is crazy. I have to measure this roof. We need to patch it. It's a three-foot patch, or is it meters? How do you measure things? Meters and yards are the same? Why don't we use the metric system? Wouldn't that make more sense? WOOO, whoa! Yeah! Hahahaha. So, I have three meters to patch. With what? What will we use to patch it? AAAHHH! Then I need to carry it up the ladder! Haahaha..."

Dave carried on, not making any sense, until I told him I was hanging up.

I called Adam. He was the only friend Dave and I shared who agreed something beyond Dave's characteristic wackiness was happening.

"Aim, he's been calling me too. He just carries on nonsense. I think it's called 'flight of ideas.' It's a symptom of bipolar disorder. My mom gave me the name of a doctor at Samaritan Hospital. I think we should take him for a ride."

This wasn't what I wanted to hear. I didn't want to take Dave "for a ride" to the psych ward. It was scary. It wasn't my responsibility.

"I don't know. I don't think I can handle this. He won't admit there's something wrong. If he doesn't want help, I can't help him," I whined. The excuses came easy. I didn't want a mentally ill husband. I didn't want to be the one to take control of his health after we'd broken up, after he'd let me go.

Doctors diagnosed Adam's mother with bipolar disorder and schizophrenia when she was in her thirties. Adam saw his mother melt down in a way similar to Dave.

"He isn't going to want to help himself, Aim. He doesn't know any better. He's sick. He needs help. We can get him help; he'll get better."

My mind raced. I didn't think I could handle standing by my estranged husband in a psych ward or while he had to be medicated to maintain a normal life. I'd seen Adam's mom when she didn't take her medication. It was scary. I didn't want to bear such unpredictability for the rest of my life with Dave.

I still thought Dave could change himself back.

The next time I saw Dave was when he showed up unannounced at my house. He brought a birdhouse, a 4x4 post, and a post hole digger.

I opened my front door to his wide grin.

"I'm here to put your birdhouse up," he declared.

I didn't want a birdhouse. Dave had been obsessively talking about and measuring for birdhouses for over two years. I was trying to move on with my life, trying to make the house I bought my own. I didn't want a monument to Dave and his insanity in my new back yard.

Before I could say anything, he was ambitiously digging a hole.

I didn't want his birdhouse, but it seemed easier to let Dave follow through with his plan than to start an argument. I was tired of trying to make sense to Dave. I ignored him and went to work on my computer. When he was finished, he came bounding into the house.

"You're all set!" he chimed, as if he'd just done me a huge favor.

"OK. Thanks, Dave," I reluctantly replied. I wanted him to go away without us having to fight or cry. I wanted to shoo him out, but once our eyes locked my heart melted. No matter how mad or maddening he was, I wanted Dave. Every time I saw him, it was hard for my heart to let him go. Nevertheless, my self-persevering brain couldn't let him stay.

"Dave, something is wrong. I don't know what else to do but send you away. You are making me crazy. You are crazy. You need to get help. I can't help you," I whimpered. I was a wreck: whiny, scared, angry, and wishy-washy.

He looked hurt, wounded. He backed away from me.

"I know," he whispered.

He left. I let him go for what felt like the last time. I'd let him go so many last times I'd lost count.

I started painting my house. When I wasn't out climbing, I painted the interior rooms. Rock climbing and fixing up my hundred-year-old house were the only activities that shut off my confused head and aching heart.

While I worked, I played the stereo, resigned to the fact that every song on every album I owned reminded me of Dave. I wallowed in heartbreak while passing the hours, comforted only by the idea that time would eventually heal me.

Hours blurred into days blurred into weeks. Sometimes I'd cry too hard to paint. When that happened, I'd pull out pictures and look at our past. Each time I looked through the hundreds of pictures documenting our travels, homes, and adventures together, I'd find a shot or two I couldn't put away.

I'd add the chosen photographs to the bunch gathering on my piano. Dave smiling big and squatting on a dirty sidewalk petting a stray dog in Prague. Dave playing in the big waves on a Cancun beach. Us together, dancing at our wedding; Dave wet from the rain.

Dave's face: close-up and buried in lush green Hawaiian pot plants. Every couple of days the collection grew.

"Aim, that Dave shrine on the piano is creepy," Jeremy said one day. "Aren't you getting a little obsessive?"

"He's my *husband*!" I snapped. "I love him! I miss him! I want him! I can obsess all I want. You don't know what it's like! I'm devastated."

Thirty Seconds Away from Death

I was alone, painting my apartment, listening to the wind rattle leaves down the sidewalk. It was a crisp, cold full-moon night. Working methodically through the fall, I'd painted the kitchen, hall, entranceway, and dining room. Now, I was edging the white trim in the living room when the phone rang.

Dave's wild voice burst into the room as soon as I answered. He was hoarse and short of breath.

"What's going on, Dave? Are you OK?"

"No, Amelia, I'm not OK. I'm out of my mind. I can't take this anymore."

"Take what? What do you mean?"

"I mean I don't want to be here anymore. I WANT TO DIE."

Whooosh. The walls closed in on me. I was punched in the gut. I squeaked.

"Oh no, David. Don't say that," I pleaded. I knew he was serious. I knew Dave didn't make threats. I was frozen, immobilized by fear, and pressed by a gravity I'd never felt.

"I'm thirty seconds away from death," he groaned. He sounded as if he was in physical pain. It was agonizing to hear him. "I have my brother's shotgun."

I screeched back into the phone.

"Noooo! David, no, please. Please, please, please don't!" I sobbed. I bolted up, breaking gravity's heavy pull. The walls fell back and started spinning.

"I'm fucked up!" he yelled. "I want to die!"

"No, no, no, no, no. Please, David. Don't hurt yourself. I'll come get you. I'll be there in twenty minutes. You wait there for me. Don't hurt yourself; don't go anywhere. I'm on my way. OK?"

Silence.

"OK? OK, David?"

"Yeah."

I'd have given anything, everything, to save Dave at that moment. Living without him, having a Planet Earth without him, was not an option. Nothing mattered but convincing Dave that he couldn't go. Our breakup, what was right or wrong, what I wanted from him and our relationship: none of it mattered. Time and experience were void. All that mattered was seeing Dave, being with Dave, having Dave stay alive.

I hung up the phone and ran to my car. I drove fast to Dave's mother's house. Arriving at the house, I negotiated the long dirt driveway. As I rounded the curve that brought the house into view, Dave was stepping out the back door. He stood motionless as I parked the car and rushed to his side. We hugged and held each other tight for a few minutes. It was a blustery night. We were shivering, so we sat in my car.

We hadn't seen each other in weeks. Despite the horrible reason for our reunion, we were energized and happy to be close. We kissed passionately in the car. We held desperately to one another.

"I'm taking you home with me," I told Dave.

Back at my house, we made love. Dave and I were always wildly attracted to each other. We were in love. We were separated and desperately unsure of our future together, but the attraction and love stood.

We lay together in my bed—our bed—and dozed off. After a few minutes, Dave was up and wandering around the house. I woke, anxious and concerned. Our passionate reunion was over and reality had set back in. I nervously followed Dave around.

"Are you OK? What can I do for you?" I asked.

"I'm OK now. I want to live here with you. You're my wife," Dave stated matter-of-factly.

I was torn. Half of me would do anything to comfort my suicidal lover. Half of me was absolutely not going to let Dave back into my house or my life without solutions to the problems that broke us up.

I convinced Dave to come back to bed. I took one of his favorite books from the shelf. I read him Bukowski's *Pulp* as a bedtime story.

He fell asleep after only a few minutes. He slept only a few minutes. When he woke, I read more. This routine went on for an hour, until I fell asleep. Dave was up and walking around the house throughout the night. I was too exhausted to check on him every time.

In the morning, I searched the Internet for psychiatrists. I called Julie at the Ginger Man to tell her I needed time off. I explained what was going on. She gave me the number of a social worker she knew. Julie thought Donna could help me find the help Dave needed.

I left a message for Donna, and then started down the list of psychiatrists. I found a nurse practitioner who worked with a psychiatrist, and she was available to see Dave the next day. Dave stayed in the kitchen while I was making calls. He must have heard me telling his story to each receptionist I got through to.

"My husband threatened to kill himself last night. He isn't himself, hasn't been himself for a long time. Yes, he's angry. Yes, I think he's depressed. No, I don't think he's on drugs. We need help."

Dave seemed content to be cared for. He offered no input on his condition or his desires. He wasn't saying much at all.

After I made the appointment with the nurse practitioner, Lucie, I collapsed on the sofa. The living room furniture was pulled away from the walls with plastic sheeting over it and on the floor. The incomplete paint job reminded me that there was work to be done. There was no comfortable place to sit. The disarrayed living room felt like a waiting room, not my home. Dave wouldn't sit; he paced around the house, opening and closing doors and drawers.

The phone rang. Donna's soothing voice responded to my curt and exhausted "Hello?"

"Amelia, this is Donna. I'm returning your call about your husband," she spoke with the familiarity of an old friend.

I explained the situation for the eighth time that day, with the backstory I'd been describing for years.

"I think taking him to see Lucie is the best thing for him now. He needs to see someone right away. It sounds like he needs help from someone who can prescribe medication. I'm not qualified to help Dave, but I may be able to help *you*. This is hard on you too," Donna said.

The thought that I should get help for myself—that I even needed help—hadn't occurred to me. I was instantly relieved. I was grateful for Donna's suggestion; I made an appointment with her for later that week.

The next morning, I ushered Dave to the car and drove across town to Lucie's office. The medical building was nestled in among restaurants, gas stations, and offices near a shopping mall. I'd driven by it hundreds of times but never noticed it.

The reception area was small and dimly lit. There was a woman behind a counter with a glass barrier, and a teenage boy sitting with his mother on a love seat in the waiting area. Dave sat across from the teenager and thumbed through a magazine.

I approached the glass barrier to introduce myself to the receptionist and sign Dave in. She handed us a packet of intake information. I sat in the open chair next to Dave, facing the mother. She glanced up to give me a sympathetic nod. Dave had no interest in filling out the questionnaire, so I went to work writing in answers. Whenever I asked Dave for his input, he answered, "You know better than I do."

Before I was finished with the paperwork, a serious, petite woman poked her head around the corner and said, "David?"

Dave gave the woman his huge, adorable smile and stood. I stood too and introduced myself to Lucie. She led us to a tiny office with three chairs and a small desk. She took the stack of papers I'd been diligently filling in and put them on the desk, then sat facing us and holding a clipboard and pen.

Lucie had an authoritative Eastern European accent. She was neatly dressed in a grey pantsuit that complemented her short salt-and-pepper hair. She leaned forward in her chair to talk to us and nodded attentively when Dave or I spoke.

"David, why are you here?" she asked.

"Because Amelia wants me to be."

"Well, I think Amelia is a smart woman. Why do you think she wants you to be here?"

Dave shrugged.

"She *is* smart," he said. "She's my smart and beautiful wife."

Lucie asked Dave questions about his state of mind that he answered with a shrug or "I don't know."

"Would it be OK with you if Amelia tells me why she's worried about you, David? Can I ask her some questions about you?"

"Yes. Amelia knows better than I do. She can tell you everything."

"I think Dave has post-traumatic stress disorder," I said. "And maybe he's showing signs of being an adult child of an alcoholic. I've been doing a lot of research on the Internet. And a friend's mom is schizophrenic or bipolar; my friend says Dave's behavior is similar to his mom's."

Lucie listened to me carefully.

"Dave's childhood was hard. He had a lot of exposure to violence, and drug use, and alcohol abuse," I said.

"Does what Amelia is saying make sense to you?" Lucie asked Dave.

"Yes," Dave said.

I was surprised, almost floored, to hear him agree.

"I do feel hurt by some of the stuff that happened when I was a kid," he said, "and sometimes I'm angry at my parents about it."

"Good, I'd like to hear more," Lucie said. "Amelia, could you leave us so we can talk?"

I was happy to bow out of the therapy session. I wanted Dave to get better, but I didn't want to be the interpreter between him and the therapist.

After almost an hour, Lucie called me back to the room.

"I need to see Dave more before giving a diagnosis," she said, "but I suspect he's suffering from bipolar disorder."

She filled out a prescription form.

"I'm giving him an anti-psychotic drug," she said, "and I need to see him at least once a week. I'll prescribe more drugs after I see how he reacts to this one."

She looked up at my worried face.

"Everything will be OK," she reassured me. "I can find the right drug combination that will bring Dave back. He'll get back to a functional level."

I let out my breath. I hadn't realized I'd been holding it.

"Meanwhile, he needs to be someplace safe and supportive," she said. "*Not* his mother's house."

I was relieved to hear this from a professional. I'd been trying to convince Dave that living with his mother and brother wasn't a healthy place for him.

"He can stay with me," I said.

"Good. And he should *not* be left alone," she emphasized.

She looked at Dave sternly.

"Dave! Can you promise not to use drugs or alcohol?" she asked.

"Yes," he said.

"Can you promise not to hurt yourself?" she said.

Dave looked from her to me, and back to her.

"Yes," he said. "I promise."

I took Dave home with me and dosed him with the anti-psychotic. He slept for over fourteen hours. When he woke, he said he'd slept better than he had in as long as he could remember.

"I like Lucie. I think she can help me," Dave said that morning. It gave me hope that Dave was receptive to treatment, but I was terrified about our future. This was a beginning. This was the start of what would be a long and difficult process. I'd been hoping for an end. I'd been wishing for an end to Dave's crazy behavior and a fairy-tale reunion.

Dave liked Lucie and I liked Donna. I'd managed, at least, to find well-suited mental health guides for the both of us. I was in shock and running on autopilot. I got lucky when Donna encouraged me to make an appointment *for myself* on the day I called looking for help for my suicidal husband.

Our initial meeting felt exactly right and cosmically reassuring. Donna was a guide, a wise teacher. The things she said made sense. She offered comfort by introducing me to concepts that felt true and obvious, though I'd never thought or heard of them.

She explained the "field of all possibilities" and the idea of allow-ing. She informed me that infinite possibilities and outcomes existed in my world. I could find comfort by allowing those possibilities and allowing what was happening to just be.

Together, we meditated. She guided me through visualizations of color and light. She taught me to demand that the universe "fix this for me." She advised me to be open to things being fixed in ways oth-er than the ways I could imagine.

Donna told me to ask for help. She encouraged me to care for my-self, not just Dave. Donna immediately became my unconditional supporter, and she rallied me to build a network of other supporters.

I called Katie, who offered to let Dave stay with her family. I called Dave's dad and left a voicemail saying we needed to discuss Dave's health. I called Jay in Portland, Oregon. Four of Dave's best friends were living there. I'd been out of touch with them since Dave and I had separated.

Jay was happy to hear my voice.

"I've been worried about you, sweetheart," he said. "I'm relieved to hear you're helping Dave. He needs help."

"You already know he's having problems?" I was a little surprised. I'd assumed Dave's weirdness hadn't been evident over the phone.

"They're pretty hard to miss. He'd call up and be frantic. He sounded drunk, carrying on and not making sense," Jay said. "At first, we thought he was abusing alcohol or taking heavy drugs. Re-cently, we collectively decided he was mentally ill."

The boys had been riding the same roller coaster as me.

"At least now I know it wasn't just me who's noticed Dave's de-cline," I said. What I didn't say was that it terrified me; this was proof that something was really wrong.

"More than noticed. We've been pleading with him to get help," Jay said. "Mark's been on the Internet, trying to figure out what's wrong with him."

"I did the same thing," I sighed.

"All four of us gave him an ultimatum. We weren't going to speak to him unless he acknowledged a problem and got professional help."

"He's getting it now, Jay," I said. "I brought him to a professional to get a diagnosis, and he's taking medication. He might be bipolar."

"I'm so glad to hear he's getting help. Because it's getting worse," Jay said. He paused. "I kind of hate to tell you this."

My stomach dropped. I clutched the phone.

"A few days ago, he went to my aunt's house," Jay said. "She knows Dave, she's known him since he was a kid. But she said he was amped up in a way she'd never seen. He was screeching and laughing and announcing his own insanity. He told my aunt he had access to guns and that he could kill himself—or anyone else—at any time he chose."

I groaned, bracing myself for whatever fresh bad news was coming.

"Amelia, I told him to keep away from my family and to stop calling me. Mark told him to stop calling too. We can't perpetuate this crazy behavior; we can't pretend it's not happening and expect him to get better."

"He told me he was going to kill himself, too," I said. "That's why I brought him to Lucie."

"We'll support him if he's getting help, but we won't stand by while he self-destructs," Jay said.

Jay was firm and determined. He'd decided the best way to help Dave. I didn't feel so assured. I had no idea what my role should be or how I should proceed. I wished I could shut the door and pass Dave off to someone else. I couldn't.

I had left Dave hoping that it would startle him into helping himself. It didn't work. He wasn't getting help. Now, he seemed so lost and confused and beyond helping himself that I was forced into a new role. A medical professional recommended Dave live with me for his own safety. I was poised to become his caregiver.

I didn't like that role one bit. I didn't have time or energy for such an all-encompassing job. I was resentful that Dave let me leave him, that he didn't fight for me, that he didn't have the wherewithal to get his shit together before we were torn apart.

That a tangible medical condition may have been to blame for these shortcomings was not reassuring.

We were separated, on the verge of divorce. Dave had never done anything to keep that from happening. Didn't that mean I was free of my wifely duties, the in-sickness-and-in-health? Couldn't I drop him off at the psych ward and wash my hands of him?

Dave brought a TV from his mom's house down to mine. He brought his lava lamp too. He was content to move back into my life. I was tense and afraid. I didn't trust him to be alone in the house. He seemed capable of wandering off and leaving the front door wide open and the stove on full blast.

He was seeing Lucie twice a week and had been given more mood moderating drugs. I was talking regularly with the Portland crew. Mark sent an Internet list of famous people with bipolar disorder.

Lucie called to check in with Dave almost every day. She'd call him on his cell phone and then call me on my landline. She assured me she thought Dave would get better.

"Your husband will come back to you, Amelia," she told me. "It may seem hopeless now, but the medications and therapy will work. He'll get better."

Lucie told me what she thought I wanted to hear: that Dave and I would be together again. Her words did more to stress me out than offer comfort. Was I supposed to want him back? I wasn't sure I did. I was heartbroken without Dave, but I was in control. I was taking care of myself: trying to have fun and be in the world while establishing myself as an independent, self-employed, home-owning single woman. I'd gained some control of my life after spinning out and losing Dave. Lucie's diagnosis sent me reeling from my steps to normalcy back to an out-of-control, uncertain future.

The medication sedated Dave, but he wasn't making any more sense or acting at all like himself. I knew I could drop him off at the hospital if he was too much for me. Lucie's advice and my gut told me that that should be an absolute last option, but it comforted me to know it was an option.

I was working full-time from home and waiting tables three or four nights a week. I worked at my computer in the dining room while Dave watched movies in the living room. I cut back my hours at the Ginger Man. The nights I did go in, Jeremy could usually stay home with Dave.

When Jeremy or I weren't around, Dave would drive away. He got pulled over regularly, often for drunk driving when he was cold sober.

After two weeks, my patience and sanity were wearing thin. I was on edge; I needed help.

Our friend Susanne offered to help me with Dave. She had a home in the country with lots of land, gardens, and animals. It was an ideal place for Dave to convalesce. Susanne was home most of the time and needed help to manage her land and animals. She agreed to watch over Dave to give me a break.

While Dave was living at her house, Susanne would call or email daily. At first, she was hopeful about Dave's recovery. He drove himself to see Lucie. He was playing music with Susanne's fourteen-year-old daughter and watching TV with the family at night.

Susanne gave Dave chores including feeding the llamas and building bookshelves.

Within two weeks, Susanne's hopefulness turned to concern. He attempted to fix molding, but ended up destroying a wall. He wasn't feeding the animals. In the garden, he stared off instead of doing what Susanne asked.

I visited Dave at Susanne's place or brought him home with me when I had free time.

As the weeks passed, Dave was less and less willing to go along with Lucie's treatment. And he was wearing out his welcome with Susanne.

One day, she dropped Dave at my house while she went shopping.

"I don't think the medicine is working. And it's too expensive," Dave announced. He was anxious and pacing.

"Dave, you have to keep doing what Lucie says. You need to help yourself if you're going to get help from me or Susanne or anyone else," I warned.

He shrugged.

We had a tense visit. He was agitated; I was uneasy. I was relieved when Susanne collected him after her shopping trip.

A few days later, I answered the phone to heavy, squeaky breathing. Susanne was crying. Her words were forced gasps between sobs.

"Davey left," she said. "It's cold and rainy and stormy and he left."

She was agonizing, moaning.

"He was barefoot in the cold rain. He was soaked. He left without his shoes. I told him he couldn't stay if he wasn't helping and taking care of himself. I didn't mean for him to walk out just then. I'm so sorry. I failed Davey."

"No, Susanne. You didn't fail. You did so much to help him."

"Amelia, he's really sick," she whispered as she caught her breath. "I don't know if we can help him." She lost her breath again, completely, and sobbed and sobbed. I was too shocked and exhausted to cry with her.

I gave up. Again. Dave didn't come back to my house after he left Susanne's house. Lucie called to tell me he'd stopped showing up for his appointments with her.

It was the New Year. I was attempting to pick up where I was back in the fall when Dave called to tell me he was thirty seconds away from death. I was making my new house a home. I was moving forward, trying to get over my failed marriage and let go of my crazy husband.

I knew I had to follow through on divorcing Dave. I needed closure if I was to succeed at getting my head together and heal my heart. I also needed to be legally detached from my off-his-meds, frighteningly unpredictable husband.

I called the divorce lawyer. I explained Dave's medical condition. I didn't want to wait until May for the one-year legal separation to give way to a no-contest divorce. I wanted to sue Dave for abandonment to be legally divorced.

I knew Dave couldn't be counted on to receive, sign, and return divorce papers by mail. I called him and asked him to meet me at the lawyer's office. He showed up and signed. We didn't own property together or have kids, so the process was simple.

The lawyer asked Dave if he understood what he was signing.

"Oh, yes, everything looks fine to me," Dave smiled big at the lawyer. "Amelia knows the best thing to do. She's great."

The only complication in the divorce was that my car was registered to Dave. We had to go to the Department of Motor Vehicles to change the registration and title to my name. As we left the lawyer's office, we made plans to meet and go to DMV. Dave was to bring the title and meet me at my house the next day.

I hardly slept that night. I remembered the night of our wedding. I remembered being pleasantly and overwhelmingly surprised to feel different after the marriage. The ceremony changed something. Dave and I became a family that day. It felt awesome.

The night of our divorce, I felt something equally profound. We were officially split. The legal termination of our union felt bloody and violent and wrong. I was sick, mutilated, missing half of me.

When Dave showed up in the morning for our DMV date, I was exhausted and depleted. He was chipper and detached. He offered to drive us and piloted the car in his new-normal haphazard way, traveling way under the speed limit and almost colliding with parked cars and oncoming traffic.

We parked in the huge, crowded DMV lot. I was surrounded by a dark, grey cloud of angst. I was lost and lonely. Crazy Dave was aloof and all-business.

He hopped out of the car and walked around to my door. I was frozen, trapped in a thick stinky filthy molasses. I opened the door and got one foot out of the car and on the pavement.

"C'mon, baby," Dave said.

"*Baby?* How can you be like this? We got divorced yesterday. Our life together is ruined. Don't you care?" I groaned. The words were like razors in my throat.

Dave stood looking down at me in his passenger's seat. He was quiet and looked puzzled. He cocked his head and put a hand on his hip.

"I don't know what to do," he sighed.

"Act like you care? Act like you care that my heart is ripped out?" I yelped. My voice was rising and shaking more with every word. The air thickened and twisted. My ears rang, the ground rocked.

I stood to face Dave, my legs wobbly.

"How can you do this to me? Why?" I screeched. I punched the air around me and swayed on my feet, weakening with each blow.

The ground fell out from beneath me. It felt as if I fell several stories before my knees hit the ground.

Kneeling, I kept punching. This time instead of contacting only air, I smashed at the side of Dave's car with my fists. I screamed as tears and snot exploded from my face.

Dave reached down to stop my punching, and I turned fast to face him. Instead of punching him, I held up my middle fingers. I knelt before him sobbing, screaming, and double-flipping him off.

"Fuck you, Dave! Fuck you! You are killing me! You are ruining me! Ooooohhhh! No, no, no, no, no..." I wailed on and on.

I leaned forward onto my hands and crawled toward Dave. He backed away with a terrified look on his face. I stumbled to my feet and staggered to the road. Once I hit the sidewalk, I started power walking toward home.

I'd escaped the molasses. The ringing in my ears subsided. Now, the world was muted. Color, edges, and sounds were all fuzzy and toned down. My house was a two-mile uphill walk away. About halfway there, I made a beeline across the busy street and into a park.

As soon as my feet touched the grass, I collapsed. I lay on my back staring at the sky. My body was too heavy to move. My heaviness sank into the dirt below me. The tears came back and ran down my cheeks to the ground. Time stood still.

After a while, I stood. I was lighter; my brain and body were fog passing through the surrounding air. I shuffled to the sidewalk and continued my walk home.

"Hey! I've been looking for you!" Dave's voice shattered my daze. He pulled up beside me and stopped the car in the road.

I turned to him and threw up both middle fingers again.

"Leave me alone!" I screamed.

Spoon with Me

With a part-sad, part-angry, mostly baffled look, Dave turned back to face the road in front of him. He drove off, leaving me alone on the sidewalk, just as I asked.

This was the start of radio silence between us. It was the start of the longest stretch of time in our twelve-year relationship where Dave and I didn't communicate.

I took the pictures off the piano. I was back to trying to get over Dave.

I went on dates, picking up guys at the hardware store and at the office where I did contract work. My heart wasn't invested in anyone I met, but I was committed to moving on and trying to have a good time. Jeremy's Japanese wife, Shiho, was living with us during her breaks from school. With her distinctive, English-as-a-second-language vocabulary, she named me "Boyhunter."

I adventured in snow and on ice. I bought ice-climbing tools for the first time. In nineteen years of rock climbing, I'd never wanted to climb ice. Something about losing Dave had made me want to try this sport I'd always viewed as dangerous and masochistic.

In March, Sugar Shack Mike and I were looking forward to spring climbing and planned a trip to New River Gorge and Seneca Rock in West Virginia. We'd be gone for my birthday in April.

In late March, Jeremy came home looking very serious.

He'd been using the pay-by-the-minute cell phone Aunt Patti had bought me for Christmas. I'd used the phone when I was homeless in the spring and early summer, then stashed it in a drawer when I moved into my new house. When Jeremy moved in, broke and displaced, I passed the phone along to him.

Now, he waved the phone at me.

"Aim, I got a message on your phone today. It's about Dave. I think you better listen," he said.

"A message from *Dave?*" I was surprised. It had been almost two months since I'd heard from him.

"No, you better listen. It's not *from* Dave; it's *about* Dave. I think it's his cousin," Jeremy explained.

"His cousin? Kathy? Oh, she's trouble. She parties hard, not a good influence on him."

Why would she call me? How'd she get that number? I wondered.

"*Aim*! Listen. I think something bad happened. Listen to the message," Jeremy insisted.

"Something *bad*?" I said bitterly. My interest was piqued, but I also felt annoyed. "Why is she calling *me*?"

I was trying to be detached. I didn't want to get dragged into Dave's family drama. I divorced Dave for a reason. I knew something bad was happening with him, or a series of bad somethings. I'd tried and tried to stand by or help, but since the divorce, I was resolved to move forward.

Jeremy held out the phone. I stared at him, frustrated.

"She says Dave is in the hospital," Jeremy sighed and pushed the phone closer.

Bam! The word "hospital" slapped me. The feelings I was trying to ignore—my concern, my love, my loss—came flooding back.

"What?! Hospital? Is he hurt? Is he OK?" I grabbed the phone from Jeremy.

The message was brief: "Amelia, this is Dave's cousin, Kathy. I thought you should know Dave is in the hospital. He's not doing good. Give me a call."

I called the number Kathy had left. It wasn't in service. I hung up and called Dave's dad. No answer. I called Dave's brother. No answer. I called his mother.

"I didn't know if you'd want to be bothered," Beverly sighed. She sounded exhausted, defeated. "He's been there for a while; they admitted him on the eleventh. You can go visit him. Or call him. He's been asking about you: 'his wife.'"

Dave had been taken to Samaritan Hospital Psychiatric Ward after being picked up by the police from the Walmart parking lot near his mother's house. He'd been living out of his car for weeks. He'd run out of places to stay.

Like me, his other friends had become frustrated and exasperated by his crazy behavior. Like the boys in Portland, his local friends had given him ultimatums about getting help. When he refused, we all turned away from him.

Dave's brother returned my call later that day. He explained how, over the previous months, he'd watched Dave's sanity crumble.

"He was walking around here naked. He'd play guitar or babble while I was trying to work. When I was on business calls, he'd make crazy bird noises!" Rick said. "He was driving me insane."

Rick told me Dave had been drinking a lot. He'd drink liquor and act belligerent. The family had yelling matches, and after one such episode Dave left for good.

The state police had called Rick more than once after Dave left his family's house. Dave was driving around and loitering in the upper middle class suburb where he grew up. The police told Rick that Dave was a nuisance.

Finally, Rick got a call that Dave had been sleeping in his car in the Walmart parking lot down the road from the family's house. The police told Rick they would take Dave to jail unless Rick had him admitted to a psych ward.

Hearing that the police suggested Dave needed psychological treatment was both validating and terrifying. As with Lucie's diagnosis, I felt relieved that I wasn't just being a pushy, over-concerned wife. I still doubted my judgment. I again felt shock and disbelief over hearing something was really, certifiably wrong with Dave.

For years, I'd urged Dave to seek professional help and receive treatment if he needed it. Yet a big part of me wanted there to be nothing wrong. I wanted everything that was happening to be Dave's choice. That way, he could choose his way back to sanity, and to me.

After getting the news of Dave's lockup, I started calling our friends. I called Adam first.

"You were right. Dave's at Samaritan. His brother checked him in," I explained to Adam. "I want to go see him."

"Aim, I don't think that's a good idea. It's pretty rough over there," Adam advised. "I'll go."

"OK," I agreed. "When will you go? Can you go today?"

I was scared. I wanted to see Dave; I wanted to support him, but mostly, I was scared. I didn't know what I'd find at the psych ward. Was he even crazier than he'd been the last time I saw him? Was he mad at me? I loved Dave as much as ever, but was that enough to turn my life back over to his insanity?

As much as I reflexively wanted to and felt obligated to rush to Dave's side, I accepted Adam's advice. I accepted being let off the hook by one of my best friends.

I was nervous and worried. The thought of Dave being locked up and alone in an institution was terrible.

"You have to get over there. Please," I begged Adam.

"I can't go today, Aim. I'll go tomorrow. He's OK. He's the best he's been in a year. He's safe in there. You don't have to worry anymore. You can relax," Adam tried to reassure me.

Nothing could reassure me then. I was sick with worry. I was worried about Dave. I was worried about myself. I knew our hard times weren't over. I'd spent the last couple of months trying to live easy, trying to be cool, trying to let time heal my failed marriage and broken heart.

I didn't want this. This felt harder than my broken heart. I didn't know what it meant to me. How committed was I to standing by my ex-husband?

I was back to being split, a person divided in two. Half of me was in love and wanted to rush to my husband's side, half of me wanted to run away and find an easy, normal life away from my crazy ex.

The next night, a group of friends gathered around my dining room table, council-meeting style.

I was comforted as we waited together for Adam to return from visiting Dave. I was reminded that many people really, really loved Dave. It wasn't just me who was hurt or heartbroken by Dave's detached behavior and personality changes. There was a whole crew who wanted him back.

As we tried to talk about the frightening present, the conversation kept coming back to reminiscing about the past. We reminded each other about times when Dave made us laugh or pulled a crazy stunt. We wondered when his newly diagnosed mental illness had started taking hold of our beloved friend. When had Dave shifted from eccentric artist to psych patient? Which of his actions were his wacky personality, and which were fueled by mental illness?

Sometime after nine, Adam threw open the front door to deliver his full report. He'd been at the hospital with Dave for hours.

"That place hasn't changed a bit since my mom was there," Adam lamented.

"Well? How is he? What's going on?" I pried.

"Aim, he's going to get better. It'll take a few weeks, but they're going to fix him up," Adam assured me. And then: "He wanted to spoon with me."

We all laughed. This was so typically Dave. "Would you like to spoon with me?" was a Dave-ism. He'd ask this of his guy friends with a suave voice and a raised eyebrow.

"Yeah, I walked into the TV room where all the patients were hanging out. Dave was standing in the middle of the room, right in front of the TV," Adam explained. "Dave turned to look at me. He clapped and pointed at me with a smile. The first thing he said was, 'Would you like to spoon with me?'"

Adam's imitation of Dave—the clap, the sly smile, the voice—was dead on. It was a glimpse of Dave. I felt relieved to know Dave was at least well enough to give one of his famous one-liners.

"I need to go see him," I sighed.

"It's pretty harsh in that place. Lunatics just walking around!" Adam dramatically announced with a sweep of his arm. He paused, and then added, "I think Dave might be the craziest one in there."

Adam explained that the other patients in the ward seemed fascinated by Dave. Typical: Dave entertained wherever he went.

"One of the other patients pulled me aside. He said 'What's *wrong* with him?! He's really crazy!'" Adam said. "I told him we didn't know, that's why he was there."

We didn't know exactly what was wrong with Dave, but Adam's analysis, based on his experiences with his own mother, seemed right on.

"We sat down while they served dinner to the patients. I used the same approach as when my mother was in that unit. I humored him to a certain point, but I was very frank with him. I asked him how long he'd been there, and he didn't seem to know. He said 'A few days.' I asked him if he knew why he was there and he said 'Not really.' I explained to him that he hadn't been himself and he'd been acting out of his mind, not making sense and doing weird things. I said he wasn't there yet, but when he was aware of what was happening, then I knew he'd be all right. I told him that the unit was a state-of-the-art, top-of-the-line mental health ward.

"He was very serious for a few minutes while I was saying all this. Then he asked me how you were doing. I told him that you'd probably be coming there to see him tomorrow, and he said that he hoped so. I told him in few weeks he'd be back to normal and everything would be cool; I'd seen it happen before. For a few minutes, he seemed lucid, like he was listening. Then he looked at me blankly and he started laughing and asked if I wanted to spoon with him again.

"They're gonna keep him a while. Evaluate him, give him meds. They'll figure it out. He'll get better," Adam confidently explained.

Just when I thought our fates were decided, that I'd done all there was to do, a new chapter began. I had a whole new set of decisions to make, a whole new set of pains and frustrations to experience. My husband—my estranged ex-husband—was mentally ill.

I had a new title for my life story. It wasn't "My Failed Marriage and Broken Heart," it was "The Man I Love is Mentally Ill." That sucked. Things had gone from bad to worse. I didn't like the twist. I had felt capable of managing our breakup. I knew what steps to take to heal my heart. I didn't have any idea how to deal with Dave being certifiable.

I felt inexorably drawn to Dave. Our hearts were like magnets that pulled us back together, no matter the pain or confusion it brought to both of us. My head had a little more survival instinct. I wasn't sure how committed I could be to a mentally ill Dave and his recovery. I knew it'd be a setback on my personal path to heart healing if I went to Samaritan to visit him.

"I'll go see him," Katie volunteered.

"You shouldn't go alone," Adam advised her. "That place can be hard to handle. And Dave is pretty whacked out. It's rough!"

Katie went to visit Dave the next day.

She came to my house straight after the hospital. When I opened the door to her, she hugged me with teary eyes.

Katie had so much love for Dave. She always had an open heart and an open door for him.

Katie is a remarkably strong woman. She's unflinching, capable, and confident. That evening, Katie's watery eyes and quavering voice were at once alarming and consoling. Her emotionality was a sign that Dave's position was dire, but seeing her so deeply moved gave me a reassuring feeling of solidarity.

Katie gave me every detail of her visit.

"I found Dave's floor and talked to the ladies behind the glass. One went to tell Dave he had a visitor, and I heard him saying, 'Katie? Katie?' and then, 'Katie!' as he realized who I was. He was jumping up and down behind the glass window like a little kid.

"I know he's messed up, and my heart was sinking, but who doesn't like such a happy reception? The woman said, 'Well, it seems he knows who you are,' and let me in. Dave grabbed me and jumped the both of us around so I couldn't help laughing. He was so happy to see me, such a sweetheart." Katie described Dave and his surroundings so I could see it in my mind.

"He hugged me and kissed me and rubbed his head on me. He needs to have his hair washed, and it was clear *he* doesn't know it. We sat down in the lounge, and hugged and held hands, and he put his head on my shoulder.

"After we settled in, he tried to have a conversation with me. He knew I had two children, and wanted to know how they were, but he thought I might have daughters instead of sons. He was trying to remember. I filled in the blanks. He asked if I was married and I said, 'Yes, to Charlie, you remember Charlie? He's tall, he's blond...' and he thought about it and said 'Yeah... yeah.'

"I think he could remember some things, but not clearly. It was as if he was calling up his memory-file on me. Somewhere in this was his consummate question: 'You know... Amelia?' 'Yes, of course, we're all old friends.' 'Yeah... how is she?' That question felt loaded. His pause wasn't the 'thinking it over' type of pause, but more of a dramatic stage pause. In my best upbeat and chipper manner, I said, 'Oh, you know, she's doing well, she's good, she's up to the same kinds of things...' 'Yeah,' he said, and I could see him thinking his own thoughts, and I felt terrible, since I knew how miserable he's been since your relationship has been suffering, and I figured he was going to start getting upset as he reflected upon all this."

Katie started to giggle and shake her head.

"You know what he said? He said, 'You know what *I'd* like to do to Amelia?' It sounded sinister. I was stumped, and just said 'Uhh...' He said, 'I'd like to fuck the *shit* out of her!' I slapped his leg and said, 'Dave!' and we roared with laughter."

Oh, boy. I couldn't help but laugh. Dave was still hilarious and uncensored (maybe more now than ever).

"He really did want to know about you, though," Katie continued, "and he wants you to know he was asking about you. We talked more about some other things," Katie's voice lowered, the laughter gone. "He's in bad shape. Despite his being glad to see me, it was obvious things aren't right at all. Sometimes he was quiet. I'd ask him if he was OK, and he'd say, 'I'm nervous,' so I'd hug him and tell him he had nothing to be nervous about. I told him he was in the right place and they would help him. I tried to be encouraging.

"After a while, we just sat there squeezing hands. I'd give his hand a squeeze, and he'd do it back, and we'd chuckle in a silly way. He gave me his ring. I told him it was nice, and he took it off and gave it to me, and made me keep it. He told me he loved me, and my family, and added emphatically that he always liked me and that he always thought I was nice and pretty, too."

Everything Adam and Katie told me about those first visits made me know Dave was fundamentally himself. Some of his idiosyncrasies may have been exaggerated, but the details of his words and behaviors sounded familiar.

"I'll go see him tomorrow," I declared, confident that visiting Dave was the right thing to do. I didn't like it, but this was my life. It was inconvenient and hard, but this was my life. It wasn't going to change or go away if I ignored Dave's illness. I wasn't going to feel better if I turned away from him.

I knew Dave loved me. This was part of why it was so hard to break up. All along, I knew we were in love and deeply connected. I knew Dave would never turn away from me if our roles were reversed. Dave was the most nonjudgmental person I knew. If he were in his right mind and I were in a psych ward, he wouldn't hesitate to stand by me. He wouldn't think of inconvenience or consequences, he'd just do what was right.

I knew it should be some consolation that Dave was mentally ill. He hadn't been in his right mind through our breakup. He wasn't able to make choices to salvage our relationship. His sick head was incapable of doing anything but go along for the ride.

I wasn't consoled. Maybe this meant Dave didn't choose to end our marriage, but maybe it meant something worse. Illness felt worse than bad choices.

"I'll bring a deck of cards. Or maybe backgammon," I thought out loud to Katie.

"I don't think he can play games," Katie said. She gave me a concerned look as if I was missing an important fact.

That was hard for me to fathom. Was his condition really so bad he wouldn't be able to play rummy or backgammon with me? I'd have to see for myself.

The next day, I drove to Troy. I found my way to the hospital, then to the right parking lot, and finally the right building. I was dizzy with anticipation. I followed signs around the hospital corridors and wound up at an elevator marked Inpatient Psychiatric Ward.

As I rode the elevator up three stories, I put an invisible protective suit over my body. I concentrated on putting up my guard. I wouldn't be infected with the negativity and disease I envisioned the third floor to house. I wouldn't assume a burden from the sick people.

This seemed to be a very important step for me to keep my sanity. I needed to protect myself.

The elevator door opened to a reception desk. I took the three paces to the desk. A nurse sat with her head down, disinterested in my arrival. I opened the sign-in book and wrote Dave's name and my name in the first two required fields. I paused at the third blank, in the column labeled "relationship." I wrote "friend."

When I was done, the nurse turned the book to face her without looking up at me.

"Visitor for David Z," she muttered.

The nurse who was sifting through files at the counter behind the desk looked up and asked, "Huh? Who?"

"David Z."

They both looked at me then.

The second nurse approached the desk and looked at the sign-in book.

"Friend?" she asked.

I was trying to be anonymous and assume as little responsibility as possible.

She stared at me and then glanced back down at the book. "*Amelia?* Aren't you David's wife?"

I didn't know what to say. I was afraid that admitting my relationship to Dave would force me to be accountable.

"Well, I was. I'm his *ex*-wife," I explained meekly.

"Hmm," she said. "He thinks you're his wife. You can help us. Telling us about Dave's behavior can help with his diagnosis."

I stood over the nurse at the counter. I gave her a loose description of Dave's unraveling. When she asked about the exact time frame of our breakup, I realized I'd been in a whirlwind for so long I'd stopped measuring time. I couldn't remember, off the top of my head, how much time there had been between the markers of Dave's mental decline. I also didn't know where Dave's idiosyncratic personality ended and mental illness began.

"It sounds like Dave's condition may have worsened since that last time you saw him," the nurse warned. "Are you sure it will be a good idea for you to see each other?"

She seemed reluctant to let me through the locked door to the ward. My heart beat faster at the thought of being denied access to Dave.

"I hope it will be OK. I think so," I answered. I was nervous, but I felt seeing Dave was ultimately the right thing for both of us.

"I'll let you in, but I'll sit with you to make sure everything goes well," she said.

I wasn't sure what she meant by that. Did she think I'd freak out? Or Dave would? Her uneasiness made me feel more confident about being there. I knew what was best for me and for Dave. Despite the circumstances, I understood that Dave and I were bound by love.

The lock on the prison-style door that separated the reception area from the ward clanked and the door slowly slid open. I stepped into a long hallway. The floors and walls were a dingy grey, green, and brown. It smelled like a hospital: a combination of bodily fluids and antiseptics.

The nurse met me and led me across the hall to a rec room. A wall mounted TV was blaring. There were three young guys and a woman about my age gathered on folding chairs around the TV; *Cops* was playing.

Dave was sitting back from the others. His gaze was fixed on the floor at his feet.

He glanced up when the nurse said his name. She set two chairs near him and motioned for me to sit facing Dave.

Dave's movements were slow, and his reactions were delayed. His eyes met mine as I sat, but stayed blank for several seconds.

When I said "Hi, David," his eyes cleared.

"Hello," he replied with what sounded like a mouth full of peanut butter. His voice had a high pitch and was slow. He was obviously on heavy-duty drugs.

"David, do you know who this is?" the nurse asked him gruffly.

"My wife," Dave cooed, "Amelia."

Our eyes were locked and Dave took my hands in his. He was emerging from his drug-induced haze.

"Are you glad to see her?"

"Yeeesss," Dave said softly.

"When was the last time you saw Amelia?" the nurse continued her interrogation.

"A long time ago," Dave answered.

For the rest of that visit and many more after, Dave held my hand fiercely and marched us up and down the fifty-foot hallway that ran the length of the ward. Every so often, he interrupted our rapid pacing to fondle the alarmed emergency exit door at one end of the hallway.

"No, David," I'd caution. "We'll get in trouble if you open that door."

Other times he opened the door to his room and tried to guide me inside.

"No, David," I'd decline. "We're not allowed to go in there."

Patients could only have visitors in the common areas.

I went back to visit Dave almost every day. The pacing became part of our routine. This routine made me feel as if we were in a movie. Dave had been obsessively writing a screenplay before, or as, he went off his rocker. One day, as we tore down the hallway, I watched Dave and saw him as a character he'd create for his story. He was suffering, but he was also living hard and dirty, like his favorite author, Charles Bukowski. He admired Bukowski's commitment to living a hard and dirty life and letting it inspire his art.

"You'll write a rockin' screenplay about this when you're out of here. Some good songs too," I said. "You're gathering all sorts of source material."

I was serious. Dave's insanity and lockup were tragic. But this was the kind of tragic, dramatic experience that fascinated and compelled him. It was ironic, almost poetic, that life had handed him such a Bukowski-esque situation.

I felt sure Dave would find a creative use for his psych ward experience after it was behind him.

While we paced, I'd ask Dave how he was feeling and what kinds of things he'd done when I wasn't visiting him. He never had much to say. If I knew a friend had called or visited him, I'd ask him about that. Many times he didn't seem to remember having had other visitors.

I'd reminisce about happier times from our recent or distant past to pass time with Dave. Often, it seemed as if he didn't remember the things I talked about. He didn't remember going to Peru three years before or Hawaii two years before.

I wasn't sure if his memory loss was from his medical condition or the drugs the professionals were using to try to fix him.

Dave was dirty. His hair was unwashed. He wasn't shaving. The staff insisted that patients manage their own hygiene. As the days passed, I realized Dave wasn't *capable* of taking care of himself.

When Dave did speak, he had only a few subjects in his repertoire.

"I'm going to buy an acre of land and build a house," is one thing he said again and again.

This was his common response to questions about his future or what he wanted.

Once, when my dad came with me to visit Dave, he tried to draw Dave out.

"What kind of house are you going to build, Dave?" my dad asked. "Will you dig a basement? What about an A-frame?"

My dad and Dave had done construction work together. My dad knew Dave's abilities and styles. He was asking questions that would normally draw Dave into an involved conversation.

In answer, Dave would give a blank look, laugh, and repeat his original statement: "I just want to buy an acre of land and build a house."

Weeks were going by, and Dave wasn't improving. He wasn't responding to the anti-psychotic and mood-moderating drugs as the doctors predicted he would. I knew nothing about bipolar or schizophrenia or the other mental disorders the doctors labeled Dave with, but, since he wasn't improving, I wondered if he'd been misdiagnosed.

I wasn't alone. Katie had been back to see Dave a handful of times since her first visit. She thought Dave had been most lucid the first time she saw him. She was alarmed to see him noticeably decline on each of her later visits.

Dave's family was frustrated with the hospital. They were having a hard time arranging meetings with the doctors or getting answers about the plan to bring Dave to a mental state strong enough for release from the hospital. Since Dave and I were legally divorced, I didn't have the right to speak with the doctors.

Dave's brother, Rick, demanded Dave be given a brain scan. Seventeen days after Dave was admitted to Samaritan, he was given an MRI.

I called to find out what happened when Dave's family spoke to the neurologist who read his MRI results. Dave's dad answered the phone with a barely audible "hello." From the sound of his voice, I knew the news was bad.

"Dave has lesions on his brain," he said.

I O U

"Lesions on his brain?" I groaned with a sinking heart. "What does that mean?"

"They don't know, honey." Rich's normally smooth voice cracked. "They have to do more tests."

"I'm going to the hospital now," I whined, fighting back tears.

"So am I. We'll see you there," Rich answered.

Dave was happy to see me, as he was every time I showed up at the hospital. He was unfazed by the doctors' MRI findings.

For the first time, the nurse suggested we sit in Dave's room. Normally, visitors were forbidden in patients' rooms.

"Dave's case has changed," the nurse quietly explained. "We're not sure he belongs here anymore. You two can have some privacy."

Dave lay on his bed with his clothes and shoes on. I pulled a chair up to the side of his bed, and he reached out to hold my hands. We sat and stared at each other.

"Something's wrong with your brain, ya know?" I said gently.

He nodded gravely and rolled his eyes with a shrug. Dave's body language and facial expressions had always been so meaningful. He could communicate volumes with a raised eyebrow. Since he was speaking less, these supplemental gestures were substituting for words more and more. It was amazing how well I understood what he meant by these telling looks and movements.

"Now we know why you've been acting so weird. Once they figure out exactly what's wrong, they can figure out a way to fix it," I tried reassuring us both.

Dave nodded in agreement, also trying to reassure us both.

Not long after I arrived, Dave's dad and stepmom walked into the room. Soon after that, his mom and cousin, Kathy, arrived.

The family had requested to talk to a doctor about Dave's MRI.

Dave sat up on his bed while we waited for the doctor. He seemed content to be surrounded by family. It was rare for the whole crew to be together.

We tried exchanging small talk, but everything was incredibly strained. We were stuck in a psych ward, waiting for a doctor to find time to discuss Dave's suddenly terrifying medical condition.

Finally, a doctor wandered into the room.

"Is this David Zagorski's room?" he asked as he glanced up from the open chart in his hands.

Everyone snapped to attention.

"I'm here to examine David. I was told about his MRI, and I'd like to do some tests. I'm a neurologist, not a psychiatric doctor. I came over from next door," he explained with a wave toward the main hospital.

"Is that OK with you, David?" the doctor asked rhetorically as he sat in the chair next to Dave's bed.

Dave answered by slapping his knee and letting out a screechy laugh.

The doctor used a hammer to check Dave's reflexes. Then he asked Dave to stand and directed him to a painting hanging on the wall.

"What is this?" the doctor asked, pointing to a tree in the painting's park landscape.

"Ahhh, mmmm," Dave made thinking sounds and pointed to the tree knowingly. After a minute, he shook his head.

The doctor continued pointing to things in the painting and asking Dave to identify them. Dave couldn't name any of the common objects.

"Sit down, David," the doctor instructed as he took notes in the chart he carried.

Dave did as he was told. The rest of us looked at one another, dumbfounded. Dave couldn't say "tree"?

"Who's that woman over there?" the doctor asked Dave, pointing to Beverly.

"My mother?" Dave ventured.

"Good. And what does your mother do for a living?"

Dave thought for a long moment before responding, "I don't know."

It was horrifying to see Dave fail the simple tests. We pressed the doctor for a diagnosis, treatment plan, any information at all about what was happening.

There were no answers. Dave's case was unusual; there was no obvious diagnosis. So began days of testing.

Dave was only thirty-five, so age-related degeneration was out of the question. Cancer seemed unlikely based on the type of brain damage. The doctors were considering Lyme disease, multiple sclerosis, Lou Gehrig's disease, HIV, syphilis, and other viruses and bacterial infections. Blood work and a spinal tap were ordered.

I left the hospital and drove straight to my Grandma's house. Aunties Rae and Fay lived there with Grandma, and the three of them offered the unconditional, motherly love I needed.

I walked through the door and straight into Auntie Fay's arms to cry. I sobbed too hard to speak for a few minutes. Then, it was still almost impossible to squeeze out the news.

"There are lesions on Dave's brain," I announced.

I explained what I'd learned at the hospital.

I was wrecked. I was scared that Dave was very sick, that my husband had brain damage. I had divorced a sick man; I abandoned Dave when he was suffering from brain damage!

Now that sick man—whom I still loved with all my heart—was being held in a psych ward with an undiagnosed progressive brain disorder. I had to get him out of there right away!

To top it off, two of the first guesses on the possible diagnosis list were HIV and syphilis. My long-term partner and lover might be sick from a sexually transmitted disease, and I could be carrying that same disease.

The Aunties and Grandma listened patiently as I rattled off my concerns. They made me tea and fed me cheese. When I finished giving them details, they started problem solving.

"First thing you can do is take care of yourself. Let's get you tested for HIV and syphilis," Auntie Rae declared. She grabbed her laptop and started searching for STD clinics.

Grandma compiled a list of relatives who worked as nurses at hospitals. She called and asked advice about getting Dave moved out of the psych ward.

I was in a murky fog. My brain was at once shutting down and racing with a million fear-based thoughts, unable to make decisions or plans.

I picked at the assortment of cheeses Auntie Fay had set out on the long wooden kitchen table my grandfather had made. As I ate, she scurried back and forth between the cabinets and me. I was offered nuts, dried and fresh berries, fresh bread, and crackers. I was grateful to be nourished—physically and emotionally—at the family table.

It was too late for making calls and appointments, but Grandma and the Aunties had a game plan for the next morning. The Aunties loaded me into their van and drove me home to gather my cat and a suitcase so I could stay at Grandma's.

The next day, I made an appointment with my doctor for a syphilis test. Rae found a walk-in clinic at the AIDS Council that would give immediate results from an HIV test. A cousin Grandma called gave me the names of the best neurologists at the best local hospital and told me what steps I needed to follow to orchestrate Dave's release from the psych ward and transfer to Albany Medical Center.

Auntie Jen made the hour-long drive from her house to join my support team. She piloted Grandma's Civic downtown, following the directions she was given to the AIDS Council. I was dizzy with anticipation, and my body was slack with surrender. I was doing the only thing I could do. I was taking the only action within my capability to do something about the Dave Situation.

Inside the AIDS Council building, the light was soft and the staff was welcoming. We waited until a woman invited me into a room at the opposite end of the hall.

I sat across a desk from the comforting woman to explain why I was there. I told her about Dave's condition, and my fears.

She directed me to swab my mouth and started the HIV test. The results would take up to fifteen minutes to show, so she tried to keep my mind occupied by educating me about safe sex.

While she spoke, I tried figuring the probability of Dave and me having HIV. It seemed unlikely.

I was confident Dave had been faithful to me during our twelve-year relationship. His fidelity was never an issue; it was a strong part of his character.

He was open and honest about his exploits with his buddies.

I remembered Dave entertaining me with the details of his weekend-long bachelor party in Montreal.

As we passionately undressed each other on the night he returned, Dave rolled onto his stomach and lifted his ass off the bed.

"Whatcha doing?" I asked Dave as I grabbed his ass cheeks through his jeans.

"Keep going; you'll see," he snickered in reply.

Challenged, I reached to unbutton his jeans. I wiggled his pants side to side to expose Dave's skin. There was a long red welt across his right cheek.

"Holy shit!" I gasped. "You got spanked!"

"Nope, not spanked. I got *whipped*! With my belt!"

"Oh, my God!" I laughed until I collapsed on top of him. He rolled to face me and began the tale.

"They took me to the usual spots first," Dave said. I knew the usual spots. Dave and I had been traveling to Montreal together for years. We had a circuit of favorite bars and strip clubs.

"But, then, we went to Club Super Sex! You know, the place with the huge rolling neon marquee uptown on Sainte-Catherine Street? The fancy-looking place? It's awesome. The girls are hot. It's like a whole other level of strippers. Anyway, Mark and Dan picked our two favorite girls to take me on the stage. They took off my clothes and whipped me with my belt!" Dave told the story knowing I'd be impressed at the height of his bachelor party antics.

The timer beeped. My HIV test results were negative.

The reassurance about my health was a comfort, but I was still consumed with worry about Dave.

The next two weeks were packed with frustration and fear. Dave underwent test after test. The doctors were running out of ideas.

I pushed to have Dave released from the psych ward. He was restless and unhappy there. Most of our visits were still spent pacing the hall. I knew he didn't belong in that hospital but, when I thought realistically, I was frightened to see him released. Where would he go? He was incapable of caring for himself. He didn't wash. He could barely speak.

I was blindly pushing forward. I was ignoring the realistic thinking. Dave wanted out; I was on a mission to get him out.

Mark and I were in close touch. He suggested I contact Heather and Chris. Chris and Dave went to college together and were tight. Chris had been diagnosed with brain cancer three years earlier. Mark thought Chris's wife, Heather, might be able to give me advice or set me up with doctors.

Though I'd only met her once before, I didn't hesitate to call Heather. The idea of connecting with someone who had lived through a similar experience was comforting.

For years, she and Chris ran a raver speakeasy, Galaxie, in Brooklyn. The place was famous—notorious—as The Fucking Serious Party Place. She and Chris were both DJs, original NYC club kids. In the years Dave and I were together, I never went along with him to a party at their club. Dave and I lived separate lives; that was part of our success. NYC party trips were his, just as rock climbing trips were mine.

Over the years, our separate lives merged. I went to plenty of shows and parties with Dave in the city, and he tagged along on rock climbing adventures with me. I knew and liked most of his friends, but something about Chris and Heather and their wild party scene intimidated me.

I remember Dave coming home after a party at Galaxie with pictures on his digital camera: room after room packed with beautiful, costumed people dancing and posing. The place was decorated with loud colors and wild lights.

Chris was a founding member of a satanic fishing gang that rode invisible motorcycles. They smoked the hallucinogen DMT, ate psychedelic mushrooms, and celebrated the lives of the famous psychonauts Timothy Leary and Terence McKenna.

Dave reported this to me matter-of-factly. He wasn't fazed by Chris's lifestyle. He loved his soul-brother and he loved hanging out with his old friends and making new ones.

"You'd really love Chris's girl, Heather," Dave lamented. "You should come with me next time and meet her."

"You think? That's not really my scene, Davey," I reluctantly replied.

"That doesn't matter. You'd like Heather. She's a great girl. She's really good for Chris."

I did meet Heather, but it was years later, after she and Chris closed up shop in the city. They had moved to the sleepy town of Woodstock so Chris could convalesce after his cancer diagnosis and during exhausting treatments.

As I dialed Heather's number, I visualized the woman I'd met at her apartment the previous summer. The day we met, Heather wore loose denim overalls and a t-shirt. Her blond hair hung messily over her shoulders. She was gorgeous. Her gigantic blue eyes were bright and focused. Her posture was perfect; she stood straight and confidently. She was graceful and relaxed, calculated and hyper-vigilant all at once. She emanated coolness. Heather was welcoming and warm. I loved her at first sight.

Heather was expecting my call. She was ready with lists of brain doctors and heaps of advice for dealing with hospitals and Medicaid. She and Chris would come to visit Dave the day after next. I was infinitely reassured.

It was April 7, almost a month after Dave was admitted to Samaritan Hospital. Things were at a standstill. Without a diagnosis, the hospital was reluctant to release him. I was maddened by the red tape, but Heather helped me understand why the medical professionals weren't rushing to let Dave go. Caring for him would be a full-time job; they must have feared he'd end up back in the psych ward— or worse—without proper care.

I met with the social worker in charge of the unit to make my plea for Dave's release. Dave's brother, mother, stepmother, and father were crammed with me into an office just bigger than a closet. I announced I'd assume the role of primary caregiver for Dave. The social worker advised me I'd have to sign for Dave's release and be responsible if something happened to him.

Though the prospect of being responsible was terrifying, I had no choice. None of his family members were volunteering for the job; no one had the time. I'm sure they were as scared as I was. We'd all been traumatized by Dave's behavior in the previous year. Since his hospitalization, we were softening and forgiving, but it didn't make his lack of control and crazy behavior any easier to handle.

I was Dave's wife. Despite divorce and brain disease, we still loved each other. We still wanted to be together. I couldn't abandon him at this juncture, the hardest moment in our lives.

Later that day, Chris and Heather arrived. Because of Dave's mysterious illness, he'd been given more privileges in the ward. He was given his own room, and his guests were allowed to sit with him there. He and I were sitting together in the room when Heather and Chris sailed in.

They were an amazing breath of fresh air. Heather carried a box of goodies for Dave, and Chris held a blossoming potted plant. Dave greeted his old friends with a huge smile and screeching. He heartily patted each of them on the back while giving them bear hugs.

Dave ripped right into the candy Heather brought and balanced the stack of magazines from the care package on his knees while we sat in a circle on folding chairs. The astringent, bland room flooded with color and was brought to life by our visitors.

Dave nodded and smiled while listening to the animated stories Chris and Heather told. He was enlivened by the visit. Though he wasn't saying much, Dave was communicating with us in a way I hadn't seen since he'd been in the ward. His eyes were bright; his smile was huge. He squinted and widened his eyes in response to the talking around him.

I say "around him" because Dave was in a different state than the rest of us. We weren't talking "to" him. He was there in physical form; his mind was someplace else. His spirit was in both places. Dave was losing the ability to communicate in traditional ways. His being had transformed, and his way of interacting was almost otherworldly.

Three days after Chris and Heather's visit, the doctors came up with a diagnosis. A blood test showed Dave had an excess of very long chain fatty acids. This was a sure sign of adrenoleukodystrophy.

There was a name for what was happening to Dave. This derailed, dream-state part of our lives had a title: Adrenoleukodystrophy. Dave had a deadly brain disease.

The psych ward team of doctors, nurses, and social workers were suddenly very available to meet with me and the rest of Dave's family. They were ready to release Dave. I was grateful for the attention and willingness to speed up Dave's release, but painfully aware that the shift was due to the gravity of his condition.

The doctors at the psych ward had no advice or information about the disease. They had tested him as a long shot only after one of the neurologists read an article in the *New England Journal of Medicine* about a man with a case similar to Dave's. No one at the psych ward felt qualified to answer my questions about Dave's condition.

Hours after hearing the news of Dave's diagnosis, I sat in an office off the long hall Dave and I had paced so often. The room was narrow, shaped to accommodate a long boardroom-style table. I was seated at the head of the table, with Dave seated close behind me. Dave's parents and brother were gathered around the table. The head nurse, head doctor, head social worker, and some other officials sat with us.

Everyone looked at me. I was somehow in charge. I was making decisions; I was speaking for Dave. He was mine. He was mine to care for, to dislodge from the psych ward, to seek treatment for. I was his. I was his caretaker, his advocate, his devotee.

I felt disconnected and terrified. Yet I nodded and answered questions at the appropriate times. I followed along as the next phase of my life unfolded around me.

As they were for Dave, things were happening *around* me. I felt removed from my mind and body. I was cruising along—or sputtering—on autopilot.

I signed the papers the social worker put in front of me. I was assuming responsibility for Dave. He'd be released to me. In exchange for this, I meekly asked questions. My signature on the forms and contracts wasn't enough to buy me answers.

"Is there a neurologist you can recommend for Dave?"

"How will the disease progress? Will he get worse?"

"Is there a way to stop the brain damage?"

I heard my voice as if it was coming from someplace outside of me.

The doctors' voices sounded as if they were reaching me from a crackly, poorly tuned radio.

"No local doctors specialize in this disease. It's *very* rare."

"We don't know how the disease will progress. There have been *very* few cases."

"We know nothing about treatment options. His brain damage is *very* severe."

What the staff could tell me was that it would take days to process Dave's release from the ward. There was a system, steps to be taken.

The small consolation to the news that Dave was a seriously ill man being held captive in a sad, dreary place was that he'd be allowed to go outside.

After the meeting, Dave went outside for the first time in a month. He squinted dramatically as we stepped from the dim building into the bright spring day. We crossed the parking lot and headed to a picnic table in the adjacent park.

Dave didn't sit for long. He was anxious.

"Let's go," he said and nodded to my car.

"We can't, Dave. You're stuck here for a few more days," I sighed. Our helplessness was discouraging; I wanted Dave to be free. Yet part of me was grateful to have time to myself before sick Dave would become my charge.

Dave wandered around the park, taking a kind of inventory of the objects there. He picked up sticks and rocks, examining each with careful curiosity. He ran his hands over the wooden seat and iron armrests of a park bench. He slapped trees, testing their strength. I followed him and touched each tree after he did. I was comforted by earth energy and the trees' unflinching stability.

After some wandering, Dave beelined for a tree stump. There was fresh sawdust on the stump and a strong wood smell. The once-massive tree had been cut down very recently. Dave patted the smooth top of the stump and collected a handful of the sawdust. He smelled the dust before sprinkling it on the grassy ground.

I stepped onto the beckoning stump, feeling grounded and secure. Dave stared up at me with a half-smile. I held my hand out to him, and he climbed up with me. It felt rejuvenating to hold my love under the sun.

After Dave stepped back to the ground, I stayed on the tree platform with my eyes closed and chin raised. I felt raw: fearful, confused, and out-of-control, but very alive and present. That moment of awareness was prayerful.

I opened my eyes and looked down. There, amidst the sawdust, I saw an intricately patterned woodchip.

I bent to pick up the piece of wood. As I held it in my hand to look closer at the pattern, I saw the letters: I O U.

I looked closer. The grain of the wood indisputably spelled out "I O U." My heart swelled and tears rose in my eyes. It was a clear message from the universe, from God. It was a cosmic nod. It was the reassurance I needed to know I was doing the right thing. No matter the fear and pain, I was doing the exact right thing at the exact right time.

I felt the universe saying, "You may be losing everything right now, but there will be a reward."

I'd lived through darkness and loss. I'd seen light after what felt like total devastation. I knew everything I'd lived through to that point made me who I was: a strong survivor. I knew, just as shitty things happened, good things happened too. I knew the brightest light comes after the darkest dark.

When I arrived at the ward the next morning, I convinced the head nurse to let me take Dave out of the hospital.

I drove us to Woodstock to see Chris and Heather. On the ride, Dave blasted the music at full volume. When I thought he wasn't looking, I'd adjust the dial to be a little quieter. Each time, he'd raise it back up. My eardrums were aching, but Dave needed to rock out.

When I parked in front of Heather and Chris's house and turned off the car, the silence was a relief. The street was shaded by huge willow trees. Each house on the street was distinct from the next, some stone, some brick, some brightly painted wood. Most had bright, intentionally wild yards. Our friends' house was a subdued cabin-style house.

Inside, the home was colorfully decorated with collectible toys, records, and vintage furniture. The walls were dressed with a variety of vibrant art ranging from a framed Alex Grey print to a 1970s velvet painting of a devil on a toilet. Everything was sacred; the most mundane household items had a place and value in their space.

Heather kept incense burning on a table decorated with Hindu deities, miniature wrestler action figures, and Buddhist prayer flags. During my self-guided tour of their art museum-like apartment, I took a long pause in front of the table. Its stillness drew me in and I knelt to get a closer look at each of the holy objects.

Heather stood behind me and said, "The altar."

She winked when I looked over my shoulder at her.

Being with Heather and Chris made me feel secure. Big chunks of time would pass when I felt OK. Heather was a gracious host: feeding us and entertaining us. All the while, she was tuned into Chris and aware of subtle changes in his demeanor that could signal a problem. She was as attentive to Dave and me as she was her husband. As happy as I felt in her and Chris's company, reality would inevitably rush back in, and in those moments Heather's eyes would meet mine. She looked at me with such compassion, I couldn't help but be soothed.

Dave was content to sit still and just be near his friends. Chris was hilarious. He told jokes and stories that kept Dave in hysterics.

Heather and Chris were spiritual warriors. They supplied me with invaluable survival tools and techniques through their example and advice. They weren't just managing a difficult, potentially terrifying fate. They were choosing to live well and gracefully. Chris's illness wasn't the end.

Dave didn't want to go back to the hospital. We left Woodstock as it was getting dark. I knew I'd taken him for far longer than the hospital staff had expected, but I couldn't bring myself to force him back there. Killing more time, we stopped at my house. Dave sprawled out on the couch while I called the ward.

The nurse on duty sounded stressed.

"We need David back here immediately. It's after bedtime," she scolded.

"He really doesn't want to go back there," I ventured.

"Well, if he isn't back here within the hour, we'll call the police. You'll be breaking the law," she explained in a schoolteacher voice.

"But he's sick," I whined. "He doesn't belong there. He wants to stay with me."

The nurse softened.

"I know this is hard. I understand," she said with a lowered voice, "but you really have to bring him back tonight. We have to follow the rules until he's released."

On the ride back to the hospital, Dave said more than he had all day.

"I don't want to sleep there. I can't sleep there," Dave told me.

"But I thought they give you drugs? Doesn't that help you relax?" I asked.

"Doesn't work. I can't sleep there. I want to sleep with you. You're my wife," Dave reminded me.

"Oh, Dave," I sighed, "I'm sorry. I don't want to bring you there. It's not my choice. I promise we're getting you out of there. You'll be sleeping with me in the next day or two."

I tried to reassure him, but I knew there was nothing I could say to make the situation seem OK. I stopped at CVS and bought Dave some Benadryl. I gave him the maximum dose, hoping against hope that the over-the-counter allergy medicine would knock him out when the heavy-duty prescription meds didn't touch him.

That night, I cleared the random books and knickknacks from the built-in shelves in my dining room. I wanted to make a sacred space that would comfort me like Heather's place did. I'd always collected rocks and pieces of wood from places I loved. And I had a collection of objects that felt magical.

I neatly arranged stones and crystals in a row. I hung photographs of my mom and Barb. I flanked Grandma Wakefield's wooden monk statues with Yoda and Buddha. I stood the miniature wrestler action figure that Heather gave me (and that looked strikingly like Dave) front and center with his arms raised. I built an altar.

Boston

Two days later, Dave was released from the psych ward and into my care. He came home with me, to my independent woman house. My already upside-down world started spinning.

I'd worked blindly to get Dave out of the psych ward. It wasn't until he stepped foot into my house that reality struck.

I panicked. Dave couldn't be left alone. He was energetic and fidgety. He didn't like being told what to do. What had I signed up for?

Dave's personality was closer to the man I divorced than the man I married. Knowing about his brain damage helped ease the strain some, but I was still reacting more like a dissed wife than a compassionate caregiver.

Dave's brother and father agreed that they would divide Dave's care with me. Dave's brother worked from home and his father was retired. We hoped our three flexible schedules would line up enough to cover Dave's care.

At the end of April, I emailed Kristen, a friend I'd grown up with. I wrote, "Currently, life is hell. I'm wondering what I did to deserve this shitty fate."

Kristen replied, "The shitty fate is Dave's, you are OK, you are healthy, focus on that."

Her words hit me hard. I was feeling pretty sorry for myself. Everyone I interacted with backed me up; my self-pity was allowed, if not encouraged. Not by Kristen. In my raw state, her message was harsh. I felt defensive. Wah! But this *is* happening to *me*, I thought.

Over the next few days, Kristen's message kept popping into my head. I considered that, despite the emotional upheaval I was drowning in, I *was* OK. I was healthy. I was capable of caring for myself and making decisions. I was choosing to care for Dave; he was the sick one, the brain-damaged one. I was choosing to care for him; I could choose not to feel so sorry for myself.

I had a care schedule set up with Dave's family. I'd drive Dave up to his mother and brother's house on Thursday or Friday and pick him back up the following Sunday or Monday. This gave me the weekend to work at the Ginger Man.

During the week, when I worked at home on the computer, Dave would get restless. I tried to get him to sit on the couch and watch movies while I kept him in view and worked at the dining room table.

Sometimes, he'd sit and watch, laughing his screechy howl at the funny parts. Often, he'd get up and wander restlessly around the house. He'd go out the backdoor and come in the front over and over. If he was gone for more than a couple of minutes, I'd get up to check he hadn't run off.

When Dave was at his mother and brother's house, he'd run off. His usual routine was to walk about two miles to Stewart's, a convenience store. He'd buy beer or a TV dinner. He wasn't fit for the public. He'd go out walking shirtless or shoeless. Sometimes he wouldn't have money to pay for the stuff he was trying to take from the store.

I'd written my contact information on a card in Dave's wallet. I was getting ready for work at The Ginger Man on a Friday night when the phone rang.

The voice on the phone identified himself as a state trooper.

"Ma'am, you're going to have to come pick David up. We've been called several times in the last couple weeks," the officer explained. He was frustrated, yet sounded sympathetic.

"Uh, um," I hesitated, "I can't. I'm thirty minutes away and I need to be to work in forty-five."

"I'm sitting out front of Stewart's with David in my car. He can't stay here," the cop continued.

"I can call his father," I offered. "He's around the corner. I bet he'll meet you."

"All right," the cop said, "but it better be quick."

I hung up and called Rich.

I didn't feel as though I could reprimand or instruct Dave's family about his care. I knew how hard it was. I understood that they didn't grasp the severity of Dave's condition. I could relate to Dave's family's denial. We all knew Dave as a strong, competent person.

It took the MRI—proof of physical brain damage—to make me realize Dave *wasn't* making choices and I had to adjust the way I treated him. Until then, like Dave's family, I didn't rein wild, rebellious Dave in.

During May, I spent a lot of time searching the Internet for information about adrenoleukodystrophy, which was often abbreviated to "ALD." Dave's stepmother, Layne, was doing the same thing. It didn't look good. There were only a few doctors in the country studying or treating ALD.

Layne made calls to find a doctor qualified and willing to see Dave. She was also in charge of following through on getting Medicaid and Social Security Disability set up. The social worker at Samaritan had started the process to be sure the hospital would be paid the thousands of dollars of bills Dave had accumulated there.

Lots of our friends and family were doing research. I learned much more from everyone's Internet findings than what the neurologists at Samaritan had told me.

ALD is caused by an abnormal gene from the X-chromosome. It usually shows up in young boys and causes behavioral changes, then dementia and death. The adult-onset version of the disease is generally milder and causes weakness or paralysis of the lower limbs. These symptoms occur because very long chain fatty acids accumulate on body tissue. This leads to the demyelination of the coating on nerves. Without the myelin, the integrity of nerve signals suffers, and things stop working in the body.

In most adult-onset cases, the myelin on the spinal cord is attacked, thus the paralysis. In Dave's case, the myelin in his brain was attacked. He had the rarest form of the disease; only about three to four percent of ALD cases result in adult-onset cerebral symptoms. I couldn't find information on treatment. Once symptoms presented, death was imminent within four years.

Despite the Internet prognosis, I thought there might be hope for Dave. I was determined to bring him to a specialist. Layne made an appointment for Dave with a doctor at Massachusetts General Hospital. The soonest he could be seen was early July.

Dave's condition had rapidly declined over three short years. He seemed to lose vocabulary and decision-making skills by the day. In early May, July seemed a lifetime away. I kept up the search for care for Dave. I called hospitals in Ohio and Maryland. I contacted research facilities, seeking experimental treatment. Layne did the same.

At the end of May, I had what felt like my first stroke of good fortune. Kristen forwarded me an email from her husband's friend, Christopher. He was a smart, connected man from a wealthy, successful Boston family. The email Kristen forwarded to me was four pages long. Christopher had gotten wind of Dave's situation and took it upon himself to help.

The four pages included names, phone numbers, and emails for doctors who were Christopher's family friends. He'd also done extensive research on ALD and included links to articles and papers about the disease. He'd located helpful organizations and contacts related to ALD. He volunteered to make calls for us.

I called Christopher right away. Based on his, Layne's, and my research, Mass General seemed like the best bet for treatment for Dave. The doctor who was most noted for his experience with ALD was Dr. Florian Eichler. Dr. Eichler had written the article that led the neurologist at Samaritan to Dave's diagnosis.

Christopher and I hit it off. He assured me we'd see Dr. Eichler. Within days, Christopher provided me with Dr. Eichler's cell phone number. He told me not to be shy; the doctor was expecting to hear from me.

Wow. My hopes soared! Finally! Not just any specialist would see us; the most renowned doctor in the field was expecting my call!

Dr. Eichler agreed to see Dave on June 10. He wanted Dave to check into the hospital so he could undergo tests and drug treatments. I confirmed the appointment with the doctor's sweet assistant, Arenia. Layne sent all the Medicaid information to the office. We were all set.

The next several days were filled with optimism. Dave was taking supplements and vitamins based on a list Mark had compiled. We were hoping to slow or halt the demyelination process. I was confident I was doing everything I could to help Dave. It felt good to be taking action.

The day before the Boston trip, Dr. Eichler's assistant called.

"Good morning, Amelia," Arenia said. "I'm sorry, but I'm calling to cancel David's upcoming hospital stay. I don't have the necessary approval from Medicaid."

My head and heart exploded. I was fragile and barely keeping it together since Dave's release from Samaritan. Seeing Dr. Eichler was the only thing I was looking forward to. All my hope and energy were fueled by the promise of the upcoming visit to Boston. I was so close to my breaking point that Arenia's two sentences were all it took for me to lose it.

"No!" I screamed at Arenia. "No! No! No! You can't do this!"

"I'm sorry, there's nothing…" Arenia tried to explain.

"You can't do this! We need to see Dr. Eichler! You don't understand! David is SICK!" I screeched. I paced violently with the phone, punching and kicking at the walls.

Arenia tried to speak again, but I screamed over her. I wailed as tears spurted from my eyes.

"Fuck you! You don't understand! How can you do this? My husband is dying!" I carried on. I cried, swore, and screamed before hanging up on Arenia.

I collapsed on the living room floor and wept. Now what would we do?

I was still on the floor when the phone rang again. This time it was Dr. Eichler.

"Amelia, I'm so sorry. The hospital won't take David without approval from an insurance company or Medicaid. I'm sorry. I can't change that. But *I* will see him free of charge. Please still come tomorrow," the doctor spoke gently.

"Yes. Yes, we'll come. Thank you. Thank you very much. I really appreciate it," I answered, dumbfounded.

I called Layne crying. I told her about the need for Medicaid approval. She had less than twenty-four hours, but Layne pledged to do whatever it would take to get the approval from the Medicaid office for Dave to stay at Mass General.

The next morning, I drove Dave to Boston. Dave's brother followed us with his mother and father. Dave and I listened to CDs and watched miles of dreary highway pass. Dave was the DJ. He changed discs often and made constant adjustments to the EQ levels and volume. He loved to blast the music at full volume.

When we arrived in downtown Boston, I got lost trying to navigate the city. Since Rick had a GPS, he took over leading the convoy and brought us in circles over the fancy new bridge two or three times before getting us near Mass General. We paid to park in a garage and found the building where Dr. Eichler's office was located.

Inside, the family checked Dave in because I was too embarrassed to face Arenia after my phone blowout. We sat in a large, open waiting room filled with colorful children's toys and books.

All the other patients were children accompanied by worried looking parents.

As we sat waiting, Dave thumbed through magazines. When I'd ask him how he was, he'd respond with a smile and a nod.

Rich's cell phone buzzed. He looked at the caller ID and with wide eyes, he said, "It's Layne!"

He answered and after a minute he brought his phone to Arenia.

Layne had succeeded in getting the Medicaid approval for an out-of-state hospital treatment for Dave! The authorization papers would be faxed to Arenia. Dave could stay in the hospital for a full evaluation and treatment.

After the paperwork was settled, Arenia led the crew through circuitous hallways to a small exam room. Moments later, Dr. Eichler arrived.

He was tall, dark, and handsome. The doctor was much younger than I expected and very laid back.

He examined Dave, checking reflexes and asking Dave to follow a pen with his eyes. He asked Dave questions: What year, month, and day was it? Who were the people in the room? Where was he?

Dave smiled a lot and occasionally had an outburst of laughter. He identified the people in the room, but he didn't know where we were or the date.

Dr. Eichler tested Dave's reflexes and asked him to alternate moving his hands. Dave wasn't able to distinguish between left and right and easily became frustrated. He slapped his hands together willfully at each of the doctor's requests.

We told the doctor about Dave's life and interests. We told him Dave was a creative, charismatic musician and artist loved by everyone he touched.

Dr. Eichler questioned Dave based on the information we gave him.

"David. You're a musician?"

Dave smiled and nodded and snickered in reply.

"What instrument do you play?"

"If you know it, I can play it," Dave stated with a grin.

"Can you name one of the instruments you can play?"

Dave shrugged.

I wanted to interject. I wanted to say, "Guitar! Dave plays guitar! He sings! He writes amazing songs and performs on stage and everyone loves his music. He's talented and gifted!"

I bit my tongue along with the rest of the family.

The doctor continued to question Dave, testing his awareness and abilities.

Even though I'd seen the doctors at Samaritan put Dave through similar testing, it was shocking and unbelievable to witness Dave's confusion and inability to express himself.

"Can you tell me what this object is called?" Eichler asked, gesturing to Dave's shirt.

"The long sleeve thing."

"And what about this?" Eichler pointed at Dave's pants this time.

"This, that, or the other."

Dave used his catch phrases as answers. I had been hearing him pull answers from this limited repertoire for a long time.

Like when he'd come home an hour late from work and I had dinner waiting cold.

"David! Where have you been? What have you been doing?" I'd whine.

"Oh, you know: this, that, or the other," he'd casually reply. Or he'd announce, "If I knew, I'd tell you!" with a cackle.

Reality whooshed in on me. This brain-damage progression had been happening for a long time. But how long? How long had Dave not been choosing his behavior? When I thought my husband was aloof and inconsiderate, was he really suffering from brain disease?

Were all my frustrations, heartaches, and subsequent choices based on this mysterious, brutal illness?

I was sad and scared learning about Dave's illness. Now, I was questioning my judgment and actions. How many years of our lives were warped because of adrenoleukodystrophy?

The doctor asked Dave's parents about his medical history and the family medical history. He asked about Dave's childhood development. He asked us all about Dave's adult personality changes.

The room we sat in was small and hot. We were six bodies crammed together. The doctor was fresh and cool. The crew that had traveled from Albany was worn out and haggard. We were tired. We were defeated. Dr. Eichler was energized and commanding.

He was also sympathetic and kind. He explained that part of his mission was to help build awareness about brain disease. With early detection, disease progression could sometimes be slowed or stopped. But often, he explained, patients like Dave were misdiagnosed with mental illness, when the symptoms were all due to ALD.

After Dr. Eichler's family interview, he instructed us to cross the street and check Dave into the hospital. The doctor ordered testing including an MRI, an endocrinological evaluation, a PET scan, blood work, and an EEG. He also planned to give Dave high doses of steroids and a trial of N-acetylcysteine.

We found our way to the hospital check-in. I was very happy that Dave would begin a treatment—even if it was a long-shot experiment. We were in qualified hands. The hospital staff was as friendly and helpful as Dr. Eichler. Within an hour, Dave was given a room. The family sat around his bed while a nurse took his vital signs and started a chart for Dave.

"I guess we better look into getting a hotel room," I said. Dave's family members stared back at me with blank faces.

"Honey, I have to get back. Layne and the girls are expecting me," Rich said.

"I have to work in the morning. Early. In fact, we better get going soon," said Beverly.

"Yeah, me too. Work in the morning. And I need to get these guys home," Dave's brother said.

Wow. Really? "No one will stay with me?" I squeaked.

"I didn't plan on it. I didn't bring anything to sleep over," Dave's dad said, and the other two nodded in agreement.

I hadn't brought an overnight bag either. I wasn't planning on staying either. I felt as though I was being abandoned, but I didn't protest. I was shocked that Dave's family didn't want to stay and hear more from the doctors. I was shocked no one wanted to support confused and sick Dave. But I didn't think it was my place to say any of that.

So, the family left. While the nurses were setting up an IV for Dave, I found a phone and called Auntie Rae.

"Dave's staying in the hospital. I don't know where to go," I explained.

"I can drive out there in the morning. Or I could even come tonight," Rae offered.

"No, that's OK," I said. "I just need help finding a place to stay. Something cheap."

Rae agreed to look for a place for me to crash. She offered again to meet me in Boston. I had no idea what I needed. I didn't know what would help me; I didn't even know I needed help. So, I didn't ask for much help and didn't accept a lot of the help offered.

When I got back to his room, Dave had been started on intravenous N-acetylcysteine. This drug has antioxidant and radical scavenger capabilities and is given to children with brain disease because it may halt or slow injury to the neurons. Dave was also started on regular doses of a steroid in the hope that the swelling in his brain would be reduced.

A nurse informed me that Dave would undergo testing the following day. The nursing team had already figured out that Dave wasn't good at sitting still. They set up a bed alarm, so the nurses' station would be notified when he got up.

The nurse left us alone in the hospital room. I held Dave's hand to keep him from pulling at the needle taped into his arm.

"This is good, Davey," I tried reassuring him. "This place is pretty cool. I think they're going to be able to help you."

Dave nodded slowly and deliberately. He stared into my eyes. I could see he was tired, but he was fighting sleep. Dave was stubborn. I didn't know how much he understood about where he was or why he was there. What I knew was he didn't want to be there and would fight against relaxing.

I turned off all the lights I found switches for. There was still a light over Dave's head that couldn't be shut off. His vital signs were monitored by a bedside machine that beeped and flashed bright lights. The room was cool, and Dave was covered with only a sheet and flimsy blanket.

"I'll be right back," I told Dave.

I asked for more blankets at the nurses' station. While I stood by, waiting for the blankets, a beeping alarm sounded.

"That's room 227," a nurse said, glancing at a panel of blinking lights. Dave's room.

"I got it," the nurse returning with spare blankets said. I followed her to Dave's room. He was standing beside his bed tugging at the IV. The nurse dropped the blankets on the chair and got to Dave's side just as he ripped the needle from his arm.

She gently steered Dave back into bed and took the ball of tape and needle from his hand.

"Be right back," she said and gave me a sad, sympathetic half-smile. She was right back with a plastic basket of medical supplies. She expertly set Dave's IV back in place.

"Let's try to keep this one in, huh, Dave?"

Dave laughed and pounded his bed with his free fist.

"We'll see," I sighed to the nurse.

After his act of defiance, Dave seemed exhausted. He rolled his head on the pillow, looking from me to the monitor beside him. His eyes were worried.

I felt the chill that had made me leave to get Dave a blanket. I spread the thin coverings over him. Three of the hospital blankets seemed to be enough to keep Dave warm in the drafty room.

"It's OK, Davey. Just try to sleep. I'll wait here until you're sleeping, and I'll be back in the morning," I spoke softly.

He nodded. His eyes gently closed.

I called Rae to find out where I'd be sleeping. She'd booked two nights for me at the four-star hotel across the street from the hospital. When I protested about the cost, she insisted that she and Fay were covering the room.

The next day, I hurried back to the hospital to find Dave's room empty. He'd been taken to get the MRI. I killed time picking at breakfast in the hospital cafeteria.

For the rest of the day, Dave was wheeled to different parts of the hospital for tests. In between tests, a dietician, a social worker, and various residents and medical students visited us.

The social worker wanted to help me find a full-time care facility for Dave. She had ideas for places that would take Dave in Massachusetts, but was stumped when I told her we lived in New York. She was so kind and eager to help that I wished we did live in Massachusetts.

The previous day, Dr. Eichler had told me he'd stop by Dave's room after he reviewed the MRI. I was eager to see the doctor, and by evening I was wondering when he'd drop in. The phone in Dave's room rang as Dave and I were resting on his bed.

"Amelia, I'm so sorry to keep you waiting all day," Dr. Eichler apologized. "My wife has been in labor. I've been here at the hospital all day, just not working. I'll see the MRI and talk to you, I'm just not sure when I'll get away."

I was touched and impressed that the doctor was calling me during such a monumental personal experience. I assured him I understood and wished him and his wife well.

I dozed at sleeping Dave's side for the rest of the evening. That night, a doctor came to the room and asked if I'd like to see Dave's MRI. He and Dr. Eichler had reviewed the scan together. Dr. Eichler

would sound and a nurse would tend to him if he moved. I knew I could leave his side and trust he'd be looked after.

A growing dread was seeping through me. I wouldn't be able to leave Dave's side. I was going to watch my husband die.

For the night, though, I knew I could leave Dave. He was the safest he'd been in years. I knew I needed to eat and sleep and make a game plan.

I wandered down the block from my hotel and into a dark, neon lit bar. I ordered a Sam Adams and looked at the dinner menu. I ordered a two-course meal. My mind went blank as I made small talk with the bartender. I ordered dessert with my second beer and pretended everything was OK.

I made it into the hotel elevator before I started sobbing. The weight of Dave's condition bowled me over. When Dave received the ALD diagnosis at Samaritan, my focus became getting him to a specialist. I was determined to find a way to treat him.

I accomplished what I set out to do, but I wasn't rewarded with a treatment plan. ALD would kill Dave. Dave had a deadly brain disease. He was not coming back. As the elevator rose to my fourth floor room, my head spun. I felt as if I was on an amusement park ride, not an elevator. The motion was so intense I fell back against the wall.

Once the elevator door opened, I staggered to my room, using the corridor wall to keep me on my feet. In the dark room, I collapsed on the bed. I was at the very center of the very most remote and lonely place in the universe.

Before we left the hospital, I called Dave's family members individually and asked them to meet me at his mom's place for an official family meeting.

In the car, I followed Dr. Eichler's advice and asked Dave about his wishes.

Dave wasn't capable of having a dialog with me, but he answered questions with nods or a "yes" or "no."

I thought I knew the answers to the questions I was preparing to ask Dave. But everything had changed. Maybe Dave's mind had changed now he was facing death. So, I had to force out hard, ridiculous questions.

"If you can't eat, would you want a feeding tube to keep you alive?"

Dave stared out the windshield at the highway we were rushing over. He raised his hand with his pointer finger extended as if scolding the road. He somberly shook his head "no."

"I didn't think so. If you're dyin', you just wanna ride it out, right? You don't want to go back to the hospital?"

"Right!" Dave announced with another wag of his finger.

"Do you trust I know what you want?" I asked. "Is there anything I should know?"

"You always know what's best," Dave said in a singsong way with a shrug of his shoulders.

This was a common reply. Dave often defaulted to my judgment. Now that everyone knew he was sick, our friends were united and telling stories of Dave's spiraling insanity. When we were separated, he'd tell people things like "Amelia knows best. Amelia knows what I need," and "You should ask my wife, she knows the answer!"

This default behavior was stressful to me through our breakup. I took it as apathy. Dave's "you know best" reply got old when I was seeking constructive input from him about our relationship and plans. I wanted the partner I married to contribute to our decision-making. I wanted him to man up.

After seeing the MRI, I understood that Dave wasn't capable of decision-making in the time leading up to and during our breakup. He was relying on me out of necessity. He trusted me, as his partner, to know the right things to do. I hoped I was up to the job.

When Dave and I got to his mom's, the family was waiting. I described everything Drs. Eichler and Raju had told me. While we sat in the kitchen to talk, Dave wandered around the other rooms of the house, peeking out windows and using his fingers to wipe dust from surfaces. He was never out of earshot, but he didn't take part in the conversation.

I could sense Dave's stress. When he strolled through the kitchen, his eyes were wide and teeth clenched. His parents and brother cried when I told them Dr. Eichler's one-year timeline of decline.

Everyone agreed that Dave should be kept out of the hospital for as long as possible. It was easy for us to agree Dave wouldn't want life support (like a feeding tube or respirator); we were all committed to honoring that. It was also easy to agree Dave would never want to live in an assisted care facility. Could we honor that? Dave was already so difficult to care for, and it would only get harder as he declined.

"I know he doesn't want to be in a home," I said, "I don't want to send him away. I think we should try to keep him with us."

"He won't be happy locked up somewhere," Dave's mom said.

"Think of how he hated the psych ward," his dad said.

"And how hard we worked to get him out of there," his brother said.

Looking around the table, I felt cheered by the thought I had all these people to help me. They felt as strongly as I did about keeping Dave out of a care facility. Maybe we could make this work.

I filled out the health care proxy the Mass General social worker had given me. This form would give me the legal power to make Dave's health care decisions. He signed it, and we all witnessed the form.

"Dave is really sick. His brain is in bad shape; the MRI was shocking. He really can't make choices or take care of himself," I lectured Dave's family.

I wanted to make it clear he needed to be watched all the time when he was with them. The severity of Dave's condition had sunk in with me; now I needed to make it sink in with his family. I needed to be able to relax when he was in their care, to feel he was safe and I wouldn't get a call from the police.

"If we're going to keep him out of a care facility..." my words tapered off. This would be the hardest part.

Everyone looked at me, waiting for me to continue. I took a deep breath.

"If we're going to keep him out of a care facility, I'll need help," I announced. I was desperate. I wasn't good at asking for help, but I knew I'd need it in the coming months. I hoped Dave's family would be able to give it.

As I got ready to leave, Dave stopped pacing and was at my side.

"Davey, you have to stay here," I told him. "I need a break. I have to check on my house and get ready for work. I'll come back for you in two days."

Leaving him was hard. I felt guilt and concern and sadness. But I craved time for myself; I wanted a break. I wanted to try to relax, which I definitely couldn't do while watching Dave. The relief I felt when I left Dave behind outweighed the guilt of not spending every moment at his side.

It was difficult for me to calculate how committed I was to Dave's care. I was divided as usual. Like during our breakup and Dave's time in the psych ward, half of me wanted to be Dave's devoted wife, tolerant of everything, and half of me wanted to run away and save myself the agony of his demise and the inconvenience of his illness. I was torn between wanting to make every remaining day of Dave's life an adventure and wanting to give up.

Part Two

Everything You've Ever Done

After our trip, I remembered it was summer. I remembered summer could be fun, and there were adventures to be had. Caring for Dave was overwhelming; he was like a man-sized two-year-old. Despite the difficulty, I felt a responsibility to myself and to Dave to keep living and experiencing the world around us.

So when Sugar Shack Mike invited me to meet for rock climbing and camping on the south end of Lake George in the Adirondacks, I readily accepted. I loaded Dave, a cooler, climbing gear, and camping gear into the car and headed north.

We met Mike at the camp site. The spot was beautiful and the weather was perfect. I dragged towels and cushions and snacks over the short trail through the woods. Even with my arms loaded with cumbersome stuff, Dave had a hard time keeping up with me. He deliberately stepped over rocks and roots. He'd stop to brush leaves or twigs from the trail.

Despite his snail's pace, Dave seemed eager to be in the wilderness. He looked up at the sky and around at the trees. Whenever I looked back to check his progress, he smiled at me.

The trail ended at the lake, where Mike reclined on a large flat platform rock. I set a cushion for Dave on the rock, and he heaved a big sigh as he settled onto it. The short walk had worn him out.

Mike and I chatted about the rock routes we planned to climb that day. The sun was still rising and casting vibrant light through the clear blue sky and onto the lake. The lake was undisturbed. Small, even ripples reflected the sun in sparkly glints. Dave was mesmerized, watching the lake through squinted eyes. I was mesmerized watching him.

Dave sat still for the first time I'd seen in months. His body and face were slack; the Adirondacks had melted his tension.

I felt a great relief sitting with Dave. It was one of the first relaxing moments we'd shared since the whirlwind of his illness brought us to the psych ward. At home, Dave paced and fidgeted; he'd wander off in the blink of an eye. At the lake, he was content to sit.

After sitting for an hour, it went without saying we weren't going to climb. The walk to the cliff was uphill, rougher and longer than the short approach to the lake that had worn Dave out.

Although Dave still referred to me as his wife and seemed most content at my side, it was unclear how much memory he retained or how much understanding he had about what was happening to him and around him. He'd wander off if left unattended, didn't speak unless spoken to, and didn't seem able to form complete sentences.

I asked Dave if he wanted to take a walk. He answered with a nod and I led us along the lake's edge. The path was flat and easy, and openings in the trees gave us gorgeous views. Dave ambled and took in the scenery. I had the rare feeling things were OK. I was in one of my favorite places with one of my favorite people. Walking in the woods was difficult for Dave, but he persevered. He, too, was happy to be out adventuring.

We walked along the lake side by side for a few minutes. I was matching Dave's pace, expecting him to need to stop for a rest at any time. When he did stop, he reached out and turned me to face him. On that perfect June day, on the shore of a calm Lake George, we looked into each other's eyes and stood close.

Dave looked peaceful, yet determined, and cleared his throat.

"I appreciate everything you've ever done for me," he said.

This was the only unprovoked statement Dave had made in months. It floored me to hear his voice form a complete sentence, and it melted my heart to know he was aware.

At the end of June, I had a longstanding reservation for two weeks in the cabin on the north end of Lake George where I'd stayed alone the previous summer—and with my family most of the summers of my childhood. After the success of our first Adirondack adventure, I was eager to bring Dave north with me.

I packed the car and navigated onto the Interstate. The day was perfect: sunny sky, warm temperature, fresh blossoms on the trees.

As always, Dave had the car stereo cranked to full blast. I'd wear earplugs because he always won the volume battle.

As we raced up the road, bound for an Adirondack getaway, I felt happy. I was going on vacation with my husband. We were listening to music we both loved. Despite the long-term forecast, that summer day of our lives was sunny and bright.

Instead of stuffing my ears with plugs, I sang along with the music Dave blasted. I sang loud and rambunctiously. Dave approved! Instead of my usual crinkled brow response to the loud volume, I was rocking out. Dave screeched along with me. He made bird noises and beeping sounds that were completely out of key with the music. I sang louder, and his crazy vocals rose to match mine.

We spent most of the two-hour ride carrying on this way. We were communicating; we were enjoying our time together in a connected way.

When our throats were raw, our voices quieted and we rode along just listening. I was struck by the scene we just lived. We were both totally whacked out characters. We belonged in a movie, I thought. If Dave were well, he'd make up characters like us for his screenplay.

Our first week at the lake was pleasantly uneventful. Friends and family visited. We cooked on the grill. We sat on the dock. Dave wandered around the huge field of a yard.

The second week at the lake, my childhood friend, Jimmy, was bringing his wife and two young children to share the cabin with me. I thought Dave's uninhibited behavior would be too much for Jimmy's wife and kids, so I arranged for Dave to be with his family during that time. The Aunties came up at the end of the week and took Dave back to his mother's house.

I was left by myself. Normally, I'd cherish alone time. I'd relish simply existing in a cabin on a lake. The stars were bright that night. I understood beauty was surrounding me, but I felt detached from it. I couldn't savor my surroundings; I was inconsolable. I felt detached and solitary.

I felt raw, as if I didn't have any skin or protective layer. I was exposed to the brutal elements: sand and salt digging into my flesh, raging fire burning me to the bone. I was dizzy with sorrow and fear. Darkness was caving in on me, suffocating. It hurt to breathe in, and each exhale was forced.

I spent hours alternating between tossing and turning in bed, terrified that something was lurking outside the window, and wandering the cabin looking for a distraction. I paced like Dave did: picking up random objects, looking out windows, wiping dust from window sills with my fingers. I ventured outside to the dock. I sat on the warm boards to look at the stars, but couldn't shake the feeling something would grab me and pull me under the dark water.

The image of Dave in the bedroom at his mother's, scared and confused, haunted me. The thought of him suffering alone was agonizing; it compounded my loneliness.

I fought to rein in my dark, vicious thoughts. I was panicking as my aching heart and worried mind spiraled out of control.

I forced myself to sit and breathe. It took all my strength to focus on my breathing until the panic subsided. I forced myself to remember "now." I took comfort in what I'd learned from talks with Donna. She taught me the freedom of allowance. I could recognize the pain, terror, and panic I felt and simply allow it.

I remembered to be alive in the moment. There was nothing else: no past, no future. In the moment, there was no dwelling on the past joys or being mournful over an unknown future. Instead, be here. Be alone in the cabin by the water with the calm air and sky. Be alone as the sun goes and darkness surrounds. Be alone. Be raw. Be afraid.

I allowed the now. By allowing it, by not fighting, the fear and panic subsided. Everything was OK if I let it be. Let it go.

I was practicing firsthand what Donna had taught me. I'd learned survival skills.

Our good friend Ken invited Dave and me to go on a Fourth of July trip. Ken and his seventy-something-year-old mother, Kathleen, planned to go to Olana, a historic artist compound and park, for fireworks. I jumped at the opportunity to take a slow-paced adventure with our older friends.

We arrived early enough to tour the grounds of the beautiful Persian-style complex. Trees spread artistically over rolling hills. The castle-like main house was perched on a steep hill that plunged to the Hudson River.

From the hilltop, the river below looked huge and grey. Across the river, the Catskill Mountains loomed. The setting was dramatic and timeless.

The serene quiet was occasionally disrupted by a train whistle blast. Down at the river's edge, Amtrak passenger trains sped over the tracks like bullets.

Dave was energized and stayed on Kathleen's heels as we walked around the grounds admiring gardens and architecture. He and Kathleen had always made one another laugh. Many times, Dave sat rapt at Kathleen's storytelling. He'd ask her to retell the circumstances of her meeting Kris Kristofferson back in the day. Today, he was comforted to be around these old friends. He happily trailed Kathleen, smiling when she spoke to him.

The fireworks would be displayed over the Hudson River. As dusk fell, we settled on a blanket on the hillside overlooking the river.

Dave was content. We enjoyed the show. When the display ended, the hundreds of spectators stood en masse and moved away from the river to the parking lots. The four of us struggled to stay together as the crowd surged. The hillside was shadowy and dark.

When we reached the light at the edge of the parking lot, I looked around. Ken and Kathleen were each within ten feet of me, but I couldn't locate Dave.

"Where's Dave?" I asked my friends. Both of their faces dropped, and they spun side to side looking for him. We scanned the immediate area, but there was no Dave.

How could he have gotten away? He moved so slowly; it seemed impossible he could cover enough ground to be out of eyesight.

Panic rose in me. Ken and Kathleen tried to calm me, but I broke away to jog around the hillside and parking lot, calling to Dave.

We were forty miles from home in a place Dave had never been. The rushing river and rail tracks with speeding trains were a few hundred yards away from where we'd last seen Dave. He could be worse than lost; he could be hit by a train or drowning in the river.

Just when I was starting to feel comfortable with our new lifestyle and confident I could care for Dave, I lost him! I was responsible for Dave's safety, his life, and I screwed it up.

I rushed to a security guard.

"Please help me!" I cried as I grabbed the guard's uniformed arm. "My husband is lost. He has a brain disease. He can't take care of himself. Can you please help me find him?"

The guard used his walkie-talkie to organize a search for Dave. He assured me there were many local police and state troopers on site, and they'd all be looking for Dave. After what felt like an hour, but was probably only a few minutes, a police car pulled into the lot where we were standing.

"We found your husband," the officer shouted out his window. "Hop in."

"Oh, my God, thank you so much!" I gasped and jumped in the passenger seat.

"We found him walking down the main road. He's just fine, ma'am," the officer comforted me as I bit my nails and jiggled my knees in his squad car.

We drove to the entrance where Dave was sitting in the back of a police vehicle. I jumped out of the car and rushed to him.

"David! Where did you go?!" I exclaimed. "I was so worried about you!"

He laughed at me and waved a hand to show me I was overreacting.

After we were reunited, I felt relieved, but still sick to my stomach. Ken drove us home in silence. I held Dave's hand in the backseat. At Ken's house, Dave and I switched to my car to go home.

As soon as we were alone, I lectured Dave. I used a whiny, grating voice to complain about how hard it was to keep track of him, how overwhelmed I was at the job of caring for him, and how frustrating it was that he had no regard for his own safety or my peace of mind.

Normally, I thought Dave didn't get a lot of what I said to him. I often felt as if my rants or complaints were an outlet for me, not a way of communicating with Dave.

Something about this night was different. Dave nodded gravely as I spoke. My frustration turned to sadness, and soon I was choking back tears.

"I've been frustrated with you for so long. I thought you were acting crazy all this time because you didn't care about me," I cried.

Dave nodded more emphatically as I continued.

"We broke up because you're sick. Your disease made your brain change. I didn't know you were sick, Davey, I thought you didn't care. I'm so sorry." My tears streamed unchecked. In my hypervigilant state, I didn't want to take a hand off the wheel to wipe them.

"And now I feel like I can't take good care of you. This is so hard," I whimpered.

"I know," Dave said.

He stopped nodding.

"I know," he repeated, with conviction.

"You know? You know we broke up because of the disease? You know you've been acting crazy? You understand?" I asked, floored at hearing Dave's voice utter the two-word sentence.

"Yes," he answered.

"Oh, David! I'm sorry. I love you. I'm sorry we broke up. I'm going to try to take care of you," I pledged. "I won't lose you again."

Deep Sea Dive

Now that I knew what was wrong with Dave, now that I had recommitted to being with him, all I had to do was figure out how I'd take care of him. There was only one problem. I had no idea how (or if) I'd be able to do it.

When we got back from the lake trip, I adopted a business-as-usual attitude. Going to work and managing my home became touchstones for me. I was precariously holding my life and head together by focusing on my everyday life.

When he was at my house, Dave would drive me crazy. I was totally freaked out by his condition. Just as his family didn't understand that he needed constant supervision, I couldn't understand he wasn't making choices when he did irrational things.

I'd ask him to stay put, and he'd wander out the front door and into the street while I was in the bathroom. He'd open his pants to piss—or worse, masturbate—in the backyard. He'd pick at my fresh paint job or pull at the sofa upholstery. As if he were a two-year-old, there was a constant risk of him getting into something he shouldn't or wandering off.

My dream of Dave's family being a major part of the care equation was dwindling. When I needed a break or had to work, I drove him up to one of his parents' houses in Clifton Park. But I still had to worry about Dave. The state police continued picking him up walking along the road or at the convenience store near his mom's house.

As the hope of built-in help from Dave's family evaporated, the uncertainly of how I could care for Dave overwhelmed me. I felt anxious and alone.

When Dr. Eichler told me Dave's prognosis, he assumed I'd seek a full-time care facility for Dave right away. The social worker at Mass General also spoke of Dave receiving full-time professional care with a "how," not an "if."

Since busting Dave out of the psych ward, I'd toured two nursing facilities. Both were horrifying. The patients were alarmingly low-functioning. Dave didn't belong in a place like that.

Maybe he should've been checked into an assisted living facility, but since Dave never did what he should do and always did what he wanted to do, I wanted to honor his choice of lifestyle. I was going to have to find a way. Dave was too fucking cool to check into a home.

Instead of realizing I was maxed out, I somehow decided it would be a good idea to paint my house. I took on the huge project of scraping, priming, and painting my 2,700-plus-square-foot house.

I felt that, at least, *this* was something I could do. Something tangible and physical. Something I could do right here in the present, and see results right away.

Plus, it had to get done; it was peeling severely. Paint flakes were accumulating on the driveway and yard. It looked pretty awful, especially when compared with the other houses on the block. They'd been modernized with vinyl siding. Mine had the original cedar shake and wood siding, and the original slate roof. I wanted to paint it to look like a Cape Cod house. Jeremy was still living with me, and he offered his help.

One sunny Saturday, Jeremy and I planned to spend the day painting. I left in the morning to take Dave up to his mother's house so we could concentrate on getting the work done. When I got back to Albany, Jeremy was painting the back of the house. He was standing on the ladder laying careful, concentrated strokes of Deep Sea Dive Blue across the wood siding.

As the morning wore on, my dad showed up to help me troubleshoot my leaky bathroom ceiling. He worked inside while Jeremy and I slathered paint on the back of my house.

We were working away, not saying much. I was feeling uneasy about leaving Dave at his mother's house. I felt guilty that I couldn't keep him with me all the time. I also felt as if I didn't want to care for Dave *at all*. I felt overwhelmed and exhausted.

I was determined to maintain a normal life. I felt entitled to some peace. I had dealt with our breakup in a constructive way. I was staying healthy and keeping my shit together. But things kept getting worse. No matter how much I tried to keep things together, they kept unraveling.

I'd endured major losses (deaths, breakups, my broken neck) with minimal complaint; I thought this should buy me grace. Dave and I had worked hard to build a strong, loving relationship (no easy feat for two such passionate, stubborn people). Together, we'd lived with and cared for Grandma Wakefield when she was dying. We'd done everything right! We should've been in positive karma surplus!

I had a house that needed fixing and maintaining. Dave should be helping me! I couldn't do it alone. I had work to do, money to make, adventures to go on. I couldn't live my life and care for Dave as he got crazier and crazier!

Oh, my God, it wasn't fair! I was good, I was faithful! This shouldn't be happening. I had paid my dues, when would the suffering end?

There was an angry, self-pitying storm building inside of me. As Jeremy stood above me on the ladder, precisely and persistently painting, my work pace slowed. I couldn't do it! I couldn't paint my house. I couldn't manage my house at all! I couldn't care for Dave. I couldn't believe the love of my life, my partner, my husband, was dying. I couldn't stand it! I stood staring at the wall in front of me.

"What's the matter, Aim?" Jeremy asked.

"I can't do this. It's not fair. I hate my life. I hate this fucking house," I whined in a defeated whisper. "I'm stuck with this house all by myself."

"No you're not. I'm here to help you. I've put a lot of work into this paint job. You should be grateful."

"Grateful? How can I be grateful? Dave is dying. My life is unbearable. I can't take this anymore."

"Oh, thanks. That makes me feel great, like all my help is meaningless. You just need to deal with the situation. Keep it together. Keep painting."

This was a rare moment of reaching out and admitting defeat for me. I needed love, some support, not this stoic cold admonishment. I sniffled as I backed away from Jeremy and the house.

Just then, Adam came bounding around the corner.

"Hey guys! What's up? Where's Dave?"

My answer was a scream. I threw my paintbrush against the house. I punched the backdoor frame. I thought, "There's no God; I have no faith." I wanted to destroy my house, myself.

I pushed inside the house screaming and crying. Adam followed. My dad came running from the bathroom. Jeremy stayed on his ladder, painting diligently.

"What happened?! What's going on?" my dad asked.

"I can't take it anymore!" I shouted. "Why is this happening? I've been through enough in this life! It's not fair!" I screamed as I ran through the house knocking things over and pushing into walls.

My dad and Adam followed me.

"I know, I know, Aim," Adam said with exasperation. "It sucks. You're right, it isn't fair."

I exploded into my bedroom. I picked up the guitar I found in the attic at Grandma Whalen's and had been half-heartedly teaching myself to play. I smashed it on the floor. I kicked over my wicker clothes hamper. I took the top and tried breaking it in half. When it would only bend, I gave up and collapsed on the bed sobbing.

My dad sat beside me and patted my back. "What can I do for you, honey?" he gently asked.

All my replies were wailing screams.

Eventually, Jeremy came ambling in. He advised: "Aim, you gotta calm down. Control yourself."

"But, *Jeremy*, don't you see? I'm sad. I'm ruined. Devastated. I'm losing everything. DAVE'S GOING TO DIE!"

"Well, carrying on and breaking a bunch of stuff won't help."

I screamed some more. Jeremy went back to painting; Adam paced; my dad asked me over and over what he could do to make me feel better.

"I don't know what to *do*," I said.

"You don't have to *do* anything," my dad answered.

My dad had a brainstorm: "Do you want me to call the Aunties?"

"Yes, I want the Aunties," I sobbed.

My dad left the room to call Aunties Rae and Fay, who lived twenty minutes away. When he returned to tell me they were on their way, I settled down. I knew I'd be soothed and nurtured by unconditional Auntie-love and compassion.

My dad and the boys could help with the house and getting my mind off things. I appreciated them, but my tears and loss of control were more than they could handle. There was nothing they could do for me in this inconsolable state.

I wandered out of my bedroom and sat to sniffle on the love seat. I announced that I was at the end of my rope, that I was done with this world. Fuck God. Fuck Planet Earth. I was done trying. I was cursed.

Adam, in his typical dark brooding anti-hero way, agreed.

"You're right, Aim. This world sucks. Life is pain. I've been telling you that all along."

When the Aunties arrived, they rushed in and gave me bear hugs. They coerced me out to the back yard, into the sunshine. We sat at the picnic table and they listened to me talk about my fear, and sorrow, and loss of faith.

My dad and Adam stayed nearby to interject words of encouragement. Jeremy kept painting, his determination its own stark show of solidarity.

Sitting in the sun in my backyard, surrounded by supportive friends and family, I felt encouraged. I wasn't happy, I wasn't accepting of my situation, but I was willing to hang on. The urgent mood lightened as we sat together in the back yard.

I felt relaxed sitting at my picnic table. I took in the day and looked around. When I glanced sideways, I saw my eighty-something-year-old next-door neighbor lying on the ground beside her lawn chair. Without thinking or speaking, I bolted from the table and bounded over the four-foot fence that separated our yards. I rushed to Georgia's side. Luckily, she wasn't unconscious, just confused. I helped her back up into her chair and stayed a few minutes until I was convinced she was OK.

Back in my yard, I felt pretty convinced that I was OK too. Despite my heartache and spiritual questioning, I felt fundamentally right in the world. My autopilot reflex to help someone in need was reassuring. Having my supportive loved ones around me was reassuring. I'd make it through another day.

Storming the Buffet

Dave was officially sick and officially dying. I was officially devastated and officially daunted. I was getting amazing support from my family and friends, but the lack of support from *Dave's* family and friends disappointed me.

Dave could barely speak and couldn't care for himself. He didn't shower without lots of help and direction. He'd wander off if not constantly watched. He required full-time care and was losing brain function by the week. His physical and mental decline was inevitable.

I was a wreck. I was miserable watching my love fade away; I was lost thinking about the future. I was maxed out dealing with the present. I wasn't sure I could handle Dave's care; I didn't know if I wanted to.

I was longing for help. I wanted Dave's boys to step up. Dave had always been so tight with his friends. He had true soul brothers. I had never seen guys so close and loving with each other. Dave would have done or given anything for those guys. He was a selfless and honorable friend. As his illness progressed, I couldn't help but think about what would happen if it were one of his friends who was sick instead of Dave. I was certain Dave would help, would go above and beyond. I was frustrated that his soul brothers weren't more present.

I wished for Mark or Jay to come home from Portland to help me. I'd hear myself saying, "Help me! I need help!" but only in my head. It didn't seem it was my place to say it out loud. I thought those guys should want to help, feel compelled to help.

I thought if I had a helper, I could surely do it. With some solid backup, with a caregiver partner, I'd have a good shot at keeping Dave at home.

In August, Jay did come home. His brother was getting married. He was in town, but very busy. He only had a day to spend with us. Jay's dad dropped him off at my place in the morning just before Layne picked Dave up to take him to a doctor's appointment. The appointment was with a New York State disability doctor. The doctor had to examine Dave to make sure he wasn't faking his illness to collect his disability payout.

Jay and I were alone for about an hour. We sat on my front porch. I told Jay how scared and overwhelmed and sad I was.

"I don't know if I can do it, Jay. I'm really freakin' out. It's so sad. It's so hard. Why is this happening to us?" I said as tears welled.

"We planned this, Amelia," Jay said, lovingly and confidently. "Before we were born. We've been connected for a long time. It may be hard for you to understand now, but I know we chose this. Dave, you, me, Mark, and Dan, lots of the people we're close to. We've been together before and we've been working up to this for lifetimes. We chose this life and these lessons to bring us closer to enlightenment and understanding. We set this up before we were born."

I cried and hugged Jay on my front porch, aware the neighbors were watching. Jay held me and told me we were going to be OK. I thought he was full of shit, but I loved him anyway, and I needed a friend who loved Dave as much as I did to be there with me. I knew even though Jay thought everything was cool, it still hurt him too.

When Dave came back from the doctor's, we decided to take an adventure drive. We drove twenty-five miles south of Albany to Athens. We hoped the little town would be a fun place to get away to and have lunch.

I parked the car, and we wandered through the streets of the small and disappointingly quiet town. We spent time hanging out along the river at a shut-down outdoor bar. Jay and I talked and kept an eye on Dave, who was restless. Dave wasn't interested in being included in another conversation that revolved around his illness and care.

I suspected Dave knew how hard the situation was for me. I think he was trying to give me space while I figured out what I wanted and could handle. That was Dave's style all along. He was never a demanding or controlling partner. He always emphasized our individuality and appreciated our separateness. He encouraged me to do whatever I wanted, even if it took me away from him.

Throughout our time together, Dave and I had accumulated a bunch of "our songs." One of them was "Together or Alone" by Sebadoh. The last song on an otherwise loud punk album, this slow pretty tune tells a love story. In a relaxed tone almost drowned out by the persistent melodic guitar, the singer explains that even though he appreciates feeling strong in a relationship, there's equal strength in and nothing to fear about being alone.

Dave loved that verse. He pointed it out to me again and again over the years. He thought the message was meaningful and agreed it was essential to be strong on one's own to be strong in a relationship.

I knew I wanted to be with Dave and wanted to care for Dave, but I wasn't sure I could handle it. I shared this with Jay. I was hoping he, or one of our friends whom he relayed my concerns to, would offer to help me. In the meantime, we only had one day together, so we made the best of our small town visit.

We headed into the only café in town for lunch. I usually had trepidation taking Dave into restaurants. There was no predicting if he'd screech or shout "Fuck!" He wasn't usually able to place his own order and was often fidgety. I dreaded making a spectacle of ourselves and disturbing the other diners. Now, having Jay along eased the tension for me. We sat in a corner booth, and Dave was relatively subdued. He ordered a burger, and we all enjoyed our greasy spoon lunch.

After we ate, we started the drive home. We passed a sign for a nature trail, and U-turned to check it out. We parked in a small gravel lot and headed to the trailhead. The trail was a wide Jeep road that meandered up and down hills to the river. Dave moved slowly and stopped to examine trees and rocks. He'd move branches and sticks from the trail so the path was clear.

As we walked through the woods, Jay pulled out a bottle of marijuana tincture. He'd boldly brought the elixir on the plane from Oregon, where medical marijuana was legal. Jay and I each had a dropper-full, but Dave was reluctant to try it.

Dave had always been a pot smoker. He continued to smoke after his diagnosis. The Boston doctors didn't give me reason to encourage him to stop. With his brain damage, the effects of smoking seemed minimal or nonexistent. So, when he took a dose of the tincture, Jay and I were shocked at his response.

When we reached the riverbank, Dave's eyes widened. He looked as if he was hallucinating: watching the space around him as if something was there.

"Oh my God, oh my God," he said.

Jay and I locked eyes. His face reflected my concern. Was Dave about to lose it?

"Ride it out, Dave," Jay urged. "It'll fade soon."

I had no idea what Dave was experiencing. He had no way of communicating what he was seeing or feeling. I was stoned and sad, overwhelmed at the thought Dave was stuck in a scary, out-of-control spot.

Jay talked to Dave, reassuring him we were there to care for him.

"It's all right, man," Jay said. "You know there's something bigger than this place. We'll help each other here, and then we're going on to bigger and better things."

He talked about his faith in our spirits extending before and after our time on Planet Earth. He talked again about our group of friends being soul-connected and spiritually conscious beings.

Dave nodded at much of what Jay said and, after only a few minutes, was calm and content.

The uneasiness Dave had experienced left me reeling. I was unsure of my ability to care for him. Did I have good enough judgment to keep him safe? Was this more than either of us could handle? On the way back to the car, I confessed my confusion and despair to Jay. Dave wandered a few steps behind us, disinterested in the conversation, or maybe trying to give us space.

"I want to run away with Dave," I admitted. "I want to take him back to Peru. To the Sacred Valley. That place is holy. I want to go there with Dave and jump off the cliff at the Pisac ruins."

Jay listened as I continued.

"I can't just watch him die like this!" I said. "I don't think I can get through this. I don't want to be here without Dave anyway. I want to die at his side! Now! Before this gets worse!" I looked back to make sure Dave was still behind us, still safe on the trail.

"I'm barely capable of taking care of him now," I said. "How can I take care of him to the end?"

On our trip to the Sacred Valley, three years before, we were afraid of the cliff edge because of the danger. With our lives wide open in front of us, we wanted to be safe and together. Now, things were different. Dave was facing certain death, and I was facing the loss of my partner and love. I wanted to go back and face the danger, let it take us. I wanted to spare him from a slow, painful death, and spare myself from helplessly watching that death. I wanted us to go willingly from this world, together. That was a better choice than checking Dave into a hospital or a home. I'd rather die than abandon my love.

"But, Amelia," Jay reminded me, "Dave doesn't want to take you with him. He never would. He wants you to stay and live. Instead of dying for Dave, you'll live for him. Instead of going with him in death, you need to honor him by living your life."

I wasn't convinced. I badly wanted to feel the faith that had gotten me through earlier rocky times. I wanted to feel the certainty that everything would work out. But I had a hard time accepting Jay's message. I was too concerned with practical earth things like Dave's comfort and my sanity.

We drove home. Jay called his dad for a ride. During the half-hour it took Jay's dad to get to Albany, Dave and I sat on the love seat.

Jay knelt in front of Dave, held his hands, touched his legs.

"I love you so much, brother," he said. "Thank you for your friendship and influence in my life."

He reminisced about their twenty-plus years together. He apologized for not being able to stay. He held himself together for a while, but eventually broke down and sobbed and hugged and kissed Dave. Dave put a hand on Jay. He gave his old friend a consoling pat and then pushed him away.

Jay stood, wiping his eyes, pulling himself together. We hugged, and he went out the door.

Seeing Jay was a tease. The day he spent with Dave and me was a glimpse at how I wanted to be living with sick Dave. Having one other person along on our out-of-the-house adventure was liberating. When Dave and I were alone out in the world, I doubted myself. I wondered if Dave was safe and I wondered if we were offending people.

Jay's presence had been a reassurance. He had been backup.

I had expected Jay to offer more help. He was the only one of Dave's boys who was a friend to me too. I had spent time with Jay separate from Dave. We'd shared spiritual discussions and gone on adventures together.

Jay had been the only one of Dave's friends to call me, to reach out, when Dave was acting crazy before his diagnosis.

I fantasized that Jay would give us more of his time, would offer more in-person support. In that fantasy, I didn't consider that Jay had a home in Oregon. That he had a job there, and a nine-year-old son.

I was giving up big chunks of my life: adventures, jobs, time with friends. Wouldn't someone else please do the same?

I was hopeful one of Dave's other close friends would step up. Where were the soul brothers he'd grown up with? I felt like I shouldn't have to ask. Someone should rush in to help.

Frank called a few days after Jay left. He was in town from North Carolina, and he wanted to see Dave. I'd always liked Frank. He and Dave had been friends since junior high school. Together they played and recorded music. He had played bass in Dave's band Tom Fiction.

I hadn't seen Frank in five years, since he moved away from Albany. I knew Dave had visited him the year before, during the time of his brain's noticeable unraveling. I had assumed Frank was among the close friends and family whom Dave had alienated during the early progression of his disease.

"Jay told me Dave is pretty confused. Will he know who I am?" Frank asked.

"I'm sure he'll know who you are. He doesn't really talk, but he definitely knows what's going on," I replied confidently. Dave was always thrilled to see friends and family. He laughed and screeched when old friends walked in our front door.

When we had visitors, Dave would sit and listen to conversation. If asked a question, he'd smile, slap his knee, or shrug. He was content during these times; he loved having company.

We made plans for Frank to visit the following day.

Early the next afternoon, I heard Dave's deep and gulping laugh from the living room as I washed dishes in the kitchen and knew Frank had arrived.

I dried my hands as I rushed to the front door. Dave stood inches away from the door, staring at Frank with a huge smile.

"Can I come in?" Frank asked Dave through the door's thick glass.

"Are you gonna let Frank in?" I asked Dave.

He laughed and stayed frozen in place.

"C'mon!" I encouraged. "It's FRANK! Aren't ya gonna let Frank in?!"

Dave laughed harder, but didn't move.

I opened the door and stepped aside so Frank could move straight into Dave's open arms.

Frank sat with Dave and me on the sofa. We relaxed together immediately and completely. Frank told us he'd come home for a family gathering. He told us about his job as a programmer, how he could work from anywhere and make his own hours.

"So, what are you guys doing for fun?" Frank asked. "What's the plan for today?"

"No plans," I said. "Just happy to be hanging out with you."

"Well, should we go out for a walk? Get something to eat?"

"Sure. Just be warned, Dave can make a scene out in public," I said.

"Yeah? What's new?" was Frank's reply.

He was right. Before the brain damage, Dave was just about as likely to make a scene as he was in his inhibition-free, brain-damaged state. Dave always talked to strangers. He never hesitated to speak his mind in public.

This was especially true if he was in a partying mood. Dave was often the center of attention.

Before Dave was sick, I was sometimes uncomfortable with his gregarious behavior and shenanigans in public. But, back then, I could walk away. I could hang back and let Dave do his thing. Now, since he couldn't talk and often didn't seem to understand, I was responsible for Dave. Keeping him out of trouble was my duty.

Frank's lightness was contagious. He and Dave had been getting in and out of trouble together since junior high school. If anyone could hang, it was Frank.

We boldly left the house. Frank drove, with Dave as co-pilot and me in the back. We were bound for the Indian lunch buffet in Clifton Park, the town where Frank and Dave had grown up. Dave loved Indian food, and he was a bottomless pit—always eating.

Dave cranked up the volume as soon as the car was in motion. The music made conversation impossible. I sat contentedly, happy to be chauffeured and to have another caregiver looking out for Dave. As I watched the trees dissolve into a green blur as we sped up the highway, I wondered if Dave turned the music up so we couldn't talk. Was he tired of being left out of conversation since speech was almost impossible for him?

When we arrived in the strip mall parking lot, Frank cut the ignition and the car was instantly eerily quiet. My eardrums were buzzing. Frank seemed unfazed by the top volume ride.

"Ready for some chicken tikka masala? Vegetable korma?" Frank nudged Dave before jumping out and opening his door. We arrived at the restaurant just before the 2:30 p.m. buffet cut-off time. I was relieved that we were the only customers. I could relax a little more if I wasn't worrying about disrupting other people's lunch.

When spoken to, Dave's replies were almost always loud. He'd screech, cackle, or sound like he was speaking in tongues. He always turned heads, which could exhaust me.

Inside the restaurant, Dave pushed past Frank and me and headed straight to the buffet. At high speed, he bypassed the plates and stepped right up to the food. I jogged through the dining room to catch up with him.

"Good afternoon!" offered one of the three restaurant workers as we stormed the buffet.

As I reached him, Dave's left hand pulled a piece of cheese naan from a basket and his right hand plunged into the greasy vat of pakora. He was oblivious to the tongs provided in each food container.

"Davey, let me help you," I instructed. "You need to use a plate."

He ignored me; his right hand emerged from the pakora squishing four pieces in his fist.

"Oh, David!" I sighed as he stuffed a pakora into his mouth.

He was smiling and nodding vigorously.

"Whoa," Frank said as he took his place in line beside us. "I guess he's going for it."

I was satisfied that, with hands full, Dave wouldn't be reaching for more food. I pointed to each dish to ask Dave if he wanted it on the plate I was preparing for him. He nodded affirmative to every single option. Once his plate was piled high, I ushered Dave to a table.

The restaurant workers hovered nearby but didn't comment.

Frank caught up with his own full plate and sat with Dave while I went back to help myself to the buffet.

"I'm sorry about that," I said to the man tidying the buffet. "My husband has a brain disease."

"It's OK. He's welcome here," replied the man with a warm smile. Then, more seriously, he offered, "I'm sorry your husband is not well."

I kept forgetting that Dave's condition was obvious. To me, he could seem like still-normal Dave just acting a little wild. To the world, it was clear Dave was ill.

Back at the table, reassured by our host's welcome, I relaxed to enjoy my meal. I encouraged Dave to use a fork, but he mostly ate with his fingers.

Throughout our lunch, the three waiters took turns filling our water glasses and clearing our plates. They each looked kindly at Dave. He smiled and laughed responses to the men serving our table.

After the three of us were satiated by our bountiful lunch, we got up to go. As we stood, the three men working at the restaurant scrambled to meet us near the door.

They stood in a receiving line and each extended a hand to Dave. As Dave shook each hand, the men bowed their heads.

"Thank you for visiting," one said. "Be well."

Right away, I knew Frank would be a part of the Dave care equation.

Within hours, he offered to ask his brother, who worked in the Disability office, to help me get Dave's benefits started. He suggested we move the audio gear from Analog Underground that Dave abandoned in his mother's basement to my house to give Dave something to do. He offered to stick around instead of going home to North Carolina.

Frank made himself available. He was present and unflustered. He wasn't an observer of the problem, but was part of the solution.

Jeremy had moved out at the end of summer, so I had a spare room available for visitors. I invited Frank to stay at my house. He agreed, and we made plans for the coming weekend. Instead of sending Dave to stay at his mother's while I worked Friday night at the Ginger Man, Frank would stay with him at home. Dave wouldn't get shuffled off for the night like a kid living between separated parents. I wouldn't worry that Dave was walking barefoot to Stewart's to buy a TV dinner and beer.

The next evening, Frank showed up with his suitcase. His arrival into our lives changed everything. Most of my friends and family were focused on my getting professional help caring for Dave. Everyone was overwhelmed by the enormity of the care required to keep Dave at home. Frank was focused on caring for Dave in the present. He wasn't overwhelmed; he was rolling with it. He had ideas for adventures.

One of the first things we did as a newly formed family-of-three was to go to Dave's mom's house and collect his recording gear and music tapes. Frank set Dave's studio up in the attic and started to identify what Dave had recorded on countless half-inch tape reels.

Frank and Dave often sat together, with Frank asking Dave for instructions for setting levels and outputs with the many dials and switches on the console before them. Dave didn't give directions or offer Frank advice, but he sat comfortably at his friend's side in front of the mixing board.

One day, while I sat at the dining room table, staring at the computer screen and trying to edit a proposal, Frank took Dave downtown. They walked up and down Lark Street, stopping in the record shop and coffee shop, and looking in windows.

Frank told me he felt as if they were in high school again, in their old stomping grounds, causing a commotion like free-spirited kids. They laughed a lot, and Dave screeched and hollered in an out-of-context joyful state—as if he was laughing at a joke that hadn't been told. As they wandered, they turned plenty of heads.

After a flustered woman stepped from the sidewalk to let them pass, Frank turned to Dave.

"People are gonna think we're tripping!"

"I *am* tripping!" Dave announced.

When the boys came home and Frank relayed this story to me, we considered what was happening in Dave's brain-damaged mind. His words were so few. Those three words were the first Frank had heard in days. I was envious that I hadn't gotten to hear Dave's sweet voice. But I was pleased to have a sliver of insight about Dave's thought processes. He felt like he was tripping. Wow.

Every once in a while, Dave would come out with some hilarious one-liner when nobody thought he was paying attention. One night, we were sitting around the living room with a crew of visitors. I was updating everyone on Dave's condition.

"One of the positives is that Dave has his very own Valium prescription now," I said, trying to put a lighter spin on things.

"I bet you like that, huh?" Charlie, who was sitting next to Dave on the couch, nudged him.

"I always *did* like Valium," Dave casually replied, with his trademark eyebrow raise.

It was funny. It was true. Hearing his voice was music to our ears.

There was no predicting when one of these gems would slip from Dave's lips.

Over the weeks that Frank stayed with us, we ventured out almost every day. Of course, we headed back to the Indian lunch buffet often. One day, after the buffet, Frank parked his car outside the fence surrounding the skateboard park. Dave grew up skating and always kept an old free-style board for riding around town.

Dave had the music cranked up to full blast. MGMT's album *Oracular Spectacular* filled the car while we sat and watched the kids skate.

Tears streamed down my cheeks when the song "Time to Pretend" played. The singer's voice sounded boyish over a psychedelic patchwork of synthesizers and booming drums.

The first verses described my mood perfectly. The song is about being young and completely alive, and completely exposed to life.

That was exactly how I felt! I was still young, still open. Yet I was beat down and exhausted by life. Dave too! I felt how sad that was: that the best years of our lives were being sacrificed to this uncontrollable illness.

But the next verse fed me inspiration. The lyrics celebrate a decision to live fast and have fun in the face of an awareness that death could come at any time. It reminded me we *do* have control—we choose how to live, and we can choose to have fun. Dave and I had always made our own decisions, and reveled in them. We'd always lived hard and fast; we'd always had fun. Why stop now? Dave was dying young, but he was alive for now. He had always lived a wild, fun, creative, inspiring life. Why stop now?

Life was flashing by like the trees on the highway. In the whoosh of time, Dave had gone from a skater punk to a husband to a dying man. Everything had changed, but everything was still the same. We were the same rich, bright people blasting music and having adventures and loving each other.

Through my tears and melancholy, I took the song to heart. In all the out-of-control planet spinning and time passing, we could still embrace the decision of how we would live.

He's Probably Whacking Off

Dave's inhibition was long gone. He reverted to a more primal version of himself. He was hungry for food and sex.

He poked through cabinets and dug into anything that appealed to him. He stuck his fingers directly into the peanut butter jar. He'd drink straight from the milk carton, juice bottle, and soda bottle successively. He'd rip into a sealed package of cheese and take a bite from the block despite an already opened package.

He loved sweets. The sound of the ice cream truck would send him out the front door every time.

Dave would unzip his pants and grab hold of his penis anywhere and anytime.

He often selected as a movie choice the copy of *Debbie Does Dallas* I'd received as a gag gift. Sometimes he wouldn't even bother to put the DVD in the player; he'd whack off to the cover.

Once, the ice cream truck turned on our street while Dave had *Debbie Does Dallas* in one hand and his hard cock in the other. Fortunately, Jeremy was there to chase after Dave and corral him back to the house before the neighborhood kids caught a glimpse.

Dave selected comic books or magazines with nudity or sexual content from the bookshelf. He'd dig through my pile of mail and page through catalogs until he found models in nightgowns or underwear. This was his favorite masturbation material. He was hilarious: sometimes sneaky, sometimes brazen, as he marched into the bathroom with his kinky finds.

One afternoon, I sat at the dining room table, typing a document for work while Dave and Frank watched TV in the living room.

Dave stood up and paced around the room.

"Bored?" Frank asked Dave. "Want to watch something different?"

Dave shrugged.

Frank knelt in front of the DVD collection under the TV while Dave thumbed through books on the shelf.

Frank read movie titles out loud as Dave opened the comic book he'd selected from the shelf. He stood near Frank and flipped through the pages.

I glanced into the room occasionally, distracted by the noises Dave and Frank made, but was mostly absorbed by my work.

Dave settled on a page and stood over Frank while Frank continued to rattle off choices for the next movie selection.

"Whaaa… oooo… uuugh!" Frank sputtered.

Startled, I looked up to see Frank staring straight at Dave's erect penis. He had looked to Dave to gauge his reaction to the movie choices. Dave was absorbed in whatever arousing image he'd discovered in the comic book and was oblivious to Frank's proximity.

"Dave! My God! Put that away!" Frank gasped as he scrambled to stand.

That's when I decided to hide everything remotely sexual.

I scoured the apartment and collected books and magazines in a paper bag to hide in the basement. I tried to curb Dave's temptation to masturbate when we had company.

Though his newfound sex drive could be embarrassing and inappropriate at times, I saw it as a gift from God, a cosmic wink. After years of being the one to initiate sex and feeling like my sex drive was obnoxiously high, Dave was now the insatiable one. While most of Dave's brain damage was robbing us of pleasure and contentment, this one change in Dave's system was rewarding and fun for both of us. We were making love more than ever. Many times it felt primal and hedonistic. Many times it felt profound and ethereal, and it was a way to enhance our nonverbal communication.

One afternoon, after I'd hidden all the sexy material in the basement, a few friends were visiting. Dave was restless. While we sat in the living room, he paced back and forth between us and the kitchen.

"Do you need something, Dave?" I asked.

He was exasperated. He widened his eyes and shrugged, but didn't slow his pace.

The bathroom door slammed; Dave disappeared.

We continued our conversation in the living room as minutes passed.

After a while I knocked on the bathroom door.

"You OK in there, Davey?"

He growled through the door; he wanted to be left alone.

"He's probably whacking off," I offered as I sat back down on the couch with our friends.

After another several minutes, Dave left the bathroom and wandered back to the living room. As he approached, he raised his hand. He shook whatever was in his fist and nodded approvingly.

"Whatcha got?" I asked satisfied-looking Dave.

He smiled big as he dropped his hand back to his side, still nodding.

I curiously approached Dave and reached out to his fist.

"Can I see? What are you so psyched about?" I asked.

At my prompting, he opened his hand to show me a wallet-sized picture in a magnet frame I kept on the fridge. I was momentarily confused to see the portrait of Katie, Charlie, and six-month-old Alex. Our friends had dressed up to look punked-out and trashy for the professional portrait. Katie looked sexy with a bouffant hairstyle and tight half-shirt.

"Oh, my God, David! You rubbed one out to Katie!" I screeched. Dave led the room in an explosion of laughter. I took the magnet from him and added it to the bag in the basement.

Dave didn't confine his masturbation to home. He'd grab his penis through his pocket or reach for it through his open zipper whenever and wherever he felt the urge. I was constantly admonishing him. I bought a whistle and blew it if Dave reached for his dick at an inappropriate time—like when we were standing on the front porch talking to the neighbors. I figured a whistle toot was less offensive to the average grocery shopper than Dave's exposed cock.

Every fall, the city of Albany shuts down Lark Street for a music and art festival. It's an infamously unrestrained bacchanalia, like Mardi Gras with a pugnacious New York attitude. This year, the internationally acclaimed performer Moby was headlining.

Adam and I loaded Dave into the car and got as close to Lark Street as possible. Though he was slow and easily tired, Dave was motivated to walk through the bustling city streets to the festival.

Dave always loved crowds, and he always loved live music. Larkfest was his scene. He surveyed the crowd with wide eyes and a big smile as we walked. If something caught his eye, he made a beeline through the shoulder-to-shoulder crowd. Adam and I followed along, apologizing for Dave when necessary.

We took a spot wedged in the crowd near the front of the stage before the Moby show began. We were inches away from the people around us and stood behind two college-aged girls. They both wore tight jeans.

Dave reached out with his index finger and traced the stitching on one of the girls' back pockets. She whipped around to face Dave. Before she could speak, I did.

"I'm really sorry! My husband has a brain disease. He can't always make good choices and doesn't know to keep his hands to himself," I explained.

The girl's angry brow relaxed as she looked from me to smiling Dave. Her friend smiled at us sympathetically.

"Oh, it's OK," the girl cheerfully replied and turned back to the stage. Adam and I exchanged relieved glances, and Dave snickered.

The music started. The crowd pushed us from behind and we got pressed even tighter to the surrounding strangers. The music was so loud it drowned our senses. The crowd moved in rhythm to the beat and bounced energetically.

I mostly watched the stage and occasionally glanced at Dave—who stared intently at the girls in front of us.

I didn't realize how impressed Dave was with the girls until he reached out to the one who had smiled at us after Dave touched her friend's jeans. He wiped his hand on her shoulder. I pulled his hand away to see a slippery mess on his palm. I looked down to see Dave's fly open.

The ejaculate-smudged girl gave us an understanding nod. She was OK with Dave touching her because she thought she understood the situation. She had no reason to think Dave had just rubbed any-thing—let alone his semen—on her. I was horrified. The ear-pounding, ground-shaking music drowned out my screechy gasp. Shocked and frozen in place, I stared at the girl, waiting for her to turn around so I could shout an apology through the wall of sound. She rocked to the music, oblivious to Dave's outright assault.

My animal survival instinct overrode my human, moral obligation to the girl. I knew the stranger deserved an explanation and apology, but was too focused on and blinded by the immediate need to keep Dave and me out of trouble I didn't stick around to give her one. We got out of there as fast as we could push Dave through the crowd.

In September, another of Dave's soul brothers from childhood, Scott, came to visit. He was only in town for a few days, but Scott came by whenever he had a free chunk of time.

One day when I worked at home Frank and Scott took Dave out.

The three boys were gone for hours, and were joyous and wound up when they returned.

"Dave talked!" was the first thing out of Scott's mouth coming in the door. He gave me a full report.

They had gone to McDonald's for lunch. As they got closer to the front of the line, and Frank and Scott were talking, Dave stared intently at the menu board.

When it was their turn to order, Frank was prepared to order for himself and Dave. Instead, Dave put both hands on the counter and leaned in to the cashier.

"I'll have a Quarter Pounder with cheese," he declared.

Frank and I were on edge whenever we took Dave to a public place. There was no telling what Dave would do. In stores and restaurants, he'd spit on the floor or screech at top volume.

Frank and Scott were delighted to have heard Dave's voice when he ordered so confidently and clearly.

When Scott told me about the McDonald's experience, I remembered other times when Dave spoke to order takeout food. He'd read from menu boards in a normal way. Those rare times were special and comforting. I could pretend for a few minutes we were just a regular couple out grabbing lunch together.

Everyone craved Dave's voice. After McDonald's, we wanted to hear more. Realizing Dave could read and recite what he was reading inspired us to try to get him to speak. Scott, Frank, and I wrote things for Dave to say on index cards. Dave sat with us, half interested in what we were doing.

We wrote Dave's favorite catch phrases, like: "Jerkin' the gherkin" and "Jackin' off billy goats with a cactus glove."

We wrote memorable quotes, like: "I looove gettin' fucked up" and "Your pussy smells like tacos."

Writing the cards flooded me with memories. I flashed back to a trip Dave and I took when we had been dating about a year. We went to Sarasota, Florida to visit Jeremy. One night we walked around town, window shopping and stopping in bars. On the way home, a skinhead couple followed our group of friends. The girl kept shouting insults at us, trying to start a fight. We ignored her as they trailed us for blocks. One of Jeremy's friends playfully jumped on his back as we tried to lose the instigating punks.

That really pissed the girl off, and she screamed, "Faggots! I'll kill you faggots!"

We slowed our pace and confronted the crazy skinhead. As our local Sarasota friends bickered with the ridiculous duo, Dave and I hung back. After a few minutes, Dave grew bored with the interaction and swaggered up to the skinhead girl.

"Your pussy smells like tacos," he announced with a definitive wag of his index finger.

Talk about a tension breaker. The girl's boyfriend snorted a laugh, apologized, and dragged his angry, bigoted friend away. As they left, Dave taunted her by repeating "Your pussy smells like tacos" in a singsong voice. No one ever forgot that classic Dave night.

All his life, Dave said hilarious, unique things. It was hard living without his voice. The index/cue card exercise was therapeutic for us. The idea that we'd hear his voice as a result was thrilling.

When we held up cards for Dave to read, he'd give us a shy knowing smile. Some cards got bigger laughs than others. He didn't read any of the cards out loud for us, but we all laughed a lot trying to get him to.

In the following weeks, all our visitors would read the cards piled on the coffee table. Everyone laughed at the memories. Many guests added a card or two. As time went on, the cards went from short quotes for Dave to recite to short story memories. Some cards were messages to Dave from his friends.

Dave often paged through the cards. Sometimes he'd slip one or all of them into his back pocket. He'd smile or nod as he looked at them.

One of my favorites was from Scott. It said, "I love you, Dave. You are my brother."

Shortly after Scott's visit, Frank decided he needed to get back to North Carolina, to his home and girlfriend. Frank left Dave and me in a vastly improved condition. We were living and having fun.

Frank's visit had given me a new perspective. He reminded me why I was compelled to take Dave from the psych ward and put the rest of my life on hold to care for him. It wasn't because I felt obligated or because it was the "right" thing to do. It was because I loved Dave with all my heart. With this reminder, I felt less overwhelmed.

Even with my better attitude, though, life was still hard.

Dave slept restlessly. In bed, he'd grind his teeth and kick his feet up and down. He'd get up in the middle of the night to wander the house.

I was less uptight about taking Dave in public, but it was still challenging. In the grocery store, he'd reach out and help himself to whatever he fancied. He'd crack open a bottle of soda, chug it, and set the empty bottle on the floor. His fingers dove into the open containers at salad bars or condiment racks. If I scolded him, he'd only laugh, sometimes spraying me with relish or hot sauce or whatever it was he was licking from his fingers.

He was like a toddler. He needed to be watched constantly. But instead of learning and progressing like a child, he was regressing— losing reason and aptitude by the week.

With his lessening brain function, Dave slowed down. He wasn't wandering off as he had in the summer. When he spent time at his mother's house, he sat and watched TV with his brother instead of wandering off to Stewart's to buy beer. He needed supervision in new ways.

On a Friday night, I left Dave in Clifton Park overnight so I could work at the Ginger Man. I slept in Saturday morning, content that Dave was safe because of his immobility.

In the afternoon, I went to collect Dave. I walked up the stairs from the basement into my mother-in-law's house. I pushed open the sticky sliding door at the top of the stairs.

"Hello?" I called.

The stench of shit choked the "o" of my hello. The smell was so powerful, the air looked brown.

"Hey, Amelia." Rick hopped up from his desk to greet me. He seemed oblivious to the smell.

"Is that your brother?" I asked Rick. "That smell?"

Rick looked around and sniffed the air.

"Hmm, he *was* just in the bathroom."

I turned to look down the hall to the bathroom. Dave was standing in the dim hallway.

"Hi Davey," I said as our eyes met.

Dave smiled at me with a shrug.

I peeked in the bathroom and was surprised to see it was clean. I'd expected to see an overflowing toilet. The odor was coming from somewhere else.

"You ready to go?" I asked.

Dave nodded and shuffled toward me.

Dave's mom emerged from her bedroom father down the hall.

"Hey, baby," she called to me.

We all moved into the living room. Beverly hugged me.

"How'd everything go?" I asked her about Dave's overnight visit.

"He spent a lot of time in his room," Beverly explained. "I got him in the shower last night, but I think he just stood there."

Dave moved away from us as we talked. He went to the other side of the room and stood looking at his mother's houseplants. He rubbed his fingers around the pots and across the shelves. He removed all the dust. He loved doing this, and he was very thorough.

Dave inspected for dust everywhere we went. He'd dust around bottles of windshield wiper fluid while I stood in line to pay for gas. He'd stand on his tip-toes to reach the top of the window pane in my grandmother's kitchen when we went to visit.

After we chatted, I turned away from Dave's mom and brother and went back down the stinky hallway. I stood in front of Dave's bedroom door. I needed to go in the room to get Dave's overnight bag, but stood frozen, knowing the source of the bad smell was in his room.

As I pushed the door in, a brown smear spread over the carpet.

"Oh God!" I shrieked.

Beverly and Rick hurried to my side.

We all stared at the carpet stained with shit. I gagged. I fought to keep the welling tears from slipping down my cheeks.

I was agonizingly aware of the four markers that Dr. Eichler had told me would lead to Dave's eventual death. The first had occurred just about completely—Dave didn't speak. The second would be Dave's incontinence. His shitting on the floor was a sure sign of the inevitable upcoming decline.

I tiptoed into the room and grabbed Dave's bag without looking at the shit pile. I pulled the door shut behind me.

I needed to get Dave out of that reeking house.

"All set, Davey?" I asked when I brought him his coat.

He nodded as he finished his dusting duty.

Dave and I hugged his family and high-tailed it out of there.

As I drove us home, I marveled with sadness and anger over the fact that Beverly and Rick seemed oblivious to the fact that Dave had relieved himself on his bedroom floor.

Between Beverly's report on the unproductive shower and the mess on the floor, it was glaringly obvious to me that Dave really needed constant care. He needed help bathing and guidance to make it to the bathroom.

Another thing was glaringly obvious. I could no longer count on Dave's family to aid in his care. They weren't available to help Dave on a level much beyond having him in the house. They weren't going to help him soap up in the shower, or guide him to the bathroom when he needed it, or keep him from wandering into the road.

That night, after Dave went to bed, I went around the apartment turning off lights and locking the doors. When I got to the front door, I hesitated, then slipped outside instead of locking it. The street was quiet. The big sycamore trees at the curb were still. I left the door open so I could hear Dave if he needed me and sat on the top step.

I thought about the crazy scene at his family's house that day. His family's inability to be caregivers surprised me. Dave himself had been a natural caretaker when we lived with Grandma Wakefield. And I remembered all the times Dave took care of *me*.

After we'd been dating for only a handful of months, I got the flu. I was home, sick in bed, for days. Dave was twenty-four years old. He was in a band, operating Analog Underground, running a candle factory, and having lots of fun with his friends. He was boyish and cool.

No matter how busy Dave was or how much attention he got for being a gorgeous, talented, charismatic man-about-town, he always had time for me. He was devoted in an old-fashioned way. He was a romantic.

Every day I was sick, Dave stopped by—on his lunch break, before band practice, whenever he had a spare moment—and delivered me things he thought would make me feel better. He brought magazines and ginger ale, Popsicles and fresh fruit. The fresh fruit came on the day I stopped throwing up, but was afraid to test it by eating. He sat by my bed and cut pieces from each of the fruits he brought and fed them to me.

I thought about another time Dave took care of me. A few months after our wedding, we got on an airplane to Mexico. When we left Albany, I had the beginnings of a cold. By the time we landed in Cancun, I had a fever, chills, sore throat, and earache. We checked into the budget hotel we'd booked and I went to bed. I woke up to Dave letting himself back into the room.

He rushed in with arms full: fresh flowers in one hand and grocery bags over both arms.

"Hey, baby, I didn't mean to wake you, but what I got is gonna make you feel better!" he cooed.

He piled his loot on top on the blankets covering my legs, and emptied one of the shopping bags.

"Look at this! Cipro—the pharmacist told me it's the strongest antibiotic! Vicodin and Demerol—these are the good shit for pain. And, of course, Valium!" Dave was like a mad scientist kid in a candy shop, determined to make me better and thrilled at the legal, no-prescription-needed drug selection.

I groggily propped myself up on my elbows. With my full attention, Dave removed the contents of the second bag one piece at a time, showcasing each item with his big toothy grin. Mango, avocado, lime, bottled water, Mexican soda, and Mexican beer were all stuffed in the bag.

"You'll be cured! I got you the remedies! And all for twelve dollars!" Dave howled.

He jumped up from the bed, scooping up the flowers and water bottle. He went to the sink in the corner and poured half of the water from the bottle before cutting off the narrow top with his pocket knife. He arranged the flowers in the plastic bottle and placed them on the rickety bedside nightstand. Next, he busted open the Cipro bottle and presented me with a giant white pill accompanied by an orange soda in a heavy glass bottle.

Dave couldn't stand to see me sick. He was always enthusiastic about caring for me. He took action to get me what he thought would make me feel better, and it always worked. His determination and care were enough to soothe away my ailments. The arsenal of cheap Mexican over-the-counter drugs fueled Dave's healing powers.

Within twenty-four hours, I was enough on the mend to enjoy Mexico.

Dave had a way of caring for me without getting down or missing a beat. His thoughtful attention to detail and deep empathy made him a natural, graceful caregiver. This quality came through in his lyrics, too. In his song "Catch" he sang:

I knew you would and
I knew you could
I knew you'd fall and
I'd be there to catch you

Sitting there on the quiet porch, hearing his words in my mind, I came to a solid decision about my relationship with Dave. Despite his erratic behavior and dwindling sense of reality, he was my husband. I was committed to his care and committed to living a full life with him until death did us part. I'd do my best to emulate the compassion and care he unconditionally gave me over the years.

I knew I had to step up the level of care for Dave. I was determined to keep him home, safe, and now clean and toileted. If friends or family were incapable of seeing to these duties, Dave couldn't stay with them.

I'd lean much less on Dave's mom and brother. It wasn't that they didn't care about Dave. Of course they did. But they just couldn't give the level of care he needed. The job was really, really hard. We weren't just dealing with the physical hardship of keeping Dave from running off and observing his every move to anticipate his bathroom needs. We were also dealing with the emotional devastation of witnessing our strong, determined loved one fail.

Caretaking was overwhelming. I often felt unsure I could handle the stress and challenge of caring for Dave. Now I saw I couldn't place my expectations for his care on others.

I had to rely on myself. Because this wasn't a group decision, this wasn't a democracy. No one else got to decide whether this would work. I was making that decision now, for both me and Dave. I was going to make it work; I was going to control it.

If someone showed up and joined us—if someone self-assigned himself into our life, like Frank did—then I'd welcome them.

But I wouldn't be asking for help. It had been hard enough asking his family for help, and that had been disappointing. I wasn't going to get my hopes up again.

What's this Guy On?

At the end of September, yet another of Dave's soul brothers, Dan, came to visit. We stayed close to home for two days while Dan was busy on the phone and Internet reporting to countless friends curious and concerned about Dave's condition. Dave was loved by so many people from different times and places throughout his life.

Dan suggested I start a blog to keep Dave's faraway friends involved in his life.

I thought Dan's suggestion was brilliant. I'd write only when I had time; I wouldn't feel obligated. It would be a service to our friends who wondered about Dave. Connecting through the Internet might help encourage others to visit and support Dave. I needed all the help I could get.

While Dave and Dan watched movies and laughed together, I got to work on my first entry on the "Life With Dave Z" blog.

When Jeremy moved out, he left a furniture set I didn't want. The furniture was enormous and heavy, and filled my garage and basement. I was furious at him for his lack of consideration. To my delight, he also left behind a favorite trinket: a wooden owl. The owl was a prized possession; I was using it to chastise Jeremy. Over the weeks since Jeremy had moved out and away to Montana, I threatened harm to his owl in retribution for his furniture abandonment.

I used dental floss to hang the owl over the toilet and photographed it. It looked like the owl was floating in the toilet.

Jeremy—and others close to us—knew the bathroom was a touchy subject. Dave would lock himself in there, repeatedly flush the toilet, and run water. Until I removed the lock, it was a mystery what Dave did in there.

"We put the owl in the toilet" was the title of my first Life with Dave Z blog post. The post explained that we appreciated everyone's concern for Dave.

"It's not always easy, but we keep-on-keeping-on by PUTTING THE OWL IN THE TOILET!" is how I assured everyone we were surviving.

I sent a link to all of Dave's and my friends and family, and right away, got encouraging responses.

Before moving to Portland, Dan lived in Albany. I'd been a guinea pig for Dan when he was in massage school and a regular client when he started his practice. Besides being a good friend, Dan was a healer. He was a spiritualist and a Reiki master.

Dan, like Donna, was one of my professional supporters. He offered bodywork that transcended our Earth relationship. He moved my energy, rejuvenating my body and spirit.

During his visit, Dan reconnected with a friend from high school who was practicing acupuncture near Albany. I knew my broken heart, confused mind, and stressed body could use acupuncture; Dan suggested Ruth would be a great practitioner for me. He introduced us and I became Ruth's client.

I was seeing Donna on a regular basis too. I wanted to withdraw from the world, but she wisely ordered me to keep my two weekly shifts at The Ginger Man. She knew it would get me out of the house and get my mind off of Dave for a few hours.

Each time I saw them, Ruth, Dan, and Donna worked on me like I was a race car making a pit stop. They understood the urgency of my life with Dave and used skill and compassion to tune me so I could stay in the race.

Visiting those healers gave me awareness and inspiration to keep my spirit tuned at home too. The altar I had built in the late spring became a powerful place in my home and part of my practice. I'd add found treasures and gifts to the built in shelves, and burned candles and incense daily. Dave added things to the altar too. He'd empty his pockets and carefully place mysteriously acquired items—a checker, a pink glass heart—among the Buddha and Yoda statues.

By the third day of Dan's visit, Dave got restless. He kept coming in and out of the back and front doors, pacing around the house, doing what we called "the perimeter check." He'd survey the house, rubbing his hands over surfaces and studying walls.

When I asked Dave what he wanted to do to relieve his boredom, he gave me his characteristic shrug and eyebrow raise.

I'd taken to writing out choices to help Dave communicate what he wanted. That morning, I wrote "drive" and "walk" on a piece of paper. He pointed to "drive," so we loaded into the car. Dave navigated by pointing the way, and we headed north. I was ready to aimlessly follow Dave's finger when Dan spoke up from the backseat.

"Isn't there a big white temple somewhere around here?" he asked.

Dave emphatically nodded his approval. We were going to the Grafton Peace Pagoda.

We meandered eastward for twenty-five miles on back roads, listening to mix CDs at full-blast. As we neared Grafton, I thought we should make a side trip to the fire tower on the way. It had been a cloudy, drizzly autumn day, but the sky was clearing, and the late-day light was beautifully soft.

"You guys mind if we stop to check out the fire tower?" I asked as we arrived in Grafton.

Dave nodded, and Dan agreed, but I sensed Dan's growing reluctance as I piloted us from the main road onto a small, twisty road and then onto a dirt road. He may have doubted my judgment as I nosed my car partway onto a steep, rocky Jeep trail before cutting the engine.

We walked the hundred yards up the trail to the base of the sixty-foot tower. Dan leaned back to get a full view and said "Oh, my." Dave answered with a pterodactyl call and started the climb up, one stair at a time. As Dan and I followed, the bone-chilling wind was whipping and the tower framework creaked and shuddered.

At the top, Dan uttered an enthusiastic "Whoa!" and Dave made pterodactyl and monkey sounds. The view was panoramic and magnificent! The sky was alive with color, and the trees were bright with the reds and oranges of autumn.

As we walked back to the car, we agreed that the place had a sacred feel. We were content on our Grafton excursion. We pressed on.

We parked along the road near a dirt driveway marked with a simple hand painted sign that said "Please walk in. Handicap and elderly people welcome—drive up."

A thick growth of young birch and maple trees lined the driveway. Dave walked slowly and occasionally stopped to squint at the sky. When he'd look back down, he'd take a visual inventory of the rocks and dirt below his feet and the trees on either side, grounding himself before moving again.

A large single-story house stood welcoming visitors at the end of the driveway. Past the house, rising from a grassy hill, was a big white stupa: the Peace Pagoda.

We traversed the wide, rolling lawn and stood at the base of the Pagoda. I stared up at the white dome, taking in its enormity. Its top was decorated by a spire with a gilded lotus crown. The monument for peace was doing its job: emanating calming vibes and creating an ethereal stillness. A grand staircase rose to the dome's stone wall base. A closed-eyed Buddha statue sat on a platform built into the wall.

Looking up, my mind was clear for a rare few moments. I watched Dave move toward the Buddha, taking the wide, uneven steps one a time. Dan and I followed him to the top of the stairs. A sign directed us to circumnavigate the dome to view bas-relief panels narrating the Buddha's life.

We circled the dome, reading each panel, from birth to death. The last one quoted the Buddha: "Life is a river always flowing. Do not hold onto things. Work hard."

Back at the top of the stairs, Dave looked down and then at me with a shrug. I took his hand, steadying his descent. As we managed the stairs, I visualized a river sweeping us from behind and knocking us off our feet. In this fantasy, Dave and I back-floated as the quick current took us away from the Pagoda. We were flowing, but our hands stayed together, we held on.

We ambled back toward the driveway, taking in the surrounding gardens and pond. A playful black lab appeared and charged us, enticing Dan and I to throw her stick.

Meanwhile, Dave shuffled over to the house and gazed in a window. When Dan and I escaped the enthusiastic dog, we headed over to Dave and saw what he was watching: a yellow-robed, bald nun arranging an altar and praying. She turned to the window, smiled, and waved us in.

"We'll start prayer in a few minutes," she explained as she met us at the door.

"Please come in. You can stay as long as you like," she offered. "You are welcome."

We took off our shoes and sat on the embroidered pillows she set down for us. She handed us wooden drums and sticks before sitting with her back to us. Another woman kept rhythm with a huge deep drum as the nun and a monk chanted in entrancing, melodious voices. A few people came in and sat behind us.

I felt warmth and peace as I drummed along with Dan on my right and Dave on my left. Dave's drumming was always forceful, sometimes right on and other times off beat. After a couple of minutes, he got up and circled the room, checking out the statues and offerings around the altar. He went into the next room and looked behind a hanging tapestry in a doorway. He alternated between sitting to drum and exploring the rooms.

I could tell from his glowing smile when he glanced at the nun that she was looking kindly at Dave as he wandered. On one of his circuits, he stopped at the altar and opened his wallet to put a bill on a tray.

After what seemed like ten minutes, Dan stood. Dave and I followed him to put on our shoes and let ourselves out the back door. Once outside, we realized we'd been sitting for almost an hour. As we walked toward the driveway, the nun scurried out behind us. She graciously thanked us for visiting. She bowed to Dave and presented him with a small paper-framed picture of the Peace Pagoda. She adamantly told us she was happy to have Dave there and she knew he was someone very special.

We left feeling peaceful and happy and grateful for our day in Grafton. Dave had led us on an awesome adventure. He put the Peace Pagoda picture on the altar when we got home that night.

The rest of October was fun. Dave and I were alive on Planet Earth. We were a loving, married couple. Since leaving the psych ward, Dave was content. I was following his lead and relaxing into our new life.

Dave and I had many visitors throughout the month. My Aunties and dad came over regularly to watch movies or have dinner with us. Dave's dad and brother would stop by to hang out or take Dave for a ride. Out-of-town friends visited. Guys Dave had recorded at Analog Underground would spend hours listening to tapes and playing with the gear in the attic.

When Dave sat at his mixer, he looked cool. He was an indie rocker at heart. Dave no longer knew how to work the dials and knobs, but he sat with authority and ease. He was comfortable behind his board.

I noticed Dave would mouth words along with me when I was singing or talking. If I said something predictable, he'd mouth or whisper the last word.

I often said, "Goin' on, feelin' strong"—a quote from a Beck song.

I encouraged Dave to say the words with me.

If I was lucky, he'd whisper "strong" along with me.

When I told him, "I love you," he'd almost always be ready to mouth or say the "you" along with me.

Throughout our years together, Dave and I didn't use the words "I love you" very much. It was a cliché, and we were generally too cool for clichés. Through thick and thin, though, I always knew Dave loved me. He was sweet and gentle and kind. He wrote and played songs for me. Those things were more valuable and meaningful to me than the overused three-word phrase.

It was only after Dave stopped speaking that I longed to hear those words. Hearing Dave utter those canned words was something I missed. I appreciated his effort to say the "you" along with me and I understood he wanted to say all three words as much as I wanted to hear them.

Dave's friend, Murph, had a motto during their college years: "I looove gettin' fucked up!" Dave had always thought Murph and his motto were hilarious. Whenever Murph came up in conversation, someone would inevitably say this famous line.

When Dave heard those words, he'd always crack up. To hear his laugh, I knew what to say.

The more I said Murph's motto, the easier it seemed for Dave to lip sync along with me. One time, I tried saying it slowly, and left the end off.

I looked Dave in the eyes and said, "I looove gettin'..."

He looked straight back at me and said, "Fucked up."

I exploded with delighted laughter.

This became the only guaranteed way to hear Dave's voice.

I was so thrilled to hear Dave's voice; I wanted to share it with others. One afternoon, I sat Dave on the love seat. I had the camera set to record in my left hand and a piece of paper with the words "Hey everybody, rock on" in my right hand.

"OK, Davey, I'm going to record you and put it on the blog for all your friends. Can you tell everyone to 'rock on'?"

Dave didn't smile, but he nodded. He wasn't thrilled about being put on the spot.

"I think we have a good message for our friends. We're rockin' on! Let's motivate everyone to rock on with us," I encouraged.

He nodded again, this time with more enthusiasm.

"Can you do it? Can you say what's on the paper?"

Dave raised his hand and motioned for us to get on with it.

"OK, go ahead. We're recording. OK, tell them," I instructed.

With a half-smile, Dave leaned in toward the camera.

"Hey everybody, rock on," he said in a slow, determined voice.

A few days later, I convinced him to say, "Goin' on, feelin' strong" for the camera. It took a lot of convincing. The recording on either side of his words is filled with Dave's teeth grinding. The teeth grinding was due to his brain damage. It was incessant.

The videos got a ton of responses on the blog. The support made me buoyant. I was pleased to show everyone that Dave was still shining his supercool self.

Dave and I spent one autumn day with Auntie Jen. We met at her house in the country, and she drove us around the back roads and countryside near where she lived.

Jen and I wondered how much Dave could still comprehend. We discussed Dave's condition, often looking to him for input. He turned his head away from us, and was disinterested in our conversation.

"I don't know if he can't understand us, or if he just doesn't care," I told Jen.

Dave seemed content on the drive. He watched rolling farm land and animals pass by his window.

"Well, I think he understands," Jen announced. "Right, Dave?"

Dave giggled in response.

We stopped at a diner for lunch.

We got out of the car. Dave had difficulty standing and walked slowly to the diner. In my mind, I questioned whether he was really up for the day's adventure.

After we ate our sandwiches, Jen looked at the dessert menu.

"Mmm, chocolate éclairs," Jen pondered.

She smiled at Dave in her teasing way.

"I know how to make chocolate éclairs, betcha you don't," she said.

Dave didn't miss a beat. He perked up, riled by the teasing.

"Betcha I do," he said.

He sat back and followed up his words with his characteristic smart-alecky wide smile.

The rare surprise of hearing Dave's voice was amazing and beautiful. Dave was still not only comprehending what was going on around him, but also maintaining his sense of humor. That "Betcha I do" was hilarious.

I marveled over and admired Dave's strength, his will. Sick, brain-damaged, and weak, he was still up for an adventure and still glad to be along for the ride.

At the end of October, Frank came back to Albany to stay with us. On his first night back, we had a celebratory pizza and beer dinner.

The simple, cheap meal tasted so good. We all ate with zeal, smiling wide-eyed at each other with mouths full. It felt great to have Frank back. Life was easier with him around.

The next morning, Frank rattled off suggestions for fun things to do and listened to Dave's responses. Some ideas got a shrug, some a smile, some a chuckle. When Frank suggested a trip to New York City, Dave went wild with screechy laughter.

We surfed the Internet, looking for inspiration to make the drive. After finding that most of Dave's favorite bands were touring in Europe or on the West Coast, we paged through the online *Village Voice*. Superdrag, a band Frank had been trying to turn us on to, would play in Chelsea in two days, on Friday night!

Friday afternoon Adam, Frank, Dave, and I crammed into my Civic and headed south. After a smooth ride, we arrived in Manhattan and parked in the first convenient garage I found. We stepped out of the garage onto the crowded avenue, and Dave promptly stopped beside a flowerpot in front of a classy French restaurant.

Those days Dave was short on both discretion and modesty. He lived in the moment and was completely impulsive about meeting his immediate needs. Knowing this, and having just finished an almost three-hour car ride, we anticipated what was about to happen. As if rehearsed, we surrounded Dave to create a shield from the restaurant window and passers-by as he emptied his bladder in the flowers.

After the pit stop, we dropped off our bags at our midtown hotel, and our New York adventure began.

We rode the subway to the East Village, always one of Dave's favorite spots. His eyes were wide and his smile was huge as we wandered along looking for dinner. We settled in for sushi on Avenue A and stuffed ourselves with Japanese beer and a colorful platter of sashimi and rolls.

After dinner, we headed to the venue to buy tickets. With tickets in hand and two hours to kill, we set out to find a neighborhood bar. It started to rain as we scoured blocks rejecting bars as too crowded or swanky. We'd almost settled on a coffee shop when we caught sight of an orange neon sign that simply said "BAR."

The place was dark and inviting. There was an indie rock jukebox and good beer on tap. It was exactly what we'd been searching for. Dave sat smiling and answered with screeching laughter and nods whenever we asked him how he was doing. The bartender watched us curiously, and asked Dave if he was OK a couple of times. Dave answered with a faraway gaze and half smile.

Finally, the bartender leaned in close to Dave.

"What are you on, man?" he asked.

When Dave only screeched and laughed in answer, the bartender looked inquisitively at Frank and me.

"C'mon," he said, "I gotta know. What is this guy on?!"

I looked the guy in the eyes.

"Do you really want to know?" I asked.

"Well, YEAH! I haven't seen a guy this fucked up in a long time," the bartender exclaimed, slapping his hand on the bar in front of Dave.

Dave roared with laughter and wagged his finger at the bartender.

As I told Dave's story and explained that we were making the best of our situation with happy adventures, Dave smiled and nodded.

Dave's newest friend shook his hand and presented him with an on-the-house shot of whiskey. This night was like any other night with Dave in New York. He was making new friends, and impressing and intriguing the strangers around him.

Days later, back in Albany, Frank, Dave, and I sat around the dinner table with plates scraped clean of Frank's delicious beef burgundy. We were sipping red wine and relaxing. Dave was content.

"Oh, maybe you'll read to us tonight, Davey," I mused. "Let's open fortune cookies."

I had a box of fortune cookies we'd sometimes dig into after a meal. Most times the fortunes were mundane and meaningless. The main perk to opening these cookies was that Dave would often read his fortune out loud.

I passed out a cookie to each of us. Dave struggled to open the plastic wrapper, so I used my pocketknife to start it for him. With the corner cut away, Dave easily ripped into the plastic. He removed the cookie and carefully shook the crumbs out of the wrapper and onto his plate before tossing the wrapper aside.

He slowly removed the paper fortune and recited the words like someone who was just learning to read.

"What do you. Want to have. To love," Dave read. He didn't say the words like a question, and his intonation made it hard to know if there was more to the message.

He paused, staring down at the paper in his hand. He raised his eyes to look at me, his face grave. Once we made eye contact, Dave smiled big and laughed. As always, his laughter was contagious.

"It's a question? Your fortune is a question?" I asked him.

He handed me the paper.

Sure enough, Dave had read it correctly. His fortune was a question: a question about love.

I opened mine and read it to the boys, "When love and skill work together, expect a masterpiece."

"Whoa," Frank said.

"I got the love. Do I have the skills?" I asked.

Dave stared at me with a slight smile, as if to say, "Love is enough, we'll figure the rest out as we go."

As with the fortune cookie, I found reassurance in serendipitous ways. At the end of October, Dave and I went to see the adaptation of the children's book *Where the Wild Things Are.*

The creatures in the movie communicated with sounds instead of words. They were a troubled bunch, trying to figure out how to work together as an extended family. Their goal was to get along well enough to "sleep in a pile."

The film was soothing. Dave sat transfixed, his normally-fidgety body still, his normally-strained face slack. I could really relate to these struggling, nonverbal monsters. Their plight and enduring love for one another was comforting. The display of nonverbal communication bolstered my growing comfort with Dave's state of being and our lifestyle.

The first week in November, we headed south again. Monday morning Frank, Dave, and I drove to Manhattan to meet our friends Dana and Daniel. They were getting married in April, and I was to be a bridesmaid. We had an appointment to try on bridal wear at a boutique.

Daniel and Frank took Dave to check out bars and music stores while we girls tried on dresses.

Afterward, we drove across Long Island, following Dana and Daniel to their home in Sag Harbor to eat pizza and sit by the fire.

The next day, we went to the beach. The sky was perfectly clear on that cool autumn day. The beach spanned limitlessly in both directions along the crashing ocean waves. It was safe to let Dave wander. It was a rare chance for him to be alone. He walked away from the ocean to the tall reeds and grass at the other edge of the sandy beach. He broke the heads off the taller stalks and ran his fingers over blades of grass.

Back in Sag Harbor, we wandered the streets and took turns following Dave into high-end boutiques. Dave's lack of inhibition was conspicuous in the affluent village. In the furniture shop he cruised into, he ran his sticky fingers over a gilded bureau with an eight-thousand-dollar price tag. The shopkeeper—a fifty-something woman dressed in designer clothes, high heels, and sparkly gemstone jewelry—approached Dave swiftly.

"Can I help you with something, sir?" she admonished.

Dave craned his neck toward her and answered with a loud screech.

"Nah, I think we're good," I smiled and turned Dave back to the door.

He chuckled loudly and slapped his leg as we made our way out of the store.

That evening, we made dinner back at Dana and Daniel's. While we lounged at the house after dinner, Daniel announced that he was going to the basement to organize tools for work the next day.

"Want to check out the basement, Dave? I built a walk-in fridge down there," Daniel invited Dave to follow him.

Dave hadn't said a word for the entire visit. He followed Daniel down the basement stairs.

As Daniel showed him around, he said, "I've still got a lot to do. It's kind of a mess down here."

Dave raised his eyebrows and said, "You're telling me!" His clarity reminded us that Dave still understood and was an active part of the world around him.

Besides the rare one-liner or prompted fill-in-the-blank, Dave's vocal communication was made up of sounds. He had a wide variety of clicks, hums, and tongue rolls. The volume, speed, and intensity of his sound effects increased with his excitement level.

His most common sound was the pterodactyl call. He could carry on this screechy blast for many seconds, for what felt like endless minutes when done at inappropriate times. The more psyched he was, the longer the screech. He often used it as a greeting, letting loose if we saw someone we knew in public.

Those of us who spent a lot of time with Dave learned to imitate the call. Dave's Dad was great; genetics allowed him to match Dave's exact tone. Together, they would howl until they ran out of breath.

I dragged Dave along with me to the mall one busy Saturday night when I had to pick up a gift. The mall had never been our style.

I parked near the one store I needed to go to, hoping to make the trip quick and painless. Dave tagged along quietly. We made it in and out of the store without incident. We were cruising down the corridor, bound for the exit, when we came face-to-face with Dave's uncle and aunt and their two young daughters.

"Dave? Amelia?" Uncle Timmy gasped, shocked to see us out on the town.

Dave responded with a full-volume forty-five second pterodactyl call. As Dave screeched, everything wound to a stop around us. Silence except for the Muzak. Mothers scooped up children. Tough-looking teenagers pushed together in a frightened huddle. Eyes widened and mouths hung open in slow motion as time stood still.

"Wow! Great to see you," Timmy managed as the rest of his family stood dumbfounded. They hadn't seen Dave in months. I'm sure the reports they heard from the rest of the family couldn't have prepared them for seeing Dave in his brain-damaged state.

The rest of the mall's denizens recovered and resumed their activity for a few seconds, but Dave stopped them in their tracks again when Timmy pulled him into a bear hug that triggered a second pterodactyl screech. This one was shorter, but followed by a series of ridiculous tongue rolls and a grand finale shriek.

Dave was happy to see his extended family. As I updated Timmy, Dave interrupted with loud sound effects and hand claps. Some of the mall-goers moved along, but many lingered to watch Dave's better-than-reality-TV show from a safe distance.

Late in November, Dave and I spent a day with Chris and Heather in Woodstock. Because of his own struggle with brain cancer, Chris could empathize with Dave in a way no one else could. Chris was my guru—the most spiritual and wise person I knew. Over the months, whenever we got together, Chris would give me or recommend books and music that spoke to the exact struggles my spirit and heart were enduring.

Chris was hilarious and joyful. He embodied a Buddha-like peace and calm. His faith was steady and inspiring. He spoke confidently about the afterlife and other dimensions. Far-out concepts I'd ordinarily be skeptical about were absolute truth coming from Chris.

Toward the end of our visit, Dave went into the bathroom. Heather was cleaning up the kitchen as Chris and I sat talking at the kitchen table, just outside the bathroom door. After several minutes, I called to Dave behind the door.

"Whatcha doing in there, Davey? Almost done?"

He sputtered a small laugh in reply.

I jiggled the door knob.

"Uh-oh," I said, looking at Heather.

"Locked?" she smirked. "Guess you're not going anywhere, huh?"

I sat back down, defeated. Suddenly I felt tired and longed for my bed, a fifty-minute drive away.

"Oh, man," I sighed, looking from Chris to Heather, "this is fucking hard. He does this kind of thing all the time. I had to take the locks off the bedrooms and bathroom at home."

I talked about my fears and concerns. I confessed how scary it was to know I had so little control.

Heather and Chris listened and understood.

Chris leaned forward in his seat and looked me straight in the eyes.

"We're on the fast track to enlightenment," he said.

It was a fast track. I studied the books Chris recommended. Books and prayers would show up at my doorstep and in my email box from friends and family. As the weeks passed, my faith and spirituality grew. And grew. And evolved and became its own. I took comfort and lessons from *Star Wars*, science, the Bible, Buddhist texts, stories of survival and loss, and my day-to-day life with Dave.

The Tibetan Book of Living and Dying by Sogyal Rinpoche became a beacon for me. From it, I learned the Essential Phowa Practice. Phowa means transference of consciousness. Its practice invokes serenity, and comforts someone close to death.

By December, I was practicing the Phowa with Dave a few times a day. I'd ask him to visualize a golden orb and great light in the sky. I told him our grandmothers were there with Yoda and Jesus and Buddha. Sometimes, I'd list as many of our dead people as I could think of. Dave would give me big smiles and nods of understanding.

Many times I'd remind us I was practicing the Phowa for myself too. We were both joining the light.

One day, Dave lay down on our bed in the middle of the afternoon. After a while, I went to check on him. I sat on the edge of the bed and set my hand on his chest.

"You OK?" I asked.

He nodded, but looked sad. He raised his eyebrows and shrugged.

We sat looking at each other for several minutes.

"Should we do the Phowa?" I asked.

He nodded faintly as he stared at the ceiling.

I started with the usual visualizations. Jesus, my mom, and Grandma were all gracing us with huge light smiles.

"We're ALL trying to get to that light. I'm going there too; I'm not sending you alone, Davey."

Dave's gaze shifted from the ceiling to my eyes. He gravely nodded and stared at me with sparkling eyes.

"Visualize your body disintegrating into light particles and traveling to the join the big light. The light particles from our bodies are floating up and mixing with the light particles all around us. It feels warm and tingly as we disintegrate."

He was especially pleased with that. His smile sparkled as bright as his eyes.

Dave was always very peaceful when I spoke about or practiced the Phowa. I knew it was working.

That December, Dave and I found an increased solidarity. The Phowa practice unified us in a new way. Synchronistic happenings and findings filled our days. Our encounters with people and places were meaningful and right-feeling.

We were both more content at home. The urgency to fill our days with activities and fun dwindled. We could sit together for hours.

One evening, Dave rested his head in my lap. We were timelessly floating, riding the sofa gracefully through the cosmos. I stroked Dave's head and rubbed my fingers over his cheeks and lips. He rolled onto his back to look at me.

"You are my mother," he declared.

His statement whooshed me back to Earth, the sofa landing solidly in the living room.

For a few seconds, my mind raced. Was this confused, brain-damaged Dave? As I watched his face, I knew this was my clear-headed, rich-hearted, wise-spirited husband giving me a message. Finding words in his mind and speaking them with his mouth was nearly impossible for Dave. When he did speak, it was to deliver truth.

Unconditional love bound us. Electrifying, glorious love pulsed through and between both our bodies. I was Dave's mother. Dave was my brother. I was Dave's daughter. Dave was my grandfather. Our relationship was the embodiment of unconditional love; we defied labels and fulfilled all human roles for one another. We were each other's guide, teacher, caregiver, and soul-journey travel partner.

Dave would page through the many books I left on shelves and tables throughout the house. He'd often carry a book around with him, sometimes holding it open to a particular page and sometimes opening it randomly to scan pages.

After Dave carried *Emmanuel's Book* around for several days—even taking it along for car rides—he gave it to me. As he handed it over, he tapped on the open page. The title of the passage he chose was "Your mind cannot possibly understand God; your heart already knows."

The prose was beautiful and appropriate. I read it to myself as Dave watched me curiously.

"Oh, I like this part. This is right on for us," I said. I read it out loud: "When you are with another human being are you really communicating with the mind? Or are you speaking to a soul and the minds are scurrying around trying to put it all into order and vocabulary?"

"You've had it with vocabulary, huh, Dave?" I offered.

He nodded and giggled.

"That's cool. I'm learning too. Our souls are taking over!" I exclaimed buoyantly.

A few days later, Auntie Rae passed along a Rumi poem she found tucked in one of my late grandfather's books. After I read it to Dave, he gave an approving smile and earnest nod. Despite his near muteness and day-to-day confusion, Dave was lucid and aware.

"Don't go back to sleep!" Rumi demands in the poem.

The dawn breeze is trying to tell you something, he explains, so you should stay awake.

Rumi goes on to describe the entrance to the afterworld—and he suggests that people can go in either direction over the threshold.

"Ooh, that sounds good!" I said.

Dave threw his head back with knowing laughter. His eyes spoke with wisdom and peace.

Not Bad

As winter settled in around us, we went out less and less. I avoided taking Dave out in the cold and slippery conditions.

We did hang out in the back yard. Some nights, I cooked dinner on the grill. Dave and I would bundle up and venture out. Often, I'd build a fire in the pit.

In the way Dave would seek out and use his fingers to remove dust from surfaces indoors, he'd clear snow from railings and window sills outdoors. He'd use his arm to sweep any accumulation from the picnic table and benches.

Inevitably, Dave would soak his gloves. I carried extra sets in my pockets.

Dave spent an afternoon and evening at his brother's apartment so I could get work done. I'd started dressing Dave with diapers because he was pissing himself occasionally. I brought him to the bathroom when I had to go, and would often ask him if he had to pee. I worried he'd have an accident when he was spending time with people less diligent about his toilet needs.

I went to pick Dave up from his brother's after dark. I let myself in and found Dave sitting on the sofa by himself and his brother and dad positioned across the room on chairs. The apartment was dark, with only the huge flat screen TV illuminating the living room. All three men were intently watching a super action movie. The room smelled bad beyond the usual stale cigarette and marijuana air.

Right away, I thought the bad smell was shit. As I inched closer to Dave, I was positive he was the source of the smell. I sat beside him on the sofa and stared at the TV screen.

My head raced. Dave didn't have a bowel movement every day. On the days he had a shower, I'd instruct him to sit on the toilet first. We had a regular schedule, and I never considered Dave would shit himself. The diapers were for catching pee.

I sat on the sofa, staring at the TV, with a sense of impending doom. I'd have to clean Dave's shit. Sitting next to Dave on the sofa,

I was nearly choking on the smell. It would surely be worse when I took down his pants.

Finally, the anticipation of cleaning Dave broke my TV trance.

"All right, Davey, let's get out of here," I announced and gave him a nudge.

I helped him to a standing position with my eyes fixed on the sofa. I expected to see a stain where Dave had been sitting, but was relieved the mess was contained in his pants.

We shuffled to my car. Dave was reluctant to sit in the passenger seat. He locked his arms between the door and frame when I tried to guide him into the car.

"You don't want to sit, huh?" I said. "Must be gross."

Dave ground his teeth fiercely. He was serious as he stared back at me.

"This is gonna suck," I sighed to Dave.

He raised his eyebrows and lifted his hand from the door in a shrugging gesture. We both knew it would be a rough night.

As I drove us back to my house, I remembered a time seven years prior when Dave and I were living with Grandma Wakefield. She was dying of lung cancer. A health aide came to the house to clean her in the morning and to help her to the bathroom throughout the day.

Dave and I lived at the house to oversee her care and make sure someone was always with her. We hadn't assumed caregiver roles. We ate with Grandma and watched TV with her, but we didn't sign up for bathing or bathroom duties.

Grandma was a private and proud woman.

One night Dave called me at a friend's house where I was hanging out. Grandma had had an accident in her bed. She was calling for help, but would not let Dave be the one to change her bed and clean her.

I reluctantly went home. Dave was apologetic.

"I'm sorry you had to come home. I would've taken care of her. I don't mind; I'd clean her, but she wouldn't let me," Dave explained.

I bathed Grandma. I cried as I did it. It was hard and gross. She was embarrassed. She kept telling me how sorry she was. I didn't want her to know I was crying; I didn't want to make the situation worse.

Afterward, I lamented to Dave about how awful the job was.

"I wish she let me do it," Dave said.

It struck me as an appalling and ridiculous thing for Dave to assume responsibility for. He amazed me. He was genuinely disappointed he couldn't help Grandma.

He'd already been such an instrument in helping her. His display of unconditional love—for me and for her—was exemplary.

Dave taught me so much by his demonstration of unconditional love.

He taught me through our relationship, with his complete forgiveness of my bad behavior and his complete tolerance for my adventurous lifestyle.

He expected the same from me. He'd compromise whenever he felt that what I requested was reasonable. But if he felt strongly, he refused to change or alter himself or his behaviors.

"That's part of who I am. Love it or leave it," he'd remind me.

One of Dave's best traits was his unconditional devotion. He limitlessly supported and served the ones he loved. As the twenty-nine-year-old boyfriend of her granddaughter, Dave would have cleaned up Grandma and her bed. If allowed, he'd have done this selflessly, without complaint.

It would be my honor to return this service to him.

Back at home, Dave made it just inside the kitchen door and latched onto the radiator. He glared at me to let me know he wasn't moving.

"All right," I sighed. "I guess we're gonna do this right here."

I reached around Dave to close the kitchen window shade. I left him to get a trash bag, washcloth, and bucket of warm, soapy water. I stripped off my clothes, put on rubber gloves that went up to my elbows, and wore a bandana over my mouth and nose. I was equipped to battle a hazardous waste scene.

I crouched beside him and struggled to remove his pants. He resisted and held his jeans up around his waist with his super-strength grip.

"Help me, Dave," I scolded. "Don't make it harder."

He growled back at me.

I stood up and glowered at Dave.

I was sad and stressed. As I stood, I was ready to argue with Dave, but when we were face to face, I only felt sorry for us both.

My shoulders slumped, weak and defeated.

As my head hung in sorrow, I saw myself standing in my underwear and rubber gloves in the middle of the kitchen. I laughed. I looked ridiculous.

Dave crinkled his nose. Other people's laughter was irresistibly contagious to him.

"Look at me!" I cried through gulping laughter. "Look at your wife. This is ridiculous!"

Dave succumbed to our laughter and released his grip from his pants.

I cut his diaper away and cleaned him. The act wasn't as bad as the anticipation.

Once again, our sense of humor got us through. Despite the literally shitty hand fate had dealt us, Dave and I marched forward, costumed in diapers, rubber gloves, and bandana masks.

As the December days grew shorter, I feared I was losing my adventure-girl edge. I was only getting out of the house for work. The rock climbing season ended. During a normal year, my flexible schedule allowed me to take advantage of the rare warm, snow-free winter days. In the past, I cherished these last-minute escapes. In the present, the Dave care schedule didn't allow me to take unplanned adventures.

While he recovered from a surgery, Sugar Shack Mike had been hiking on the state land near his mother's house way up north. In December, he was feeling well enough to plan a first ascent of a mixed route—both ice and rock—he'd been scouting since the previous spring. He invited me to be his partner.

"The ice is coming in on that cliff I've been telling you about," Mike told me over the phone. "Do you want to go for a first ascent?"

"Oh, that sounds awesome," I sighed. "I don't know about leaving Dave overnight though."

"It's a beautiful place. You'll love it," Mike said.

"I'm so out of shape. I haven't been going outside at all," I lamented.

"This will be good for you," Mike encouraged. We'd been climbing together for five years and had become good friends. Mike understood a hard-core adventure was essential to my sanity.

"I might be *too* out of shape," I continued. "I might not be able to keep up with you! Is it a long hike to the cliff?"

"Nah, you'll do fine. It's mellow. Probably an hour."

The seed was planted. The more I thought about getting away and going on an ice climbing adventure, the more I knew I really wanted—needed—to find a way to pull off it off.

Frank was planning to be in town for the holidays, and would stay with us. Dan would also be in town from Portland and offered to help with Dave care. The Aunties were an ever-present and supportive force.

I wasn't having success finding a professional aide to stay with Dave. So, the team of friends and family was my only hope for relief from caring for him.

Dave didn't eat or use the bathroom without direction. He wet his pants or the bed with more and more frequency. Caring for Dave was becoming more than just sitting with him to make sure he didn't run off. More nursing duties were required: giving him meds, changing and cleaning him, and feeding him. It felt like too much to ask. At the same time, I felt as though I'd break if I didn't get away.

One night, the Aunties showed up to share takeout sushi with Dave and me. I filled Dave's gaping mouth with chopstick-full bites of California roll and spicy tuna with lots of wasabi. He chewed each mouthful with watering eyes.

"Too much wasabi?" I asked.

He slapped his knee and screeched. His smiling open mouth and finger pointing at the glob of wasabi signaled that he wanted more, and I kept shoveling it in.

Rae and Fay giggled as they watched Dave eat. In his fun and always-entertaining way, Dave made the meal a hilarious event.

Hanging out with Dave was mostly fun. He was content to watch movies—usually a rotation of the same five favorites—or enjoy snacks. Having company made things less daunting. Dave was distracted with guests around.

After dinner, I came out with it.

"Please say no if you're not comfortable with the idea. I'm wondering if you two would be available to help with Dave if I go on an overnight ice climbing adventure," I squeaked to the Aunties.

They glanced at each other, both with knowing smiles, before nodding in unison.

"Sure!" Auntie Rae said with a clap, as if she was accepting a favor, not granting one.

"Well, you know there may be bathroom issues. And I'm hoping Frank and Dan will help too. And it's not till next month, so things may change..." I rambled about my reservations.

"Oh, Aim," Auntie Fay interrupted. "We'll be fine. We have time to figure out the details and practice what we'll need to know how to do while you're away. Are you going with Sugar Shack?"

I gave the Aunties details about the trip. We all agreed to do our best to make it happen.

Throughout our relationship, Dave and I were always overbooked at the holidays. There were many family members and friends who expected visits.

This Christmas, I didn't feel obliged to go anywhere or do anything special. I knew none of our family and friends had expectations for Dave and me. We had the indulgence of staying home.

On Christmas Day, we ended up with a house full of family. We ordered sushi and feasted.

While the family ate, Dave moved to the sofa and turned on the TV.

The dining room was overflowing with Dave's young sisters, my Aunties, our dads, Dave's stepmother, and my grandma.

Dave selected a movie and adjusted the volume to high.

The movie was *The Hangover*. The living room filled with lots of swearing and off-the-wall dialogue. Dave screeched at the most obscene parts.

I was over trying to protect the rest of the world from Dave's lack of a filter. So, it was Christmas dinner. So, Dave was blasting a movie completely inappropriate for the mixed company. So?

None of the social or etiquette protocols applied. We were surviving. Dave wasn't dead, and I wasn't a complete emotional wreck; that's all that mattered.

I'd shifted my energy to caring for Dave, not worrying about the impression we were making on those around us. We were reduced to a fundamental level: life and death. Social niceties became an indulgence. If things went smoothly, if we got through a social situation without Dave exposing himself to urinate or masturbate, if something wasn't spilled or broken, we were in great shape.

If Dave wanted to play *The Hangover* for Christmas, then so be it. No one minded.

After the movie ended and everyone was full of sushi, we opened presents.

Dave's dad presented us with a large, elegantly framed photograph of Dave and me hugging on the sofa. It was a recent picture. Dave and I were both smiling so big, our teeth shone and eyes were squinty. We looked like kids: happy and careless. The portrait was the most touching gift we could receive.

My dad gave Dave industrial strength, heavy-duty rubber gloves big enough to fit over his winter gloves. My dad had seen Dave soak through his gloves while removing snow from surfaces many times. The rubber gloves were his solution. He found a way to help our helpless situation. The gloves were the most practical gift we could receive.

After Christmas, the weather was clear and warm, so we got out of town for the first time in weeks. We drove three hours west to where Aunt Patti lived with her three sons and husband.

Patti's home is always stocked with all kinds of food and drink. She's a tireless hostess.

The day we arrived, she fed Dave treat after treat.

As Dave sat in her kitchen, Patti made sure he was satiated.

"Do you want something to drink, Dave?"

He replied with his standard eyes-wide nod.

"Well, I have soda—grape, orange, or cola, there's juice—cranberry, grape, orange. Cappuccino? Hot tea? There's beer in the basement," she offered.

Dave smiled and shrugged at each of Patti's suggestions.

"I bet he wants cappuccino," I called from the living room where I'd settled in to play video games with my cousins.

"OK, cappuccino it is. Oh, and I have biscotti to go with that," Patti chirped as she dug through her cabinets.

Dave sat contentedly for over an hour. Patti chatted while she presented cookies, brownies, ice cream, and candy to Dave. He ate every morsel like he hadn't had food in days. I could hear his lips smacking over Patti's conversation.

Eventually Dave wandered to the living room. He carried a huge plastic cup filled with soda. The cup had a lid and straw. Patti was an organized and thorough mother and caregiver. She was equipped for Dave-care.

He sat down to watch my young cousins and me battle with plastic guitars. We took turns standing in front of the TV trying to hit the notes on the game *Guitar Hero*.

Dave sat silent and transfixed until I hit a bad note. When that happened, he'd erupt with laughter. He never laughed when my cousins made mistakes.

Daily I was reminded that Dave was present.

I savored the bad notes. When I turned to Dave as he cackled at my errors, his eyes sparkled.

We were having fun. Dave soaked in Patti's motherly care. And he thought it was hilarious that I couldn't match my young cousins' video game skills.

That night, Patti set up the guest room as if we were staying at a hotel. She even set chocolates on the pillows on the perfectly made-up side-by-side twin beds.

She made Dave's bed with a waterproof bottom sheet and bed pads.

I had the best sleep I'd had in months.

Patti's house felt safe. Patti and her family were unfazed by Dave's condition. She was prepared: from the covered cups to the protective bed coverings.

The separate beds made it so Dave's kicking and turning didn't disrupt my sleep. Dave must have been comatose from his full belly because he didn't get up once in the night.

The next morning, the pads on Dave's bed were soaked. The sheets were mostly spared. It was easy to pull away the soiled linen and put it in the wash. Cleaning the protective waterproof sheet was a breeze.

That morning, Dave spoke for the first time in weeks. My cousin Anthony asked him how he was.

"Not bad," he nonchalantly replied.

It was this kind of occurrence—Dave casually speaking—that caused Adam and me to fantasize that Dave had concocted his brain disease as an elaborate gag.

Back in Albany, the three of us sat in the living room and I told Adam about our trip to Syracuse.

"Dave had no trouble replying to Anthony when he asked how he was. Dave said, 'Not bad.'"

"Oh, nice one. I would have liked to have heard that," Adam mused.

"Yeah, he was so casual, it felt like he was his normal self," I sighed.

"You sure you're not faking this whole thing, Dave?" Adam razzed, "The joke's on us, huh?"

Dave snickered and nodded knowingly.

The joke was on *all* of us. I think Dave was as unknowing about when he could speak as the rest of us.

After our Syracuse trip, I bought a waterproof sheet and bed pads. I imitated Patti's bed-making style.

I learned to prepare for the inevitable. I slept easier.

By the New Year, I'd adjusted to Dave's muteness. I knew what his shrugs and nods meant. We'd carry on together using sounds— squeaks, screeches, clicks, and hums.

Occasionally, Dave would still read from cue cards or fill in blanks to appease those around him. Attempts at words could be frustrating and tiring for Dave. Instead of pushing him to talk, I joined in the silence.

At first, it had been so hard for me to accept Dave's lack of speech. Sometimes, I worried his needs weren't being met. Most times, I'd been frustrated or offended. I was a sensitive wife with hurt feelings.

I knew his brain was injured; I knew this wasn't his choice. But I also knew Dave! I knew stubborn, determined, trickster Dave. I knew Dave who always did whatever he wanted, saying things like "I don't care if it's wrong, it's how I'm going to do it!" He prided himself on his rebellious ways.

Just because Dave was sick with a vicious brain-eating disease didn't mean he wasn't the nonconformist I knew and loved. In fact, his disease was an extension of his core. He got ill and died the way he lived: in a distinctly Dave way—in a self-sufficient, apathetic-to-norms way.

Though Dave was losing control of his body and brain, the survival of his strong-willed determination was a gift. A big part of him was preserved. He could still make choices. He could plant his feet firmly in place and be as unmovable as a one-ton block if he didn't want to go somewhere. He could lock his jaw and swivel his head practically 360 degrees if he didn't want to eat something.

But, he couldn't talk. His brain couldn't make the necessary connections for him to form words.

Dave was stubborn in beautiful self-preserving ways. He was wise and intelligent. This combination helped him improvise for his lack of speech. Dave's eyes and facial expressions were so communicative.

As I grew more comfortable with and accepting of our new life, I opened up to receiving Dave's subtle messages. I learned to stop taking things so personally and to stop reacting without thinking first. I learned to appreciate the pieces of Dave that were shining through the brain damage and to try to accept that neither of us could control the effects of the progressing disease.

As I settled into this new way of life, two things returned: my sense of humor and my ability to relax. Dave had never lost these things. He was sick and dying, and undoubtedly confused, but he was relaxed and able to laugh.

He laughed while I cried and made a mess of the living room by breaking records one-by-one in my hands. He laughed when I shouted at him, "Are you systematically trying to destroy everything I love?!" after he innocently tugged at the seam and pried the upholstery off the arm of my new love seat.

At first, his laughter would only make me more sad or mad or frustrated. I felt as if he didn't understand what I was going through; I felt alone. Little by little, I realized I wasn't alone. Dave was right there with me, with bright, wise eyes looking at me and shining love. He was laughing because he knew this hopeless tragedy was part of our greater divine comedy. He was laughing because he was overwhelmed by love and truth.

I know this because he told me. When I accepted his silence, when I relaxed and laughed with Dave, our communication deepened. He didn't have words, so I tried doing without them too. We started spending time sitting together and looking at each other. And laughing and smiling and kissing and touching.

When I stopped speaking *at* Dave, I heard his voice again. We'd stare into one another's eyes, and I could feel his message. He'd laugh, nod, and smile responses to the silent words in my thoughts.

One night we sat facing each other on the love seat. I was sad and feeling overwhelmed. Dave was intent on soothing me. He looked at me calmly with love and peace.

"It's OK," I heard him say. "Everything is totally OK. We are going someplace so much better than this. We planned this. We are doing this amazing thing together and everything's going to be great."

Energy Beings

The universe was delivering me a survival manual, one book or human interaction at a time. In January, *My Stroke of Insight* by Jill Bolte Taylor showed up in my mailbox. This chunk of my survival manual came from Frank's girlfriend, Anna.

Taylor is a brain scientist who suffered a stroke. In her book, she chronicles what it was like to lose the use of her left brain, and the experience of living from her right brain's point of view.

At first read, parts of the book made me feel defensive.

"I needed my caregivers to teach me with patience," she wrote. That hit a nerve.

"You don't know what it's like to be a caregiver!" I thought. "You can't know the frustration that comes with being a caregiver."

Then I read on.

Taylor describes her struggle to recover, and her awareness of her body's reaction to emotion. Through the recovery process, Taylor notices her mind's ability to choose emotion and reaction.

I realized her condition and subsequent awareness were invaluable. I started to see that Dave's condition came with gifts of immeasurable lessons. I understood that I could choose to learn a new patience. I could choose to absorb Dave's right-brain peace and nonlinear thinking, and live closer to enlightenment because of it.

Inspired by Taylor's memoir, I searched the Internet for more about her experiences. I found an eighteen-minute TED Talk that was so moving and informative, I wanted to share it with everyone I knew. I watched it over and over, and played it for visiting friends and family. It was a great crash course for our visitors. In the video, Taylor gives a blow-by-blow account of her stroke.

She explains the differences between the right and left hemispheres of the brain. The right hemisphere, Taylor says, "is all about this present moment. It's all about right here, right now."

She says, "I am an energy-being connected to the energy all around me through the consciousness of my right hemisphere. *We* are energy-beings connected to one another through the consciousness of our right hemispheres as one human family."

The right brain knows, "We are brothers and sisters on this planet, here to make the world a better place. And in this moment we are perfect, we are whole, and we are beautiful."

The left hemisphere "Thinks linearly and methodically. Our left hemisphere is all about the past and it's all about the future."

She explains that the left brain sorts through the "enormous collage of the present moment" to assign and analyze information.

"The left hemisphere thinks in language... It's that little voice that says to me 'I am. I am.'" This, she says, is what makes us feel we are individuals, separate from each other.

On the day of her stroke, Taylor lost the function of her left hemisphere. At the onset of his disease, pieces of Dave's left hemisphere were the first to go. His left hemisphere was the most damaged.

Taylor explained that when her left hemisphere stopped generating "brain chatter", she couldn't distinguish her body from the wall. She could only feel energy.

"What a tremendous gift this experience could be," she says.

Taylor made a full recovery after her stroke. Through the process, she learned, "We are the life-force power of the universe, with manual dexterity and two cognitive minds. And we have the power to choose, moment by moment, who and how we want to be in the world."

Taylor's explanation of the brain made perfect sense. Dave was a living example. Her description of losing left hemisphere function and seeing light and knowing her place in the vast universe put words to the look in Dave's eyes.

Taylor helped me let go of my left-brain articulation and ego-driven desire to control. This wise, experienced scientist gave me permission to relax into the magnificent energy around me. Dave was already doing that.

Taylor helped me see I could choose how to approach being a caregiver. I could choose to be patient. I could choose to see Dave's condition as a gift. We were connecting in ways beyond the ego; we were closer than ever. Our lives were more meaningful. We were feeling our connection with energy, the Force, light. God.

Everyone cried when watching the TED Talk in our living room. It was clear to me, and many of our friends, that Dave was living between the worlds. He was riding close to death, but still grounded on Planet Earth. His left brain was disintegrating, and his right brain was taking over.

Bit by bit, my faith was growing. I was growing into the spiritual being I was born to be. But, I was still on Planet Earth, and my husband was still dying. I still felt exhaustion and frustration. I still yearned for a less painful existence; I still wished I could do the human things I loved.

Mike and I set the second Sunday in January as our ice climbing adventure start date. As the weeks passed, I scheduled times for the Aunties, Frank, and Dan to stay with Dave while I was away. I'd be gone for two nights.

I felt worn out; I knew I needed to take time away from home and sick Dave. Still, I was concerned about leaving Dave. He was unpredictable, especially with the bathroom. He wore diapers most of the time, but still had accidents.

Sometimes, he'd put his hand in his pocket to pull his penis out of his diaper and piss down his leg. I was vigilant about taking him to the bathroom every couple of hours, but I ended up cleaning piss from the floor and washing Dave's clothes almost daily. He'd wet the bed most nights, soaking a diaper, pajama pants, and the layers of bed pads.

Dave only had a bowel movement every couple of days. I insisted he sit on the toilet before I'd shower him. So far, there hadn't been any shit accidents at home, but I knew it was only a matter of time.

I hoped Dave would be comfortable enough to let his friends help him with his bathroom needs. I hoped the job wouldn't be too much for the caregivers. I knew it was almost too much for me.

I didn't know if Dave understood time or planning for the future. He was aloof or frustrated when I tried involving him in decision-making. I was calling the shots, yet Dave was still present enough that I needed to consult him about major choices. My leaving for two nights was a big deal for everyone involved.

A few days before I left, I sat with Dave on the sofa.

"So, Davey, you know I'm going away this weekend, right?"

He shrugged.

"I'm going on a kick-ass ice climbing adventure with Sugar Shack Mike."

Dave had always supported my adventures and pushed me to climb bigger and harder rocks. I knew healthy Dave would be excited about my Adirondack plan.

"It's going to be a first ascent; it should be pretty awesome."

I told him the details. He smiled and nodded while I spoke.

In my mind, I filled in the blanks of our one-sided conversation with what I thought Dave would say if he could.

He'd ask how high the cliff was; he'd want to know what gear I'd bring, how I'd protect the route; he'd encourage me to be safe.

"I don't wanna leave ya, Davey," I said. "I'm gonna miss you."

Dave looked at me with raised eyebrows and wide eyes.

"Is it OK? Someone will be here the whole time, either the Aunties, or Frank or Dan."

Dave's gaze locked on me. He reached out, squeezed my hand, and nodded gravely.

He understood me. It was a comfort he didn't protest my getaway, but it made me feel sad to know he'd surely recognize my absence.

The second Sunday in January arrived. I left close to dusk. I pulled away from my warm, bright house, leaving Dave with Frank and the Aunties, and ventured north into the cold evening.

I felt a mix of relief, guilt, and excitement. It was good to be on my own. I was desperately aware of leaving Dave's side and the potentially stressful situation I put him, our two friends, and two Aunties in. I was exhilarated to be setting out on a backcountry ice climb, a potential first ascent.

Driving north, I was psyched. I hadn't left town on an adventure since the cold of winter set in. Taking Dave out in the snow was an unnecessary risk and hassle.

Driving north was always a release for me. Since I was a kid, driving to the Adirondacks meant I was leaving day-to-day life for adventure. I was leaving structure for wilderness. Many of my best memories start with a drive north.

I stopped thinking about what I was leaving behind and started focusing on where I was. The familiar mountains were welcoming and comforting me. I couldn't help but smile as I steered off the highway onto Route 73, the road that winds through the High Peaks. Even in the dark, I recognized the landscape and was put at ease.

I was on my way. I had made the choice to go away. I had set up care for Dave. I was ready to focus on my adventure. I was comfortable in the Adirondacks.

My comfort lasted for thirty miles. As I passed out of the part of the Adirondack Park that I was most familiar with, it started to snow. Big, wet flakes fell fast. I was driving into a storm.

As I ventured farther from home, then farther from the woods I was familiar with, the driving became hazardous. I kept a white knuckle grip on the steering wheel as I tried to follow the road through white-out snow. With each gentle curve, the tires lost their grip on the snowy road.

I finally got to Mike's mother's house an hour after I was scheduled to arrive. The house was old and drafty. It was cluttered with antique furniture draped with afghans and pillows. I covered myself with blankets, cozied onto a pile of pillows, and ate the food Mike served.

The next morning, we woke up early to start our mission. Our heavy packs were loaded with ropes, harnesses, ice axes, ice screws, rock climbing gear, water, and food. We were bundled in layers of long underwear, fleece, and down. We wore snowshoes and used ski poles.

The first part of the approach was easy going on a Jeep trail. Snowmobiles had packed the trail, so our snowshoes cruised along on top of the crust. Deep snow lined the sides of the trail. The accumulation was over three feet, and snowdrifts gathered by the wind were as high as four feet.

Mountains, hills, and cliffs surrounded, standing tall over the tree line. The landscape was beautiful but foreboding. It was the Adirondacks, but not the part I knew and felt at home in.

I'd just read *The Andean Codex*, the story of J.E. Williams' spiritual journey in the high mountains of Peru. He learns from indigenous people who call the spirits of the high mountains *Apus*. I was moved by the idea of the mountains as God-like spirits. I've always felt protected by the not quite as high, but majestic, Adirondack Mountains. I'm moved by their energy and holiness.

As I trudged through the snow, surrounded by the ominous, unfamiliar mountains, I prayed to the Apus. I prayed for protection and guidance on the adventure we were starting. I prayed for clarity and strength. I prayed that the mountains and clean air surrounding would purify my toxic and stagnant-feeling body and mind.

At a seemingly random spot, Mike led us into the woods. The deep, heavy snow was like quicksand. With each step, the snow filled in over my snowshoes and buried my calf, knee, and sometimes thigh.

Mike led us deeper into the woods. I tried to keep up. I put one foot in front of the other, but often slipped back half the distance I covered with my steps. The virgin snow was heavy and slippery. The farther we went, the steeper the terrain.

The trees were thick, and a layer of low grey clouds hid the sun. Travel in the woods was dark and uninspiring. Right away, I felt out of shape. From the couch at home, I'd hoped my enthusiasm would be enough to override my lack of physical conditioning. On the trail, my enthusiasm dwindled and my chest and legs burned. My pack felt like it was loaded with rocks. My feet and hands were cold, but my body was hot and sweaty.

I fell behind and lost sight of Mike. I felt discouraged and wondered how I'd do on the ice climb if the walk in was so exhausting. We'd been walking for an hour, and I felt as though I couldn't go on.

I tried to concentrate on the majesty of the mountains, now hidden behind the trees and low cloud cover. I tried to focus on my prayers to the Apus. With each strained inhale, I visualized light and energy from the trees and mountains entering my body. I felt my breath travel through me, oxygenating my blood, giving me strength. With each exhale, I released tension and toxins, sending my stress to the light.

This routine worked for about ten minutes. Then I gave in. I was tired; I felt pathetic. I wasn't the adventure girl I believed I was. I was exhausted. I was sad. My life was overwhelming. I was lost.

"Mike!" I shouted into the stillness. There was no answer; he was long gone. I was alone. I wanted to give up. I didn't care about the adventure. If Mike answered, I'd insist we go back to his truck. I wasn't up to this challenge.

My pace slowed, but I kept moving. I was following Mike's tracks. The incline had become so steep that his path started to switch back, cutting the steep terrain into a longer but more manageable route.

I started to cry. I cried so hard my whole body shook. I was alone in the woods, with only the Apus to witness. I wailed. I sobbed. Snot and tears covered my face and froze to my scarf.

The enormity of my charge overwhelmed me. My struggle in the woods mirrored my real life trials.

I had a sense of giving up, releasing my rigid determination. I had been counting myself strong and unflinching. What I thought would be an adventurous recharge was devastation. In the woods, I was weak and defeated.

In my release, I saw the source of my despair: Dave was dying.

Life was hard; caring for sick Dave was painful and exhausting. I'd been determined to stay strong, and the arduous hike had melted that strength. I was stripped raw. With my defensive edge gone, I was filled with anguish over the root of my hardship: Dave was going to die. Soon. And there was nothing I could do about it. It didn't matter how strong I was.

I plodded on, one foot after the other, slipping and sniffling. Close to three hours after we left the car, I saw a 200-foot-tall cliff. I'd made it! My heart leaped though I was still dripping tears and choking on my sobs. As I closed in on the cliff, I saw Mike sitting on his pack with his back against a tree, looking up at an icy corner at the edge of the rock face.

The last thirty feet to reach the ledge where Mike sat was steep. To get there, I had to climb over snow-covered boulders. Even so close to the destination, I felt I'd never reach the rock. My effort to mask my tears halted as soon as I slipped backwards on the final approach.

"Mike! I can't do it," I gasped and sat in the snow.

"Amelia?" Mike was confused. In over five years of adventuring together, he'd never seen me give up or cry.

"It's OK. You're here. You did it," Mike encouraged.

"No! I mean I can't do *anything*! Oh, my God," I wailed.

"Dave's gonna die. I'm taking care of Dave *while he DIES!*" I coughed out the words through sobs.

Mike stood and moved to me. Wordlessly, he took my backpack from me and helped me stand.

"I can't do *anything*. This is too hard for me. The hike, the climb, my life. Dave's gonna die," I squeaked. "Dave's dying. Right now he's home dying while I'm here."

Mike arranged my pack across from his and motioned for me to sit. While he waited for me to ascend the last few feet, he poured a cup of tea from his thermos and pulled a bag of trail mix from his pack.

When I sat, he offered me the nourishment.

"I know. I'm sorry," he said. "I'm really sorry, Amelia."

"I don't know what to do," I confessed.

"You don't have to do anything. Just sit. Breathe. We can eat lunch and go home," Mike consoled.

"I mean I don't know what to do about *anything*. My life. Dave," I wailed.

"You don't have to do anything," Mike repeated.

We climbed. Mike led the new route. I followed him up the corner and traversed under an overhang, wedging my ice axes into cracks in the rock where the ice wasn't thick enough to stick into. I climbed to the spot where he'd stopped, over a hundred feet above the ground.

Together we examined the last fifty feet of cliff. To finish the route, Mike would have to lead up a sheet of ice barely thick enough to cover the slab of rock. I had fun following the first pitch and encouraged him to keep us going. It looked scary and hard, but Mike decided to try it.

After about twenty-five feet, the ice was so thin it shattered under the blows of Mike's axes. He couldn't safely go higher, so he downclimbed back to where I hung from an anchor made from screws in the ice. We would have to retreat.

We rappelled down from the route to the safety of the ground. There, we drank more tea and ate the pancakes left over from breakfast. Mike led the way out. He followed our path from the morning for a hundred yards. Then, instead of staying on the path when the trail steepened, he took off his pack, set it on his lap, and sat in the snow. Mike slid down the mountain on his ass, weaving between trees, gliding over the deep snow.

Before taking off my pack, I wondered about the possibility of gaining so much speed I'd be unable to stop before slamming into a tree. I decided it was worth the risk and took off after Mike.

The ride out was weightless and fun. I imagined that I'd shed a hundred pounds of tears; without them, I could defy gravity.

Back on level ground, we found our way back to the Jeep trail. I felt a huge relief and a new peacefulness.

I looked to the mountains I'd prayed to that morning. I thanked the Apus for my safe adventure. I was grateful for the strength to get through the day. The sacred energy of the mountains empowered me.

The skyline captivated me. I was at once invigorated and exhausted. I'd undergone a tremendous release. My skin and muscles felt loose on my bones. I'd been completely worked, but felt no tension in my body.

I gazed back into the woods from which we emerged, and a literal weight lifted from my shoulders. In my mind's eye, I saw a silver plate of armor floating from my back to the mountains. When the armor met the mountains, it melted, and I felt a flush of tingly heat spread over my shoulders and down my back. The Apus had absorbed a heavy piece of my stress and suffering.

I saw bright sparkling light on the skyline, and again when I closed my eyes.

Back at the house, I checked my voicemail. There were two messages, both from Frank.

In the first one, his voice was shaky and intense.

"Amelia. Hi. Everything is OK here, but we need some advice. So, um, if you could give a call, that'd be good."

In the second, Frank's voice sounded relieved and almost giddy.

"We worked everything out. Call when you can; Dave would like to hear your voice."

When I called home, I got the full report.

Dave had shat on the bathroom floor, next to the toilet.

Auntie Fay volunteered for floor duty, and Dan tried to shower Dave. He turned the water on and Dave stepped into the tub. The water only hit half of him, but it was enough to soak him.

Dan shut off the water and called to Frank for help. Together, they got Dave's clothes off, including his comically soaked diaper. They turned the water back on and managed to get one of Dave's legs back in the tub. Dave locked his death grip onto the guide rail on the outside of the tub. He wouldn't budge.

That's when Frank made his first call. For several minutes, Dave screeched and growled with feet planted and hands gripped immovably while water sprayed out on the floor and the three boys. Finally, Frank and Dan maneuvered Dave into the tub and got him clean.

That's when Frank made his second call. In that message, Frank's voice had a recognizable sound of accomplishment, a sound I empathized with. It felt awesome to beat Dave in a battle of wills; he was the most stubborn person any of us had ever known.

I knew firsthand how hard the ordeal must have been for the boys. Dave was almost impossible to move if he was determined to stay in a place.

Frank and Dan's love and devotion shone that night. It was a relief to hear they were handling uncomfortable and difficult situations with so much grace and humor.

It felt amazing to know I had backup with Dave's care. It was beautiful to know how deeply our friends were committed to helping Dave.

After the report, Frank handed the phone over to Dave. I could hear his smile by listening to his breathing. I told him my ice-climbing tale, and he responded with an occasional snicker or cackle.

When I told him I'd be home the following day, and I loved him, he screeched.

My worst fear about what could go wrong while I was away had happened: Dave shat. But everyone survived.

Dave was dying. But that night—and for many more to come—Dave was alive, and his characteristic screech told me he was waiting for my return. We'd be together the next day.

I didn't know what I was doing, or what I was going to do. The Apus helped me see I didn't need to know, and Mike reminded me I didn't have to do anything. I was standing by my love; that was all.

When I came home, Auntie Rae looked me up and down.

"You look good!" she complimented.

"I do? I'm tired. That was a hard adventure; I feel like a softie," I confessed.

"Something's different. Your posture is better. You're not hunched," she explained as she studied me.

A few days later, Dan gave me a massage. He maintained his role as pit mechanic—trying his best to keep my mind, body, and spirit connected and strong—and had been massaging me whenever he was in town.

When the session ended, he gave me an approving nod.

"What?" I asked, trying to decipher his knowing grin.

"You feel different. That weird, foreign chunky thing that's been stuck on your back is gone," Dan explained, "I could really dig into your problem spots."

My mind flashed to the walk out of the woods, the silver plate of armor disappearing into the mountains.

After the massage, Dan delivered some great news. He'd decided to stay in Albany. He and his brother, Mark—Dave's best friend since childhood—would be moving back to Albany from Oregon.

"We'll be around to help you with Dave," Dan offered.

Dan explained that he and Mark had started making plans to move back East. They'd leave Portland in March and were looking for an apartment in Albany starting in April.

"It'd be perfect if we could move into your upstairs apartment," Dan suggested.

"Oh, my God, that'd be awesome!" I agreed. My upstairs tenant had just renewed her one-year lease. She always paid her rent on time and was sweet as could be. As much as I wanted the boys to move in, I couldn't ask her to move out.

I was feeling more and more acceptance about Dave's and my lives. I was soulfully aware of the big picture.

I wasn't getting any better about accepting tangible, realistic, earthly responsibilities. I depended on the help of my friends and family. They were easing my burden, but they were accumulating their own burden.

Dave's sickness was a devastation to everyone. My backup needed backup.

In just over two months, Mark and Dan would be around; there'd be two more helpers. That was an awesome, reassuring fact. But two months might just as well have been two years; it was an eternity.

I'd been overwhelmed by the chore of setting up Dave's Social Security and Medicaid benefits. His stepmother had helped me by filling out paperwork and making calls.

The process took months. We'd been to the Social Security office and the Disability office. Dave had been to see doctors for evaluations. Someone from the Medicaid office came to visit our house to evaluate Dave's needs.

Medicaid approved him to receive professional home care. His benefits would pay for a part-time home health aide.

I was ecstatic until I started calling the home care agencies on the list Medicaid gave us. At each one, the best they could do was put us on a waiting list for an aide. "We don't have anyone free for an assignment," they'd say. "We don't know when we'll be able to send you someone."

I figured out that what they really meant was, "You have to wait for someone to die, then you can have their aide." The shortage of aides was that serious.

Calling the agencies was exhausting for me. I loathed the process. We had a need and the resources to pay, but we couldn't get help.

In the meantime, Dave's stepmom found an assisted-living facility that had a daycare program. I could drop Dave off when I needed to work. They'd feed him, clean him, and keep him busy with activities.

The woman who ran the program was our age. Right away, she felt like a friend. Dave was comfortable with her. Otherwise, the place housed senior citizens and severely handicapped people.

I was grateful for the option. It was a relief to have a safe place to take Dave, but it was heartbreaking to leave him there.

The care team was maxed out. We were all tired. The situation seemed hopeless. I wasn't comfortable leaving Dave at the daycare facility. It defeated the purpose of having him at home where he could be comfortable and happy. It was stressful for him. It was also unrealistic for me to keep Dave at home all the time without some professional help.

Somewhere near the end of February, things lightened up.

One night, I cooked a Thanksgiving worthy family-style dinner. Dave and I enjoyed the company of Frank and Dan. It was a like-old-times dinner party: we were laughing and reminiscing and having fun together.

The conversation kept coming back to Dan's plans to move back to Albany. We were all thrilled.

"Too bad we can't just move in here," Dan lamented.

"I know. I agree, Dan," I sighed.

"Wouldn't it be perfect if your tenant would just move out?" Dan continued.

"Of course! But she's not gonna 'just move out.' I'd love to have you guys upstairs," I said. "But you have to understand, I can't just ask Kim to leave. We have a lease; and Kim's great!" I explained.

A few minutes later we heard a car pull into the driveway.

"That must be Kim getting home from work," I said.

I was surprised to hear a knock on my back door. Kim usually kept to herself.

I opened the door to Kim's worried expression.

"Amelia, I need to talk to you," she began.

"Sure, Kim, what's up?" I encouraged.

"God, I hate to do this. I know you're going through a lot. I know you don't need more stress," she paused.

I couldn't imagine what was worrying her.

"I want to move out. I have an opportunity to move into a condo in my daughter's school district. I'd like to break the lease and leave here at the end of March," she blurted.

I almost screamed! I wanted to jump up and down and hug her.

Instead, I managed to stifle my welling giggles and smile.

"That's fine with me, Kim," I said. "I understand. Congratulations on the new place."

She stared back at me.

"*Really?* You don't mind? It won't put you out?" Kim asked, relieved.

"Actually, it'll help me. I'll rent the apartment to friends who'll help with Dave. It'll work out perfectly."

When I went back to the dining room, the boys sat wide-eyed and silent.

"Did you hear that?" I squeaked.

"Thank you, Universe!" Dan proclaimed, raising his eyes and arms to the sky.

The universe kept delivering. A few days later, the phone rang.

"Hello, Amelia. This is Denise, Mary's mom."

Mary was my ex-roommate and good friend who had moved to Florida. She'd been checking in on me and—like everyone I knew—had heard about my inability to get professional help to care for Dave.

"I know someone who might be able to help you," Denise said. "My friend Kathy has worked as a home health aide. I think she's looking for work. Do you want her number?"

When I called Kathy, Denise had already filled her in on the situation. She was ready to meet us.

Kathy's voice was like a character from a commercial. The voice that's full of warmth and reassurance. The voice that'll sell you the sanity-saving, life-enhancing product you never knew you needed.

Without hesitation, I arranged for her to start work as soon as she could, a few days later.

That day, the doorbell rang. It was Saint Patrick's Day, but I still wasn't prepared for what greeted me when I swung open the door. There stood a petite woman with short, bright red hair that framed her smiling face. Her green sweater complemented her shimmery green eyes. Not a leprechaun, but surely a fantastical being!

Here was the manifestation of my months-long fantasies for a helper. Kathy radiated warmth and kindness. And she was confident! She marched into our home with the command of an ER doctor and the ease of an old friend.

In the woods, I faced a deep truth. I'd been blaming my angst on the inconveniences and details of Dave's illness and my responsibilities. By staying focused on the day-to-day dilemmas, I could ignore the ultimate truth: Dave was going to die. Really, the inconveniences and details were a distant second to the one fact that mattered: Dave was going to die.

In the woods, I opened to that truth. I let go of the protective shield that had guarded me until I was ready. I felt changed after the silvery piece of armor floated from my back and dissolved into the Adirondack mountains.

When the armor came off, it seemed like the care equation changed, too. Maybe I had been holding everyone at bay, so only the hardiest volunteers got through. Now, it felt like the space around Dave and me was opening.

The help was coming in waves. It didn't pour in all at once. Dave's friends from Portland were coming, but not right away. There was a daycare option, but it didn't work for everyday use. There were funds for home care, but there had been a delay while I found an aide.

I was learning to allow the help to come. Little by little, I was learning I wasn't in control of the ride.

I had to reevaluate how I'd ride out the end of Dave's life. I could stay stressed and angry. I could keep struggling for control and keep falling back on my long-standing, stubborn resistance to asking for help. From literally my first memory, I had this emotional glitch that kept me from asking for help, independent and self-sufficient at all costs. My consolation for the losses I endured had always been that I felt strong and self-sufficient. I believed I didn't need anyone else. I built that armor to protect myself from needing, from feeling weak and vulnerable.

Now I could see how acknowledging my need for help and asking for it—despite my pride and stubbornness, despite my ingrained sense I shouldn't need it—could indicate strength, not weakness.

It was also a way to acknowledge the value of my helpers. My asking for help would benefit us all and strengthen the care team. Asking for help meant being truthful.

The Mother of All Parties

When Kathy arrived, she brought spring with her. Dave and I emerged from our winter cave recharged. Having Kathy around was a relief. She was competent and capable. Dave and I trusted her authority immediately.

Kathy was cheery and kind. She smiled with her whole body—all of her shined smile. She was soft-spoken and tender.

She was also strong and determined. She wasn't shy about making herself at home; she wasn't shy about caring for Dave.

Dave smiled with Kathy. He was at ease around her. I was at ease around her. She seemed to know what was best.

On Kathy's second day with us, she let herself into the apartment and found Dave and me in the kitchen. We were huddled over the waffle iron, peeling pieces of warm waffle off the griddle and popping them into our mouths.

She squealed with delight.

"Oh, I like your style! You guys are great," she managed through her giggles.

Dave and I kept eating, laughing between bites. We lived on a primal level, like two hungry, pleasure-seeking little animals.

In the spring, a small group of our closest friends cushioned us. Together, we balanced in a non-space and non-time place. We simply existed together. We partied like kids, like there was no tomorrow. We were vibrantly aware of how precious each day was.

We had a full house on most weekends. The guest room futon and living room couch and love seat were often crash pads for overnight guests.

In March, I made calendar month schedules for the refrigerator. I set up an official care schedule for Dave. The time was divided among Kathy, the Aunties, my dad, Dan, and Frank. I had plenty of people willing to help cover my time away from Dave. I scheduled time for the caregivers to visit so Dave and I were entertained and kept company.

The care team recovered from the winter doldrums, the end-of-our-ropes desperation we endured through the cold months.

We were all eager for the support system to grow by one when Mark moved back in April. One afternoon, Dan and I sat with Dave as he watched *Airplane* and laughed on cue with the funny parts.

"It's gonna be so nice when your brother gets here," I remarked to Dan. "One more set of hands will be awesome."

"Oh yeah," Dan slyly answered. "Two sets of hands would be even better, right?"

"Uh, right," I said. "But what do you mean? Who else?"

"Our cousin, Murph! Murph wants to leave North Carolina and move in with us," Dan announced with equal parts glee and trepidation.

Dave let out a whooping laugh, and it wasn't in response to *Airplane*. He'd heard what Dan said, and he responded with a hysterical, dramatic cackle.

Dan's glee came from knowing Dave would be thrilled to have the infamous cousin Murph around; his trepidation came from not knowing what my reaction would be. Murph's reputation preceded him. After all, he was the originator of the notorious line "I looove gettin' fucked up!"

Coincidentally—if such a thing still existed in our world—the only way I could get Dave to speak was to say, "I looove gettin'..."

Dave would invariably fill in the blank with "fucked up."

So, the party was getting cranked up a notch. Who was I to argue?

"All right, Dan, I guess we're really gonna have a houseful!" I acquiesced.

Of our partying crew, Heather was the one to remind me of logical things. Having lived with a sick husband alarmingly close to death for nearly four years, she'd had time to collect her thoughts regarding death. One night we were talking on the phone and she asked what my plans were for Dave's remains.

"You may not want to think about this, but—especially if his family is going to want a say—you might want to start making plans for what you're going to do with Dave's body when he dies."

She had a point. And I didn't want to think about it. But it would be easier to discuss things with Dave's family *before* the dying. It would be best to deal with any conflicting interests ahead of time.

"Uuuuhhh," was my reply.

"Have you given it *any* thought?" Heather gently prodded. "Burial? Cremation? The after party?"

Heather told me about her plans for Chris. She'd follow the Tibetan Buddhist traditions as closely as possible if Chris died. The body should be left undisturbed as long as possible. This allows a better transition into and through the *bardo*—the in-between state after death and before rebirth. Heather explained that it was customary to wash the deceased's body. She'd insist on washing Chris.

I hadn't given the topic much conscious thought.

I knew Dave and I both wanted to be cremated.

Years prior, when we were in our early twenties, Dave recorded a band called The Clinkers. "Clinkers" is a term that refers to the chunky parts of the remains after a cremation.

Dave was super enthusiastic about the band and considered producing their debut album. He wanted photographs of a crematory's interior for the album cover.

Around the same time, I was modeling for a photographer. We were doing shoots at St. Agnes Cemetery, where my mother, grandparents, and Aunt Barb were buried. I was familiar with the cemetery and loved working on an artistic project there. It was a welcoming and serene place.

The photographer suggested we work inside the crematory. The man in charge of cremations was an old friend of his. When we set the date, I asked if I could bring my camera too.

I was thrilled to get a private tour of the crematory. The brick building was peaceful and beautiful. My old 35mm camera jammed that day, and I never got to shoot for the album cover.

But I got something else that day. I went home with a sense of relief. I'd always been creeped out by embalming and burial. I was glad to see another option.

"Davey, if I bite it, I want to be cremated at St. Agnes, OK?" I told Dave after recounting my day at the crematory.

"OK. Me too. I don't want to be buried either. Ick," Dave replied. "But let's not bite it anytime soon."

Like Heather and Chris, I was taking great comfort in Tibetan Buddhist teachings and practices. I wanted to wash Dave's dead body. I wanted to keep him in the house long enough for friends and family to say goodbye and long enough that I was comfortable letting him go.

The next day, I called Dave's mother.

"I want to talk to you about what we're going to do with Dave's remains," I ventured. I had no idea what Beverly's wishes were. I braced for the worst: that she'd insist on embalming, showing the corpse, Christian ceremony, burial.

"Well, I'm pretty sure Dave wanted to be cremated," she replied.

I was instantly relieved. If we agreed on cremation, I was sure everything else would fall into place.

"I have a friend who runs a crematory," she continued. "I've already talked to him about handling Dave's body." She didn't know which crematory her friend oversaw, but she gave me his name.

"I believe you know Dave the best, Amelia. I trust you'll follow his wishes," Beverly said, relinquishing decision-making authority. "It would mean a lot to me if my friend does the cremation."

Next, I called Dave's dad and asked him the same question.

"Oh, honey, I know you'll do what's best. He's your husband," was Rich's reply.

Cool! We all agreed. I Googled the name of Beverly's friend. The search led to the website for St. Agnes. Beverly's friend was the man I'd met all those years ago. His crematory was the one I hoped to use. Coincidence? Synchronicity? Reality. My reality required coping with heavy-duty human emotion and loss, but it also seemed to be a connected and fated series of things working out exactly as they should.

The next day, I called the funeral home my grandmother used to bury my mother and grandfather. The aged man I spoke to knew who I was, or at least knew who my grandmother was.

"I'm so sorry your family has endured so much loss," he sympathized. "It was such a shame that your grandmother lost two daughters."

He assured me he and his son would be there to handle taking Dave's body from our house to the crematory. He'd help me reserve the chapel connected to the crematory for a memorial service.

The first Saturday in April was moving day. Mark and Dan showed up early that morning. Adam was there to help, and we all unloaded boxes from Mark and Dan's overstuffed cars.

A little later, a huge moving truck inched toward the house down my narrow one-way street. We paused in our work to watch the driver skillfully maneuver the truck backwards into my even narrower driveway.

Ninety-pound, five-foot-five Murph—the most distinctive character of the bunch—hopped down from the ten-ton truck's cab with a gigantic smile and enthusiastic wave.

Adam took a step forward.

"Welcome to Amelia's Home for Wayward Boys!" he shouted in a barreling voice.

Right away, Mark and Murph's names were written in on the empty spaces on the April refrigerator calendar.

With the boys came many stories. Every one of us had watched Dave's mental unraveling from a different perspective. We all compared notes.

The boys all agreed Dave never wanted to let me go. He faced our breakup with equal parts denial and confusion. He never gave a straight explanation of what had gone wrong.

We lamented how fucking devastating it was that, while we were breaking up, Dave didn't have the brain capacity to fathom what was happening to him, why he was losing his beloved.

He'd told Mark that he carried with him the letter I'd written after our fifth anniversary as a reminder of what he needed to do. Mark said he used it like a manual. He'd take the worn page from its crumpled envelope stored in his pocket and review it.

He'd say things like, "Amelia thinks I need to have a car and a job. I'm looking into getting a car; it's always easy for me to pick up work. She does know best."

Frank and Dan knew about that letter too.

Frank told me that when Dave unexpectedly showed up at his North Carolina door a year before—eight months after we'd stopped living together—he spoke of me lovingly and never mentioned we were apart.

Murph got a surprise visit from Dave around the same time.

"He was out of his mind. I mean, Dave was always a little out of his mind, but, whoa buddy, he was really out there. He wanted to go drinking. We walked downtown and partied all night. And I lost him. All I could do was go home and wait. He showed up in the morning like nothing happened. Said he slept in a bush outside a church."

Murph was saddened by his own story. He still felt guilty for losing Dave.

"I knew something was wrong. He wasn't himself. He talked a lot about you, Amelia. He kept saying he needed to write a song for you."

All the boys agreed that Dave had played like a sometimes-annoying broken record: "Amelia is the love of my life. I love my wife. I belong with Amelia."

I listened to these accounts like a teenager hearing about her crush. It was validating and warming to know I'd been right to hold on while Dave was losing his mind and slipping away.

Despite the relative peace I'd settled into at home, I still craved adventure. I'd been camping in the Adirondacks since I was a toddler. I'd been programmed to go north when spring arrived, and craved a getaway.

With Kathy and the boys available to back up the Aunties and Frank, I knew an adventure getaway was possible. There were plenty of people around to care for Dave.

I wanted time to myself, away from the Home for Waywards. I loved having a busy house and lots of visitors, but I needed a chance to be alone.

So, I sped up the highway one evening in late June, driving to Lake Placid on autopilot. I'd made that drive innumerable times, and it always felt so good: the start of an adventure in one of the best places on the planet. Dave agreed; we'd made the drive many times together.

By the time I arrived at the Lake Placid Pub and Brewery to eat dinner, I'd settled into being alone. It felt good to be by myself, independent.

I liked to camp by myself, but I had only done it near my car. That night, I planned to hike a flat couple of miles to Marcy Dam, a popular camping spot where many High Peaks trails converge or originate. I wouldn't be near my car, but there would be other campers at the dozen campsites and lean-tos.

I planned to stay at the bar until the sun went down. I'd walked or skied the well-marked wide trail into Marcy Dam many times. I planned to follow it after dark to set up camp and go to sleep after a good meal and a beer.

Sitting at the bar, sipping IPA, my mind lost the original excitement of independence. I missed Dave. I missed my adventure partner and my love; I wanted him there with me. A flood of memories washed over me.

Shit, shit, shit. Lake Placid wasn't the same without Dave. He should've been with me, but he couldn't be. So maybe I should've stayed with him.

I tried to differentiate between having an adventure and running away.

I contemplated rushing home. Shouldn't I be spending every moment at his side? I knew it made a difference to him. I knew he missed me when I wasn't with him. I was sure he understood my intentions, my devotion. He was most content with me at his side.

Or should I practice being alone?

Weren't we also transcending time, space, and humanness together? Couldn't I practice being with Dave while I was alone? Here in Lake Placid, about to walk into the woods? Alone.

I almost cried. I held my breath and drank beer until I was pretty sure I wouldn't burst into tears.

Oh, my God, I felt so sad. I knew I was learning. My faith was growing. I believed. I believed Dave was evolving, moving to light. I believed I was with him despite time and space; we would always be connected.

But I felt so sad. Lake Placid couldn't cure it.

Lake Placid was Dave Zagorski. He was everywhere; he was everything.

I stuck to my plan. I paid my tab and stepped into the crisp not-quite-summer night air. I drove to the trailhead parking and hoisted my loaded pack onto my back.

My sorrows faded as I walked through the quiet woods with my headlamp lighting the way.

In no time, I arrived at Marcy Dam. Right away, I knew I wouldn't get a spot. There were tons of people, including an entire troop of Boy Scouts. I'd underestimated the popularity of the camping spot.

I kept walking. I picked the trail that led to Mount Marcy, but also to Phelps Mountain. I'd hiked Phelps a few years before and remembered it being an easy climb. I also remembered there was a campsite about halfway to the summit. Even if someone else was camped there, I could get away with setting up somewhere nearby. I liked feeling secure camping near other people, but I had no desire to hunker down with dozens of Boy Scouts.

The climb that once felt easy was strenuous in the dark with a heavy pack and a stomach filled with dinner and beer.

The campsite was just under a mile farther than Marcy Dam. It was empty. I'd be sleeping alone, three and a half miles from my car, near the summit of a High Peak. Pretty cool.

I set up my tent and sleeping gear, and then bushwhacked a few hundred yards away to stash my food in a bear canister.

I cozied into my tent and lay in the dark. I felt satisfied and sleepy.

I wondered if I should be scared, but easily decided I shouldn't. Another thing I was learning was that there's nothing to be scared of. The worst thing was already happening.

I fell asleep visualizing Dave at my side. I visualized my love as light, pouring from my heart as a bright beam and seeping from my skin as a hazy glow. In my mind's eye, the light enveloped me and Dave in a white cocoon, inside a woods cocoon, inside a sky cocoon.

"I'm with you, Davey," I said out loud.

He smiled next to me.

I slept soundly until the dawn. I crawled out of my dewy tent and into a sunrise glow that was thick and sparkly like the love light that had filled me up, connected me to Dave, and put me to sleep the previous night.

Coffee and breakfast fueled me as I set off on the trail. It was about four and a half miles from the campsite to the top of Mount Marcy. Judging from the map, I had about 2,400 more feet of elevation to gain to reach the 5,300 foot summit.

Ascending the highest Adirondack peak for the first time in my life was savory. Dave had always been enthusiastic about accomplishing the biggest or best feats. He always encouraged me to climb, hike, and adventure harder, higher, and farther.

We had many conversations over the years in which he'd challenge me to surpass adventures I considered hardcore enough.

One night, a year after we were married, I staggered into our apartment sore and tired.

"I got rained out of climbing, so I stopped and hiked Giant Mountain!" I proudly announced.

"Giant, huh? I never heard of it. How tall is it?" Dave demanded.

"It's 4,600 feet high! And it's steep as a motherfucker! You gain 3,300 feet in three and a half miles!" I barked.

"Yeah, hmph, but it's not the highest. Marcy is the highest."

"Giant is the twelfth highest," I groaned. "It's high enough, Davey!"

"You gotta go back and climb Marcy! Do the highest!" Dave playfully gibed.

I was never offended by these bantering debates. Dave didn't mean to undermine my accomplishments, only voice his confidence I could do more. Dave saw the best in me; he always let me know he admired me and stood behind me.

So, there I was: climbing the highest peak! I was doing it for Dave. Even in his weakened, frail state, Dave was a strong, encouraging force motivating me.

All the way, I did it for Dave. I did it because the worst thing was already happening to us. The worst thing was happening, Dave's brain was disintegrating, he was dying, I was losing my love. But, still, I was in the most beautiful place feeling peace and love and alive on Planet Earth.

In the months leading up to his death, besides speaking telepathically, Dave and I were connecting on other levels beyond normal human scope. We laughed hysterically at nothing, or more likely at something bigger than us we didn't quite get. We both knew things, understood things like never before. We were living on multiple levels at once. It was as if we were tripping, existing in a non-drug-induced psychedelic daze.

As Dave shifted between the worlds, I read and prayed a lot. I read about Buddhism, death, dying, and brain injuries. I prayed to Jesus, Yoda, Buddha, dead relatives, and the light. All of this was bringing me closer to the place between the worlds, too. I was letting go of my old life as a normal person and wife to Dave. I was morphing into a spiritual being and soul partner to Dave. I was laughing more, worrying less, and relinquishing (the illusion of) control.

One night, Dave and I saw something unearthly on our physical plane to match what had been going on in our minds for months. It happened in the bathroom while I was undressing Dave for a shower. He was leaning against the wall as I pulled his pants from his ankles one leg at a time.

As I stood up to face him and help him step into the tub, I saw what looked like faded snowflakes dancing all around us. Dave was wide-eyed and glancing side to side. We looked back and forth from each other's eyes to the sparkling glints filling the room. The floating shapes pulsed and oozed. They had a jellyfish-like opacity and fluidity. They stayed with us for a few minutes as we went about our business of getting into the shower.

Dave wasn't speaking at all about anything by this time, and I didn't verbalize the peaceful feeling or the sense we were in good company with the little light creatures. Instead, Dave and I had a complete mutual understanding about what was happening. We were both simultaneously mystified and unfazed.

That night was like any other in our whacked out lives. It was a reassurance about the choices we were making and the faith we were embracing. It was just another night in the bathroom with Dave.

In the winter, Heather had mailed me a book, Timothy Leary's *Design for Dying*, with a note that read, "Chris thought you should read this." I added the book to my bedside collection of survival manuals.

One night in June, I sat in bed next to sleeping Dave and paged through several books. I'd learned from Dave to just open a book randomly and receive a message. I opened *Design for Dying* to a chapter titled "Dying? Throw a House Party!"

Leary wrote, "When I learned that I was dying, I was thrilled... I posted a sign in my home, 'The Mother of All Parties.'"

He explains that he invited his friends to come visit, and advised, "Instead of treating the last act in your life in terms of fear, weakness, and helplessness, think of it as a triumphant graduation."

It was so cool that respected scientists, authors, and spiritual teachers had written works that perfectly articulated my experiences. Often, when I was weary and confused, I'd feel completely validated simply by opening one of these works. When I was doubtful that I was proceeding correctly, there was always documentation from a wise person to give an encouraging nod.

We would host our own "Mother of All Parties!"

Dave's character shone in his mute last months of life. Besides old, devoted friends, new friends were showing up to hang out with Dave.

Friends I worked with at the Ginger Man, who didn't know Dave before he was sick, were eager to spend time at the Mother of All Parties. We were really having fun. It was a good place to be. Dave's closeness to death didn't intimidate or scare anyone. People weren't coming over out of obligation; they were coming to hang out with a rock star.

One of my coworkers, Chrissy, relished repeating stories she'd heard while hanging out with Dave's crew. Her tales always began, "In the Legend of Dave Zagorski..." To her, Dave was a character of almost mythical stature. When she met Dave, he hadn't been diagnosed but was showing signs of brain damage. To those of us close to him, Dave seemed to be going through a particularly weird spell. To Chrissy, he was a hilarious, carefree nonconformist.

Chrissy fit right in at the Home for Waywards. She hung around enough to get a good dose of reminiscence about Dave's wild, hard-partying past. She saw videos of Dave and his friends in high school, and Super 8 footage from Dave's candle factory and recording studios. She saw the mounds of Dave's half-inch reel-to-reel tape, recording equipment, and musical instruments that littered our house.

She glimpsed Dave's past and character through friends' stories and our old pictures. His style was still intact—his clothes, haircut, mannerisms, and adorable face were the same as ever—but Dave couldn't speak or tune a guitar. What he did do was laugh, screech, cackle, and give hearty, loving slaps on the back or squeezes on the knee. He gave hand signals for "more beer" or "pass the joint." He smiled so big and bright! He radiated Daveness!

Old friends of mine who didn't know Dave well were visiting, too. Lisa, my dear friend since fifth grade, told me that my house was the most peaceful place she knew. After spending the day with us, she called to express her gratitude.

"I know it's hard. It's probably not always peaceful for you guys," she said. She checked that she wasn't offending me and then continued. "It feels so safe. It's like you're living in a Zen sanctuary. Visiting Dave is like going to a retreat, going away from the world's stress to a place where what really matters is happening: love and devotion."

Another line that struck me from Timothy Leary's book was "How you die will speak volumes about how you lived."

Dave's dying was a party. He was still attracting new friends and inspiring old friends. Dave was basking in good times and love.

Dave lived truthfully. He lived fully. He cared deeply for his loved ones and for people in general. He lived compassionately. *

His dying was speaking volumes about his beautiful life. His inspiring, memorable qualities seemed to be mirrored in the people and occurrences surrounding him as he died. Before he got sick, he'd taught us all so much through the example of his heartfelt, soulful way of life. As he died, those lessons ripened.

Dave was so weak he needed help to stand. Sometimes it would take two people and a walker to move him.

His grip stayed strong though. He liked holding hands and squeezing. He ground the knuckles and squished the fingers of many unsuspecting friends.

Kathy's presence as our aide allowed Dave to stay in. I didn't have to drag him with me on errands. He seemed relieved not to endure the hassle of using stairs and loading his weak body into the car.

On the first Tuesday in July, Dan called as he was leaving work.

"I just heard on the radio that there's a free rock show at Jillian's! It's starting for happy hour. There will be three good bands. I'm on my way there; we should all go!" Dan said.

"You mean, we should bring Dave?" I asked. I'd become so settled into the easy routine of staying home I hadn't considered an out-of-the-house adventure in weeks.

"*Yeah*, we should bring Dave! It's a beautiful day. There's a free show! That's what Zagorski's all about!" Dan reminded me.

I hung up and turned to inquisitive looking Frank and Dave.

"You guys want to go to a free rock show downtown?"

Frank looked at Dave with a knowing grin; Dave screeched a pterodactyl call.

The easiest way to get Dave out of the house was to sit him in the wheelchair so two of us could carry it down the front porch steps. We'd roll it up to the open car door and, with a lot of encouragement, Dave would stand and shift his weight to the car seat.

Sometimes Dave would get stuck. He'd be crouch-standing over the car seat and his knees would lock.

"Oh, David!" I'd say, "You gotta *sit*. You're not there yet."

He'd stare back at me and laugh. Sometimes he'd shrug. He couldn't control his body. He didn't want to be stuck.

So, to unstick him, I'd tickle his sides or push on the back of his knees. If that didn't work, I'd shield his head with one hand and with the other push his torso with all my might into the car.

He'd accompany my struggle with sound effects: a screech, growl, howl, or signature combination of all three.

That Tuesday, Dave's body was agreeable. Frank and I got him into the car with little effort. I drove us into the heart of downtown at rush hour. We found a huge parking space directly in front of Jillian's that was easy to nose into.

The double doors were wide open to the street, and there was a break in the curb. Wheeling Dave into the club was simple; we were—again—in the exact right place at the exact right time.

Murph and Dan were seated at the bar. They had prepped the bartender before our arrival. He happily shouted, "They made it!" as Frank rolled Dave up to the bar.

The bar had a low section, just the right height for a wheelchair.

I ordered beers for myself and Dave. Murph got a straw ready for Dave's beer and plunged it in as the bartender set it in front of him.

As usual, Dave was right at home.

Ambitious from Tuesday's outing, the crew rallied for a Fourth of July party that weekend. Friends of ours were hosting a serious bash at their country home surrounded by acres of rolling land and a spring-fed pond.

Mark, Dan, Murph, Frank, Dave, and I made the drive to the country equipped with reclining lawn chairs, camping and overnight supplies, and a half-keg of beer.

We arrived like a troupe of characters. To move the wheelchair over the rough ground, Mark and Dan picked it up and paraded Dave like royalty across the driveway and lawn. Frank and I carried the keg, and Murph's arms were loaded with paper bags holding snacks, plastic beer cups, and water balloons.

Dave surveyed the land and the party people with a casual glance, backed by his one-wife-four-wayward-boys entourage.

The day was grand! People we'd never met pulled chairs up to Dave and had casual—though one-sided—conversations with him. Dave drank beer and ate bits of all the offered food. He stayed awake and engaged.

The sun went down, and many guests left the party.

Frank and I set up my spacious four-person dome tent in the yard, next to the pond. The three of us fell fast asleep as soon as our heads hit the camp pillows.

Dave slept soundly between Frank and me.

Dave woke up fresh. Frank and I helped him to stand outside the tent. His bare feet were rooted in the ground as he took in the magnificent landscape. He was unwavering and strong. It was the first time in weeks he'd stood unassisted.

It felt as if we were on a piece of magic land that was energizing Dave. He was an extension of the Earth. He was every bit as self-sufficient and indestructible as the planet.

The following weekend, one of my oldest and dearest friends, Kristen, was passing through town. She made plans to stop by with her husband and two young sons.

Kristen hadn't seen Dave in years, since before he got sick. I wondered how she'd react. Dave's condition was shocking for someone who'd seen him earlier in the summer, let alone for someone who'd last seen him healthy and strong.

Dave was skin and bones, a skeletal frame; his ribs poked out over his nonexistent stomach, and his baggy clothes hung loose. His eyes bulged from his gaunt face. He was tired and often slumped over.

His laugh was weak, his movements slow.

Dave perked up having the kids around. He and Julian, the seven-month-old, locked eyes and practiced telepathy. It was easy for me to see the deep communication going on between the two because I'd experienced the same mode of communicating with Dave. Dave and Julian stared, smiled, and squealed at one another. A subtle shift in Dave's eyes would cause Julian to explode with giggles.

Evan, the two-and-a-half-year-old, entertained us with his precocious piano skills and inspired Dave to accompany him with drumming. Evan motivated Dave. Dave had always loved sharing music with kids. Even in his emaciated, weakened state, he was getting and giving an inspired surge of artistic energy interacting with Evan. It was awesome.

Dave hardly ate. I'd try to feed him anything I was eating to encourage his appetite. For weeks, he'd mostly turned his head away from food, but I could usually count on him eating certain candies and fruits.

The day Kristen and her family visited, Dave was ravenous for cherries. Along with cold cuts and salads, there was a huge bowl of fresh cherries on the table.

While everyone else ate sandwiches, I fed Dave cherries. I bit into each one to remove the pit. This was the quickest and easiest way to deliver them to Dave.

Later, Kristen and I talked in the kitchen.

"I'll never forget how you fed Dave cherries today," she said. "You're making sure he enjoys every little detail of his life. It's a tiny example of this huge lesson on love you're giving everyone who knows you."

I'd been concerned that Dave's condition would disturb Kristen and her family. I was so happy to hear that, instead, she saw what was most important and real to Dave and me—our love.

It was meaningful that even someone fairly far removed from Dave's dying experience was touched by it, that something as simple as a cherry could broadcast love.

Dissolving into Light

In the middle of July, I came home from waiting tables, exhausted and discouraged. Mark was sitting on the sofa watching TV. Dave's hospital bed was against the wall next to the sofa. He was half-sleeping, eyes partially open. I leaned over him and his eyes shifted to glance at me, but didn't focus.

My heart ached. I felt rotten; a sickness in my stomach and heart was painfully eating its way out from the inside. The ache in my heart pulsed through me and down my legs. I collapsed to my knees regularly, sometimes crying, sometimes screaming, sometimes praying.

I managed to stay standing while I made a pronouncement to Mark.

"I can't do this anymore," I said. "This is killing me. How am I supposed to live like this?"

Mark responded with his characteristic inhale and pursed lips. He raised a hand in weak gesture to near-comatose Dave.

"You won't be doing it much longer," he said.

"Really? You *really* think he's going to die?" I asked, still shrinking under the gravity of my day-to-day life.

I felt as if Dave could hold on forever. He was so tough, so determined, so stubborn. Even mostly confined to bed, Dave was still lively. His life force was strong.

"Yes. Yes. This won't go on for much longer," Mark repeated with calm confidence.

He was Dave's best friend, after all. He was wise and observant.

His words whooshed me back to reality.

I spent a lot of time trying to maintain what I *thought* was reality. Or, maybe, what I thought was supposed to be reality. What was normal, what was expected, what was *real life*. But more and more, as Dave approached death, the deeper, truer reality appeared. The holy-shit-*this*-is-what-our-lives-are-about reality.

I was investing a lot of energy into maintaining life while Dave died. I had to paint my house. I had to make enough money to pay the mortgage and keep my health insurance. I'd have these break-through moments when I'd let go of the drive to be normal. I'd accept what was really happening. Money, obligations, and the head-strong compulsion to keep it all together would dissolve.

Oh yeah: my love is *dying*. He won't be here on Planet Earth much longer. I'm not in control of the ride. Paying bills, balancing the checkbook, changing my oil—all these things may be important when your husband isn't lying in a hospital bed borrowed from hospice, unable to focus his eyes on you but still shining love through his every pore.

Dave was dying, and the God force inhabited our space. Wisdom and truth were oozing from Dave's condition. He was dissolving into light from his pure-love heart.

So, this was it. The End.

I reread my favorite parts of *The Tibetan Book of Living and Dying*. I was practicing the Phowa every day with Dave.

Sometimes I'd let him know I was sending him to light, and other times I'd meditate next to him or in the next room.

Throughout each day, I lit Tibetan incense for meditation and a clean environment, and candles on the hospital tray next to Dave's bed. I lit candles and incense on the altar. I'd chant "Om Mani Padme Hum" to the Buddha of Compassion and "Om Ami Dewa Hrih" to the Buddha of Limitless Light.

Dave and I spent many hours staring at each other. The house was bright with radiant light. Dave was radiating light.

Hospice was sending someone to the house almost every day. There was a nurse, a chaplain, a social worker, and a bunch of volunteers who'd check in to see if we needed groceries or prescriptions.

We were surrounded by help. We were surrounded by peace. Tibetan lama Sogyal Rinpoche writes, "Death can be very inspiring." I took that to heart. We existed in sacred time. Dave's dying was filling us with comfort.

All of his visitors were having a ball hanging out with Dave—even if he couldn't speak, couldn't walk, and would barely eat. His eyes were clear and bright. He smiled big, he laughed, he squeezed hands.

The people visiting from hospice were able to get to know Dave. Without words, he could convey his Daveness. He continued to impress and be lovable.

The last months of Dave's life really did become "The Mother of All Parties." People and love filled our home. We partied like we were kids, like nothing mattered but the time we were sharing together.

Many of Dave's and my friends and family visited. I had an open-door policy. Dave came with a crew. He had many, many friends from all times in his life. He was always making connections and new friends. Our lives together had always been filled with great people.

No one missed the opportunity to see Dave before he exited Planet Earth. Everyone was invited to "The Mother of All Parties."

Dave's bed was in the living room. A sofa, love seat, and six wooden dining room chairs surrounded it. The bed was on wheels, so it could be moved to be in the prime spot. We'd roll Dave into the dining room if everyone was eating. We'd pull the bed into the center of the room if we needed to fit more people.

Besides the flux of random visitors, Dave and I had steady support from a few very special friends. Chris and Heather regularly made the drive from Woodstock to spend a day with us. Eve, one of my best friends since high school, was driving three hours from Syracuse almost every weekend. Frank was ever-present. Though he lived a plane ride away, he was always available and often at the house. The guest room became Frank's room. The Aunties spent many days and evenings, and some vigilant overnights, at Dave's side, enveloping him with motherly love and security.

Early in the last week of Dave's life, the hospice nurse, Shirley, told me Dave was probably not going to live through the weekend. She was the expert. I was confident that she understood the timeline.

I still couldn't see the subtleties of Dave's decline. He was so alive. He was *so* alive. He was so strong and so himself. I took hearing his voice for granted. Despite his muteness, I could hear his voice. He spoke to me with his eyes, and our hearts and souls were so deeply connected that we no longer needed words.

He was shifting into the final stages of dying, yet my connection with Dave was deeper than ever. We were closer than I knew was possible. So, they—Mark, Shirley, many of our guests—told me Dave was very close to death, and I understood that they were probably right, but what I knew was how alive Dave was. We were both the same amount of alive; we were alive together.

I'd read a lot over the year that I knew Dave was dying. I learned about the dying process from first-hand accounts and spiritual masters. I had a pile of fresh reading material from hospice. I'd learned so much directly from Dave. He was calm; he had released control. Mostly. There was a part of him that still held on. How could someone with so much life, someone as huge as Dave, just let go?

We—the boys upstairs and the close crew—all agreed, in a mostly unspoken way, that we had to let Dave go. We were holding on to him, keeping the party going. Dave was still fading away. The ALD was eating his brain. His body was exhausted. The life force in Dave, flowing from Dave, filling the house, was so strong that we were all brimming with it.

In the end, we needed to make a conscious effort to let Dave go. Through his death journey, I was learning that death was not the end. I was learning first-hand about how closely the worlds of life and death were linked. Both were real and constant. Everyone would inhabit both realms. We were connected and always would be. So, it was OK for him to die. It was OK to let him go. Letting him go would set him free. He was—we are—going someplace bigger and better.

Dave hadn't been eating. He wasn't even drinking very much. The day after Shirley told me Dave wouldn't make it another week, I ordered a bunch of sushi. Murph, Mark, and Dan were hanging out; the Aunties were over. Dave's bed was positioned near the dining room table, where we were all picking from the sushi that had been delivered.

Murph decided that Dave should partake with us. He offered Dave a piece of California roll. Dave's mouth opened wide. He smiled and snickered as he chewed the rice roll. After he swallowed, he opened his mouth at Murph like a baby bird. Dave was a bottomless pit; he accepted piece after piece of sushi.

It was joyous to watch Dave eat with such enthusiasm. He was indulging. He was enjoying his humanness. The group gathered at his bedside cheered him as he ate. We were thrilled to see him nourished and enjoying the food.

Later that day, I went to an acupuncture session with Ruth. She'd just returned from a workshop about how to help dying people. She emphasized that those close to Dave needed to let him know it was OK to go. This wasn't news to me, but hearing it from Ruth really drove the point home.

She'd learned techniques to guide and reassure the dying. She offered to visit Dave.

On Wednesday, Ruth came to the house. Mark, Murph, and I left Dave's bedside to let Ruth move in. The afternoon light was softly surrounding as we drove to the Biergarten. None of the three of us wanted to leave Dave; time with him was precious. We were quiet as we drove, in a sort of gooey slow motion.

At the bar, I sat between the boys, protected and comforted by my brothers. We were on a special mission. Leaving Dave with Ruth was a kind of ceremony, a step in the dying process, in the letting go. Drinking beers together at the comfy bar in the afternoon was an exercise for the three of us; we stepped away from hanging on to Dave toward acceptance.

Visitors were calm and always caught the peaceful vibe. Thursday night, the small group that gathered around Dave was particularly in tune with one another. We all sat close, smiling and sharing little bits of jokes and stories between long stretches of silence. The light was low and air was thick with incense. The house was an oasis. Things inside moved slowly and lovingly. The friends gathered around Dave were soothed by one another's presence and Dave's peacefulness.

Dave was mostly sleeping, with minutes of wakefulness here and there. He hadn't eaten in two days and was only taking water with a swab. We all knew he was close to dying.

I sat next to Dave. The night felt romantic. It felt exactly right. I knew Dave was content: surrounded by good friends and music. The poetry of those moments made me think of Charles Bukowski— Dave's favorite author. It seemed romantically appropriate to read poetry while Dave lay dying. It was Dave's style; I knew he'd appreciate it.

I could picture him, alive and well, joking in his light, hilarious way.

"One day, if I'm sick and dying in my bed," I could see him saying, "I want everybody hanging out having a good time. Drinking good beer, listening to Tom Waits, and reading some dark, dirty Bukowski!"

My bookshelves were stocked with plenty of Bukowski short stories and novels, but no poetry. So, I went to the computer and searched the Internet to come up with a complete list of Bukowski's poems. The beauty of a book is paging through to find the perfect read. Without a book, I selected poems based on the intrigue of their titles.

I picked "Alone With Everybody" and "Are You Drinking" based on titles alone; both seemed fitting for the group.

Then I remembered Mark and Heather's fascination with the number 27. Dave and I were married on September 27, and I was starting to buy into the 27-as-a-meaningful-number thing. Without reading it, I selected the twenty-seventh poem from the complete list as my third choice.

I printed the three poems and brought them to Adam.

As Adam paged through the print outs and cleared his throat, our cat, Abby, made a rare appearance. She walked into the room and right over to Dave's bed. She stared up at him sleeping and shifted her weight on her back legs. It looked as if she was about to jump up on the bed. This would have been completely out of character for Abby, so we all noticed and were captivated watching her.

Adam read "Alone With Everybody" and "Are You Drinking" first. We nodded our approval and commented that each felt appropriate.

Then, Adam started "Confession."

We all gasped when he read the first line—Bukowski compares the wait for death to the suspenseful pause we had just witnessed, of a cat getting ready to jump on a bed.

Adam read on. Bukowski imagines his own death, describing his lifeless body. He's not worried about dying, just about his wife being left with his body. So he writes some compensation into the poem—he wants her to know he has the highest regard for their life together, even the hard parts. He ends the poem by telling her what he found hard to say in life: "I love you."

I squeaked at the last line. Tears seeped from my eyes. It was as if Dave opened a book, turned the page to "Confession" and recited those words.

And even Abby—our cat since our early days—was in on it. Everything in the poem echoed what we were living, but the cat jumping on the bed part was just uncanny.

When his brain was intact, speaking the words "I love you" wasn't hard or fearsome for Dave. Now, his brain damage made it impossible for him to deliver those words to me. Though Dave's eyes spoke "I love you" to me many times, I still longed to *hear* him say those words. Through this synchronistic poetry reading, Dave communicated. I was sure of it. I heard him say "I love you." That night, after months of his muteness leaving me longing to hear him utter those three simple words, I felt as if I heard Dave's voice.

Friday, out-of-town friends arrived. The close crew that had been present for much of the yearlong party was assembling.

Jay called from Portland. He told me he'd known his August visit would be the last time he'd see Dave alive. He wasn't worried about Dave, he was checking on me. He told me he was checking as my friend and as a duty to Dave.

"Dave wants me to make sure you're OK, Amelia." Jay's intention was a comfort; I felt reassurance.

"I'm confused," I confessed to my far-away soul brother. "I know I'm supposed to be letting him go. I want to make his transition as easy as possible. But I want to crawl into his bed and hold on to him."

"I just got back from an ayahuasca ceremony," Jay said, referring to a hallucinogenic brew usually consumed under a shaman's care.

"I saw Dave there," he continued, "on the other side. He told me he's been living between the worlds for a while and is ready to leave Earth. He told me he'd be there to guide the rest of us when it's our turn to go; he's content to be the first."

Jay's far-fetched medicine-induced tale was music to my ears. It felt right and true.

"Do whatever you want to, Amelia, do what feels good," Jay instructed. "Dave is ready to go; your love will transcend when he leaves this body."

I hung up the phone and crawled into bed with Dave, in the living room, in front of our gathered friends. It felt amazing.

By Saturday, the house was full. Norm, one of Dave's best friend's from college, was staying upstairs. Frank and Eve were in each of the downstairs bedrooms. Many other friends and family stopped in during the day.

Dave's brother and mother spent hours at his side. Dave had always been close with and protective of his older brother. I knew Rick was one of Dave's hardest goodbyes.

Rick and I talked in the kitchen. I urged him to let Dave know he'd be OK, that he was ready for Dave to let go. I thought it was important that everyone give well wishes to Dave for his journey.

He'd been through so much, he'd taught us so much, and now it was time to go.

Rick and Dave were both headstrong and rebellious. Neither would take no for an answer. I'd worried that Rick would fight Dave's death, that he wouldn't want to let his brother go. I was wrong. Rick wanted Dave to be at peace.

Together, we went back to Dave.

"Brother, I don't want you to suffer. You can go now, Dave; it's OK to stop fighting," Rick encouraged Dave.

"We'll be all right, Davey," I said.

Dave looked at us with his ever-clear eyes and nodded.

I dropped a Kris Kristofferson record on the turntable. It was a family favorite. The comforting sound of "Me and Bobby McGee" washed over us like warm whiskey.

True to form, the crew partied Saturday night. We ate and drank, laughed and cried. We took turns sitting on the bed with Dave.

Scott was scheduled to arrive from Portland in the afternoon, but hadn't shown up by nighttime. Scott was the last of Dave's tight group of brothers to visit and say goodbye. He'd grown up with Dave; they'd been in a band together for years.

By 10:30 p.m., I was exhausted. Dave had been dozing for much of the day, and his moments of wakefulness were dwindling. I wanted to sleep with my husband. I asked everyone to leave and move the party upstairs.

After the apartment cleared out, and the room was silent, Dave opened his eyes wide at me. I sat up, leaning over him.

"Oh, David, I love you so, so much," I sighed.

Dave lifted his head from the pillow and rubbed his nose to mine for the sweetest nose-kiss of all time. He stared into my eyes. He was aware, awake, and present.

Around midnight, Scott arrived. I crawled out of the bed and up the stairs to give Scott time with Dave.

Upstairs, I sat with Norm, almost too exhausted to be coherent, and explained how right everything felt. The friends who had arrived were connected by a perfect blend of energy and love. Every song that played while the stereo was on random mode felt like a message from Dave.

Norm and I had only met a handful of times over the years, and we weren't close. Our talk on the couch was a manifestation of the exact point I was trying to make. We were in the right place at the right time. Norm told me how Dave always made it clear how much he cared for and loved me. It meant so much to hear this from Norm.

I slept beside Dave until 7 a.m. Sunday, when his panting woke me up. He wasn't able to get a full breath. I held Dave's head and kissed him. He looked at me with awareness. I reassured him with words; he reassured me with his eyes.

I spoke us through the Phowa practice. I told Dave to dissolve into the light. I told him, "It's all true."

One of Dave's favorite stories involved Sheila and her husband, Dick. After Dick's death, Sheila got word from a relative who had spoken to a medicine man. The medicine man had seen Dick in a dream. Dick wanted Sheila to get the message, "It's all true." Sheila and Dick had agreed whoever died first would find a way to communicate if what they believed about the afterlife was true.

The closer Dave was to death, the more I felt it all really was true. My faith was growing.

Holding Dave as he died was amazing. Our bodies slipped away and into each other. Everything I'd practiced from *The Tibetan Book of Living and Dying* was serving me. The Phowa practice was bringing cosmic light into the room, into me, into Dave. The dead people I'd visualized and described to Dave as smiling at us and shining light were light bodies surrounding us in those moments.

I felt complete comfort and great peace. Dave's eyes were steady and loving. Everything was perfect.

The last three breaths Dave took were profound. I knew they were the last. He was light. He was love.

I walked across the dimly lit living room and dining room to the altar. I lit incense and candles and prayed, "Om Mani Padme Hum" and "Om Ami Dewa Hrih."

After twenty minutes, the rooms filled with tremendous light. The sun had burned through the morning clouds and came blazing through the windows.

I woke up the boys upstairs. I called family and friends. I wanted to keep Dave at home for the day so people could see him before he was cremated. I'd wait until everyone who wanted to visit had the chance.

In the early afternoon, Sugar Shack Mike called. He told me he woke up thinking of Dave and me.

"Dave appreciates everything you've done for him," he said, as if he'd just had a conversation with Dave and was relaying an important message.

People filed in throughout the day. Some stayed a while, sitting on the sofa next to Dave's bed. Some just peeked in. Some joined me in chanting or praying.

At one point, I stepped onto the front porch to look at the day outside my house. Molly—the eight-year-old who lived across the street—saw me right away and squealed.

"Amelia, Amelia, Amelia!" she yelled. "Come here! Look at my drawing!"

I crossed the street and walked into her enthusiastic bear hug. Molly pointed to her sidewalk chalk drawing. She'd drawn herself holding hands with Dave. Flowers surrounded them, and a hand-trace turkey stood next to them.

"I was very sad, and crying in my bedroom," she said, "because Dad told me Dave died."

She knelt and sketched a little as she talked.

"But then I looked out the window, and Dave was looking down at me," she said. "Dave said, 'Don't cry, Molly,' and he gave me a smile. So I knew I didn't have to be sad! And I came out here to draw."

By evening, the house had cleared out. Heather and Chris arrived. They had spent the day traveling from Cape Cod. I asked Heather to help me wash Dave's body before the funeral director took him away. We both wanted to honor the Buddhist traditions of cleaning the body and allowing it to sit for as long as possible to assure a smooth transition.

While the crew stayed upstairs, Heather and I brought cooking pots filled with warm, soapy water to Dave's bedside. We played Dave's music on the stereo and washed his body.

While I tenderly swept Dave's body with the warm washcloth, Heather massaged her fingers through his hair and over his face. I shaved the stubble from his chin.

Heather combed Dave's clean hair, trying to lay it flat. His unruly hair kept flopping to the side. We laughed at the imperfection, the untamable personality the hair was taking on. Finally, Heather set the comb down with a satisfied sigh. As she did, Dave's voice came through the speakers. The song that had just played was a live track, and Dave wrapped it up with a gracious "thank you."

Heather left me alone with Dave. I crawled into bed with him for the last time. I hugged and kissed him and cried.

Upstairs, I cried more, this time in the arms of my living friends. We opened beers and toasted to the immortal Dave Zagorski. Dave had only just passed his thirty-seventh birthday on Planet Earth, but he'd live forever in our minds.

Eve, Frank, Heather, Chris, Mark, Dan, Norm, and I took our beers downstairs. Mark and Norm presented me with a bottle of Veuve Clicquot—my favorite champagne, and appropriately, named for a widow. We sat around Dave's bed, sipping champagne and listening to music.

"When I woke up this morning 'We're Gonna Rise' was in my head," Eve said. "It was the first conscious thought I had. I was awakened by the room brightening with sudden sun."

I played the Breeders song. Layers of female vocals hum over simple guitar notes, except for one screechy guitar and wild drumming crescendo. The lyrics lament that beliefs, rules, and strategies are inconsequential, yet light shines and peace prevails. The song was the perfect blend of melancholy and acceptance.

"That's how I feel," Eve said with wide, teary eyes.

"Play '200 Bars,'" Chris said. "Dave loved that song."

I cued the Spiritualized song next. A steady rhythm builds as a woman's monotone voice slowly counts from one to 200. As she nears 200, the instrumentation grows more complex and intense. Vocals explode, confessing confusion, losing track of time, and feeling used and tired.

"That's a good one," Chris said with a wise smile.

After we spent an hour savoring the company and music in profound moments of time, the funeral director arrived. We toasted over Dave's body one last time. Then he was taken away to be burned.

Part Three

Vortex of Emptiness

Dave died. It happened. It happened and I was strangely OK. I was acutely aware of my aliveness. I had an easy sense that Dave wanted it that way.

Frank had an idea of what Dave wanted, too.

Two days after Dave died, after we finished planning the "celebration of life" ceremony for the following weekend, Frank made a suggestion.

"Wanna go to DiCarlo's tonight?" he ventured as we walked the six blocks from my house to where we were meeting friends for dinner.

"Uh, *yeah*," I replied with a giggle.

DiCarlo's was the classiest of the local strip clubs.

"Remember that first time I came to visit after Dave got sick?" Frank said. "I got the distinct impression he wanted to do something nice for you. He wanted to show you he appreciated you. He wasn't talking much, but he still managed to communicate, you know?

"So I asked him what he wanted to do for you. I listed ideas: take you to dinner, take you to a movie, buy you a present, buy you a plane ticket. He just shrugged or rolled his eyes at each of my suggestions. Until I said, 'strippers.'

"Then he went nuts, nodding and smiling and slapping my back.

"So, I know he wants you to go enjoy a strip show! You get whatever you want now, Amelia. You ready for a wild night?"

Dave and I had been enjoying strip shows together from the early stages of our relationship. On our first trip to Montreal, the $35 per night hotel we stayed in was in the heart of the sex shops, arcades, and strip clubs.

Dave and I never hesitated to live it up or indulge in what a place had to offer us. We were both open-minded and loved to see each other have a good time. So, strippers were cool by us. And—in typical Dave style—he'd inevitably make friends with the performers.

That night at DiCarlo's, I felt invigorated. I felt doubly alive. I was living to honor Dave. I was hyper-aware of my experience, the richness of life on Planet Earth. I was grateful for the opportunity to indulge in human pleasure, the appreciation of the human body. And beer and good friends. Mary was in town from Florida, and she and Frank bought me limitless lap dances. In proper Dave-style, we made friends with our favorite dancers.

I talked to two dancers, Evonka and Russia, about my missing husband. I explained how each interaction I was having wasn't just for my pleasure but also on Dave's behalf.

After the strip club, the logical next step for living richly to honor Dave was to go see a rock 'n' roll show. Thursday, I drove Jeff and myself to New York City.

Manhattan felt soft without Dave. The noise sounded muted to my mourning ears. The ebb and flow of traffic and people blurred around me. I was cushioned by the fast moving life buzzing by. The city soothed me by sweeping me along into its flow, a flow that Dave had savored. Without him, I soaked in Manhattan for the both of us.

In the days after Dave's death, life was easy. Nothing mattered. I couldn't make any mistakes; I couldn't go wrong. I was close to the Light. I was lodged in the present. Everything was OK. Living close to death, watching my love's body fail, had somehow liberated me. I felt unafraid and buoyant. I had been through years of heartache that ended with the greatest loss imaginable, and still I was OK. I was alive and joyful and grateful, and poised on the brink of the rest of my life.

I thought a lot about Jesus and Obi-Wan Kenobi.

Obi-Wan's words, "If you strike me down, I shall become more powerful than you can imagine," took on new meaning. Dave was still with me. I knew it; I felt him. And Dead Dave was more powerful and ever-present than Alive Dave could have been.

Jeff and I met up with our friend Lisa and pranced around the bright city—digging the people and sights—until the sun went down and we found our way to the club where The National was playing.

The National was a band whose music I was introduced to after Dave and I separated.

I loved them at first listen. Their emotive guitars and melancholy lyrics were a soundtrack to my heartbreak. Their rocking edge and full, enveloping sound were a soundtrack to my survival. Some of their lyrics were about Dave and me.

When Dave and I had been broken up, lines from "Apartment Story" swelled my heart with longing and my head with memories. The song describes a couple's beliefs plummeting headfirst from a high-up secure place. The tone is heartrending yet hopeful. The couple is together "behind the couch" and is going to be all right. The "behind the couch" line struck me in an undeniably personal way.

When Dave and I were still a new couple, in our early twenties, we stayed the night at a friend's apartment in Queens after a party. We slept on the floor behind the couch in a living room full of other partying kids. In the morning, as everyone woke up and sat around the living room drinking coffee and recapping the previous night, Dave and I secretly made love. That's what the National song is about: me and Dave behind the couch.

And then—in the broken up time—everything we believed *was* plummeting. It hurt. That music sounded like my pain.

The National stayed with me, the music soothing me at times and helping me cry at others.

The band was touring to support their latest album, one with lots of tearjerker songs that seemed to be written for a young widow.

The song "Sorrow" summed it up best. The singer pleads to not be left alone, but wants to dwell in broken-heartedness and not move past a lost relationship.

Listening to The National that night at the club, I started sobbing during the first chorus of the first song. I didn't stop crying when the concert ended and the music stopped. The lights came up, but I was frozen in my darkness. My make-up stained cheeks left stains on Jeff and Lisa's shoulders as they tried to console me while hundreds of people spilled past us out of the club.

That Friday, I made it back to Albany in time to receive out-of-town guests. Dave's and my best friends showed up on my doorstep one by one.

The Mother of All Parties continued. The theme was love. And joy. Because Dave was love and joy. Together, Dave's friends and family basked in love-joy. I was surrounded by the coolest people I knew, and together, we were surrounded by light and the spirit of Dave.

The full house stayed up late, catching up and reminiscing. Friends and family from all over the country joined the locals.

In the morning we drove in convoy to Saint Agnes chapel.

High windows lit the little room attached to the crematory. Swirling dust particles sparkled in streams of sunlight. We hung prayer flags and poster boards decorated with pictures of Dave. The exotic flowers I ordered earlier in the week had been delivered and placed around the room. Their bright colors pulsed in the soft glow. The scene was set. The room was spectacular.

Almost 200 people squeezed in and spilled from the chapel.

Sheila led the celebration-of-life ceremony. There was a lot of crying but there was much more laughter.

Dave's friends and family told hilarious stories. Everyone who spoke said Dave had changed their lives. Dave was a walking, breathing lesson. His pranks and antics liberated us! He taught us by living in a way that put fun and love above everything else. He showed us what was important. He was genuine and truthful. He really lived in the now, without trying or talking about it.

The hilarious stories were uncensored despite the multigenerational audience. They were as real as Dave—unapologetic and shocking.

Chris told the story of meeting Dave for the first time on their college campus. They took LSD together within hours of meeting and unfolded universal secrets and truths for the rest of the day.

Chris recalled ruefully that Dave had taken him to a place much better than normal.

The last speaker was Jay, beloved friend and the drummer for Dave's band. Jay had been learning guitar and practicing Dave's songs. He played "Pablo Azul," and it was so beautiful.

It was beautiful to hear Dave's music played for a gathering of people who loved him so dearly. It was beautiful that Jay learned the song in tribute and honor to Dave. It was beautiful that I could see Dave in Jay and feel Dave in the music. There he was! Still with us on Planet Earth—just in a new way.

Dave had been influencing us all since the moments we met him. He'd been bringing us together and creating life parties, and he'd continue to do so—even in death.

That night, after everyone had wandered off to sleep, Jay and I stayed awake. We touched hands with eyes closed, and I felt energy flow between us that caused our fingers to pulse. Just as when he played Dave's song, I felt Dave in Jay then.

I thought, "Just like Jay is Dave to me, I'm Dave to Jay." We both embodied our friend's spirit. We comforted one another by bringing Dave close and inviting his spirit into us.

Feeling Jay's grief eased my pain. We had both loved Dave so deeply; we were both so impacted by our loss. Part of me wished for a special grief because Dave was *my* partner. Part of me wanted to keep the pain to myself. Dave was mine!

A bigger part of me knew that sharing love, sharing Dave, sharing pain was far more beautiful because it was right and true. We are all the same; we are all united. Holding pain and not sharing Dave was selfish, ego bullshit. If we let go of the ego, we find peace.

Our friend Shawn was known for making paper cut-outs. After Dave's funeral ceremony, Shawn left a chain of paper robots taped to my back door with the words "thank you" written, one letter on each figure. I was touched by this gesture. Gratitude was one of the greatest truths and lessons we all learned.

Over the next few days, everyone left to go back to their lives in other places. Everyone left me with love. Just as I was grateful for the presence of friends throughout my life with Dave and through Dave's dying, those friends were grateful for Dave and me sharing our love and sharing our lives. Thank you was the theme; mutual appreciation enveloped our group of souls.

I knew I wasn't ready to go back to life. I wasn't even sure what my life was. What was I doing if not caring for and living with Dave?

Work was out of the question. Fortunately, I had money saved and could afford to float along for a few months.

I was eager to go outside. As always, I craved adventure. I longed to go rock climbing. I set up an Adirondack rendezvous with Sugar Shack Mike.

A week after the funeral ceremony, I met Mike at one of our favorite camping spots in a grassy clearing next to a rushing brook.

I arrived in the evening to Mike's established campsite. He had a huge pile of wood set near the fire ring and a rock table built to accommodate a stove and kitchenware.

Mike welcomed me to my home away from home in the woods.

We picked through Mike's assortment of fresh fruit, granola, crackers, and cheese as we paged through our guidebooks and discussed climbing options for the following morning.

I felt like a wounded animal. I was injured and weak, but I was safe and being cared for.

We rose early and set out to our climbing destination. I was eager to climb. I was eager to reclaim my adventure-girl lifestyle.

Climbing was my passion, my most favorite way to spend my time. I thought it was what my sick heart needed.

We started on an easy climb, one I'd normally cruise up without difficulty.

After ten minutes and fifty feet of climbing, I cried. I felt scared and incompetent. I felt lonely. Rock climbing was *my* thing. It was the thing I loved to do, the thing I did independently. It should heal me, not hurt. But, as in every other thing and place in my life, Dave was missing from it. Rock climbing sucked without Dave on Planet Earth.

At first, I sniffled to myself. I thought I could get it together and finish the climb. Minutes passed as I shook and shuddered.

"Are you OK, Amelia?" Mike called from his belay spot on the ground below me.

I moaned in answer. If I opened my mouth, I knew I'd sob.

"What's up? Is it hard climbing?" Mike questioned.

I moaned again.

"You're totally safe. It looks like you have good gear there. Do you want to take a hang on the rope?" Mike made common reassurances and suggestions for a struggling climber.

I composed myself enough to say, "It's not the climb!" before I exploded with squeals and choking sobs.

I held on to the rock face as I cried. I felt the rope tightening me to the wall where it attached to the gear I'd placed to keep me safe.

Mike was pulling the rope tight to secure me so I could hang and lower to the ground. This process is one that climbing partners usually discuss, but Mike and I had climbed together long enough to trust the system and each other. We both knew I needed the ground.

I slumped onto the rope like a beat up old doll, my head rolling side to side as I gulped through sobs. Mike lowered me to the security of the ground.

Instead of touching down with my feet, my legs buckled and my ass touched the earth. I looked up at Mike.

"How am I supposed to live without Dave?" I asked.

Mike put his arm around me as he sat beside me. He undid the rope from my harness and sat in silent solidarity.

Mike offered me water and a bandana handkerchief.

If I was a wounded animal, Mike was the kindest wildlife rehabilitator in the land.

In his sanctuary, I was consoled.

After I collected myself, Mike finished the route I'd attempted. I followed the climb with the security of a top rope. I didn't have to place gear to protect the route, and there was no risk of falling farther than the stretch in the rope tied to my harness.

I should've moved to the top with ease; the route was well within my ability.

Instead, I struggled through every move. My body felt infected with a debilitating illness. My muscles felt atrophied, my blood felt thick and dirty in my veins. I couldn't get an oxygenating breath. I fell limp on the rope several times. I wasn't strong enough to climb the ladder-like hand and foot holds. With each movement, I groaned like someone injured.

I made it to the top of the climb, removing Mike's gear as I went so we could be done with the climb.

Back at camp, I apologized to Mike.

"You drove all this way. The weather is perfect. I wish we could climb, but I just can't. I'm sorry."

"It's OK, Amelia. I realize now we shouldn't be climbing anyway. We should honor Dave. Doing nothing is OK. Things are different. We shouldn't expect anything to feel normal."

So, we honored Dave. We didn't need to climb. Instead, we sat. We walked in the woods. We swam. We sat with the rocks and trees. We skipped stones in the still spots on the brook. We were aware of our loss. Life didn't need to go along as we'd planned on that weekend.

That night, Mike built a sweat hut. He put big rocks on the fire to heat up. He constructed a dome with tree branches, and covered the branches with tarps to make an enclosure. The hut was just high enough for us to crawl into.

After several hours, Mike put the superhot rocks in the middle of the hut. He poured water over them to fill the hut with hot steam.

We sat in the wet, penetrating heat. After a while, Mike left me alone. I sat and, as I chanted, the tangible world disintegrated. The steam enveloped me and drew me at once into the ground and up to the sky.

Time and space disappeared. I was alone in the universe. I felt complete emptiness inside me and around me. Losing Dave had opened a vortex of emptiness.

I imploded, and everything felt right again. I sensed the vastness around me. The vastness became me. It comforted me.

The sweat hut gave me an awareness of the emptiness enveloping me, and a comfort from knowing I could fill that emptiness. The emptiness hurt brutally, but the consolation was that it could be filled. Anything could happen. Just as the most unimaginable bad thing had occurred, the most unimaginable good thing could be waiting for me.

I wanted to be alone in the weeks after Dave died. The exception to my solitude was Heather and Chris. They'd been living with Chris's brain cancer for four years. They dwelled close to death. They offered support and comfort no one else could give because of their life circumstances.

I spent many days and nights at Chris and Heather's place in Woodstock. Dave and I had spent a lot of time there during his illness, and it had always been a sanctuary for us.

Heather and I were inextricably connected by the similarities of our hardships, as were Chris and Dave. Brain diseased Chris spent a lot of time in the between-the-worlds place.

One night, Heather invited me to see a performer named Jackie Greene at the theater down the road from her house. I didn't know Jackie Greene's music, but I trusted Heather, and I longed to be near her and Chris.

The show was otherworldly. The roll 'n' roll swirl was intoxicating. Jackie Greene music made me feel close to Dave music. A cute boy playing guitar is universal: Jackie Greene was Dave on stage. He entered my heart on behalf of Dave. Music tells universal, cosmic truth and unifies the living and the dead.

I conversed with Dave in my head. I asked him to choose a new lover for me when the time came.

Heather and I went out to smoke on the patio. A bright green bug landed on my plastic beer cup and rode back inside with me. He climbed from the cup to my arm. Heather and I put our hands and arms together to let the bug crawl between us. Finally, he stayed on me—climbing up my neck and through my hair. That bug was Dave.

He hung out on my head to give me messages through my music-infused, stoned and drunk haze. I had visions of alien beings procreating, fucking by touching forms to one another, by inserting spiny tubes up vertebrae. I was blessed with peaceful knowledge that infinite beings and experiences exist in our loving universe.

The next day, I sat with Chris under the picnic table umbrella in his sunny backyard. I told him I was considering an open-ended road trip out West. Frank had asked me to drive his car out to Portland. He and Anna were moving and wanted to ride together in her car.

"I need to get away," I told Chris. "My expectations for returning to normalcy are setting me up for disappointment."

The familiarity of home screamed a reminder that something was missing. Dave was gone, and there was a black hole lurking in every space where he had been.

"Well, whether you go or not, I have something for you," Chris said as he stood and went inside.

I sat expectantly. Chris had been supplying me with mind-changing and faith-intensifying ideas over the previous year. He'd become a guru to me: a teacher and guide to spirituality and death.

A few minutes later, Chris returned to drop the purple softcover book *Be Here Now* by Ram Dass on the table in front of me.

I took the book to the yard and flipped through the two-page spreads of art and prose. With each turning page, the fantasy of a cross-country journey solidified into a plan.

T-H-A-N-K-Y-O-U

Three weeks after Dave died, I got on a plane to Nashville. I flew to a place Dave loved, to see one of our best friends. I was consumed by grief and empty without my love, yet I was finding solace and celebrating Dave's life by visiting the places and people he cherished.

On the plane, I realized I wasn't afraid of crashing; I kind of wanted to crash. The times I had been most afraid of crashing, I realized, were when I didn't have Dave at my side. When he was at home and I was traveling without him, a crash would have separated us. This time, crashing would mean getting to be with him.

I sat with my eyes closed, visualizing my body dissolving into radiant light. In my mind's eye, I saw Dave as a light being, smiling a glowing, toothy Dave grin. With each bump of turbulence, I was ready—almost relieved—to give up my life.

During this time so close after Dave's demise, I couldn't help but wish for my own death. Part of the faith I'd gained in caring for dying Dave was that there was more to existence than Planet Earth. I believe in cosmic, expansive, infinite life. And Dave exists there. Dave exists here, too, but he's not always easy to see. In my humanness, when I was grieving, it was much easier to see he was *not* here.

On my way to Nashville, my death-facing faith was strong, but my keep-on-keeping-on, alive-on-Planet-Earth faith was shaky. I had lived intimately beside and aware of death for so many months that going back to life was hard. Letting go of Dave and staying grounded on Earth felt impossible, like a contradiction.

I had learned to surrender to death. I had learned a lot about acceptance and relinquishing the illusion of control. I had learned to meditate and pray like never before. In the new quiet and darkness, I had seen the light.

Frank and Anna were waiting for me in Nashville. They would soon leave for their new home in Portland, Oregon. It would be my job to get Frank's car—loaded with so much stuff there was barely room for my rock climbing gear and me—out to Portland.

I landed with a sense of weightlessness. I felt free. I wasn't responsible for anyone. I didn't have an agenda. Instead, I was unanchored, bouncing with no bounds. This wasn't an alienating feeling. I relished my freedom and my oneness. I felt unified with the world around me without any obligation to commit to anyone or anyplace.

I wandered around Nashville with Frank and Anna. I sat in their back seat gaping out the car window with a naive freshness. I was savoring life on Planet Earth. I took pictures and ogled sights and landmarks like a wide-eyed tourist.

For the trip, I'd packed a Nalgene bottle loaded with about a third of Dave's ashes.

I'd decorated a pill bottle to use for carrying around smaller quantities of the ashes. I kept that pill bottle in my purse and took it out often to blow or sprinkle bits of Dave in special spots.

I saw and felt Dave everywhere. Maybe my naiveté resulted from looking at the world with what felt like four eyes: mine and Dave's. I saw and appreciated things as he would've. When traveling, Dave was enthusiastic and adventurous. He never tired. He wanted to see and experience everything.

I remembered the time Dave and I flew to Amsterdam to start a tour of Western Europe. We took a red-eye and had a long wait to get through customs when we landed.

From the airport, we took a train downtown. We didn't know exactly where the hotel we booked was, so we ended up wandering with our heavy bags over cobblestone streets for quite a while. When we made it to our room, I collapsed on the bed.

"Sleep! Finally!" I sighed with relief.

"*What?!* Sleep? But, Amelia, we're in *Amsterdam!*" Dave gasped as he stood over me.

"But I'm so tired. We have all day. And three weeks after today. I want to rest," I moaned with drooping eyelids.

"No way am I sleeping!" Dave replied and repeated, "Amelia, we're in *Amsterdam!*"

Later that day, Dave woke me from my nap. He sat on the bed and whispered to me about his afternoon's adventures until I stirred.

In the hours I slept, Dave had eaten lunch, walked through several neighborhoods, and checked out many coffee shops—he already had a favorite—and a few bars.

"Let's go!" Dave burst out when I sat up in bed. "I'll take you to a coffee shop you'll love. We'll get you some cappuccino and Orange Bud, and they have these yummy baguettes too. And you'll love Claudia! She runs the place; she plays great music."

When I got to Nashville, Dave's spirit was energizing me as he always had on our travels and adventures. He was there urging and enlivening me.

"I know where we have to put some Dave," Frank announced as I scattered ashes around a statue of eight larger-than-life naked people dancing around a naked woman playing a tambourine. The playful, almost-naughty forty-foot statue centered in a flowerbed in the middle of a busy street impressed me.

"His favorite Nashville guitar shop!" Frank continued. "Dave loved that place, and there's a room with a couch where they keep all the best recording gear. He could hang out there for hours."

"Let's go!"

Frank and I sat on the couch in the recording gear room. We chatted nonchalantly while I tried to be inconspicuous dumping ashes from the pill bottle onto Frank's and my palms. We left some Dave in the gear room without causing a scene.

Frank and Anna were ready to leave the next day. Most of their possessions were already being shipped to Portland. The rest of their stuff was crammed into Frank's Nissan and Anna's Honda. They had been staying with their friend Naomi and awaiting my arrival.

We spent the evening with Naomi, eating barbecue and watching country bands. I spent the night in my sleeping bag on Naomi's sun porch. My first night away from home was a comfort. My old friends, and a new one, soothed me.

Naomi left for work before I woke up. I used a piece of paper from my journal to make paper doll robot cut-outs like the ones Shawn had left for me after Dave's memorial service. I wrote the letters T-H-A-N-K-Y-O-U, one on each doll, and taped them to Naomi's door. I was grateful to her for opening her home to me, for reminding me about the possibility of new friends.

From Nashville, I drove to see an old friend. Jake and I had known each other for fourteen years, since we'd lived together in a house with a bunch of other college-aged kids.

Jake lived in Kansas City, and I hadn't seen him since Dave and I stayed with him while driving cross-country nine years earlier.

I told Jake the story of Dave and me. I talked for hours about the nine years of love story that had unfolded since I'd last seen him.

I tried to articulate my pain.

"Dave and I broke up. When he was losing his mind, and we didn't know why, we stopped living together," I explained.

"Without Dave, I started rock climbing more and more. And I started boyhunting. I missed him. I was wrecked. But, somehow, I was secure in knowing he was out there. I could still have him. We weren't together, so I tried to fill my life and heart with adventures and boys.

"I didn't like it, but when we broke up, I was surviving without him. So, I know I can do it. I know I can live without Dave. I thought the broken-up practice time would help me now. I lived without him before, so I thought I could handle doing it again.

"But now he's not out there. I can't find my way back to him. When I think about that, I feel so, so sad and sick and broken.

"Now, the trick is knowing he *is* still there. Just in a new way. I gotta keep my faith, trust the universe. Drop the ego; drop the control, the human mind. I need to learn to have Dave in this new way.

"I've been practicing sending him to the light. We practiced together. I've learned so much, gained so much faith. I feel like it should be easier. I can't understand why I hurt so much."

Jake offered me unconditional love and friendship. He listened. He welcomed me into his home after years of little contact. His presence in my life reminded me that time and space don't mean all that much when it comes to love. Jake and I were connected; we always had been. Some people, some friends, are just that way. Time and space are irrelevant in the scope of those relationships.

I was learning to apply earthly time and space disconnect to that between the living and the dead. Dave was with me.

Spending time with Jake was soothing. When I left his home to continue west, I taped T-H-A-N-K-Y-O-U robots to his door. I left refreshed, with a bit more peace.

My next stop was Colorado Springs. My rock-climbing uncle lived there and offered me a place to stay.

A day or two before I arrived, I talked to my dad. He'd decided to rendezvous with me in Colorado Springs!

We spent a few days climbing on the slabs and otherworldly rock formations in and around Colorado Springs.

One day was the best I'd had since Dave died. I climbed hard and had to use serious focus. I was fully exhilarated and, by day's end, worn out. As our climbing crew packed up, I snuck away to a nearby stream. The beauty of the place overwhelmed me. The narrow stream playfully splashed over mossy boulders. The running water felt rejuvenating. The sun was setting, and the air was glowing golden.

As I sat by the water, I thought back on the day and realized Dave hadn't been the focus of my thoughts. Climbing was. I let go; I surrendered to the consuming nature of climbing. In doing so, I felt happiness and peace; I unconsciously released my desperate grip on absent Dave.

By letting him go, in releasing my sadness and my wishing for him back, I was rewarded with him all around. I saw Dave in the beauty of the day. I felt him in my climbing strength. I saw him in the stream and sunset. I sprinkled some Dave in the water and said a prayer of thanks; I chanted Om Mani Padme Hum.

I didn't know anyone in Boulder, but it was too cool a town to pass by.

Boulder felt homey, welcoming, and profound. It was the Promised Land: cute boys, legal marijuana, fit and happy people, healthy food. Boulder is a sacred place.

I checked into the hostel and started living in Boulder.

Everything felt right to me there. It was reassuring to be in a new place by myself. The sense of a new beginning invigorated me.

I wasn't ready for a new beginning, not right then. The sense that there was potential for a new life in Boulder gave me hope. For the time being, I was finishing something. I was living Dave's dying. I was sad and lonely, but that felt right too. I was supposed to be sad and lonely. I was widowed, alone, without my partner.

I was in one of the country's coolest climber towns; there is a lifetime's worth of rock climbing surrounding Boulder. I had to find a partner! I went to the climbing gear store and left my number. I went to the library and used the Internet to post my info on climber meet-up sites.

In the evening, I headed to the climbing gym. People were spilling out of the gym into the parking lot. The air was savory with the smell of grilling burgers. The gym was passing out free beer and burgers! Climbers were swarming the place.

Talk about being in the right place at the right time.

I met James. He was from England and traveling solo. I'd found a partner.

We shared burgers, beers, and good conversation, and ended up leaving the party together to go hang out downtown. While we were sitting at a bar, I was digging him: a cute climber boy with an accent.

In my head, I said to Dave, "I hope you don't mind me being with this guy. It feels so weird, and almost wrong."

Just then—out of the blue—James said to me, "You know, my middle name's David. I'm James David. Both are family names." I hadn't mentioned a thing about Dave, my marriage, or my recent loss. In my everything-is-connected and I-keep-getting-my-mind-blown way, I was floored. Why was he compelled to say that, just then?

Well, it was all I needed for a sign. From Dave. From heaven. Whatever. From that moment, it felt right to be with James David. It was part of my healing and part of my adventure.

We spent the night together. We talked about rock climbing like it was dirty. Together, we were sexy.

We were both too proud to admit hangover or exhaustion the next morning. Reeking of last night's beer and sex, we headed to Clear Creek Canyon to climb some rocks.

After spending a few days climbing together, James and I decided to tackle a long, difficult route up the Maiden—a towering rock formation in The Flatirons on the edge of town. The guidebook description enthralled us; we knew the route would be awesome and challenging.

The hike in was confusing and long. We wound on dusty trails through desert brush. The magnificent Flatirons beckoned on the skyline before us, but as minutes passed, the rock didn't seem to get any closer. The sun blasted the exposed landscape with laser rays. The dry air felt like sand in my lungs.

After forty-five minutes of walking, James complained about not feeling well. He blamed his condition on "dodgy take away," but I suspected he was scared of the route we were about to do. We turned around.

I was disappointed. Back at the parking lot, James rushed into the bathroom and I wandered around looking for other climbers.

I saw a young man and woman sorting through climbing gear in the opened hatch of a Subaru.

"Hey guys, are you getting ready to go climbing?" I asked.

"Hey, yeah, we're thinking about climbing the Maiden today," the man replied. "You?"

"I was planning to climb the Maiden, too, but my partner isn't feeling well," I said.

"Maybe you can climb with us!" the woman said. She dropped the harness she'd been adjusting and turned to face me. "It would be great to have a third person in our party."

"Totally," the man said. "This is Erika's first multi-pitch route. It would make it a lot easier on her to have someone to share the ledges with."

"Perfect!" I said and held out my hand. "My name is Amelia."

"Great to meet you! Thank you for joining us," the woman said as she shook my hand. "I'm Erika. This is Micah."

Erika and Micah intended to do a much easier route than the one James and I had planned. I'd been disappointed to lose the opportunity to tackle a difficult climb that would challenge my technical limits. My disappointment turned to renewed excitement. I'd still get the chance to summit the magnificent rock formation. The route I'd take with Erika and Micah would be technically easy, but exciting and fun.

I also knew having a third person in their party would take the pressure off Erika and would be invaluable to my new partners. Our teaming would be beneficial to us all.

When James emerged from the bathroom, I handed him my car keys so he could get back to town and convalesce.

I set off on the confusing network of trails for a second time.

"James and I weren't sure we were on the correct path to the Maiden when we took this trail earlier," I said as we walked. I hoped Micah and Erika were more familiar with the approach.

"I've been to the Flatirons before. I'm never sure of the right way to go," Micah confessed.

We took hours to get anywhere. The network of trails was confusing, and the directions we had were unclear.

Sweaty and tired, the three of us stopped. We stared at the Maiden in the distance

"It never seems to get any closer," Erika sighed.

We bushwhacked, skirting rampant poison ivy, and pressed on up steep terrain.

Once at the rock, we weren't clear where any routes were. The descriptions we had didn't match the rock before us.

"I printed this topo from the Internet," Micah said as he unfolded another sheet of paper from his pocket to supplement the scribbled route description he'd transcribed from a friend's guidebook.

I studied the sheet.

The topographic diagram of the Maiden in no way resembled the rock we were standing in front of.

"I don't know, Micah," I said. "This picture doesn't make much sense. This has got to be the Maiden though, right?"

"Right?" Micah answered.

Erika let her backpack slide from her shoulders and tumble to the ground. She sat on the pack and guzzled from a water bottle.

"Do you want to look, Erika?" Micah asked.

"Nope," she said with a smile. "You guys got me this far. I trust you can figure it out."

Micah and I looked at each other and shrugged.

"I don't know, dude," I said. I pointed to the crack in the nearby wall. "We're definitely looking at a rock climb. This has to be the Maiden."

"The first pitch is 5.6. It should start on a bulge and move right to a crack," Micah said after he reread his notes for the umpteenth time.

"I don't see the bulge, but that looks like a 5.6 crack," I said. "Let's do it."

Micah looked at me, at the wall, and at the papers in his hands for a full minute.

"Do you want to lead it?" he asked.

"Heck, yeah!" I said and dug through my pack for my harness. As the tag along, I didn't know if Micah would want to share leads with me. The fact that I got to start the climb was a welcomed bonus.

We divided the route into six pitches and had a fun time wandering up the mellow chunk of rock. The features were impressive; part of the route climbed a spine of rock so narrow I could see a hundred feet down each side of the thick spire.

Micah handed all the leads over to me since he was intimidated by our lack of certainty about the route. Nothing about the rock matched his papers. The climbing was well within my ability and I loved deciphering my way up the unknown route, so I was happy to take on the role of leader.

We became fast friends, laughing and enjoying the scenery together. At the summit, I sat taking in the panoramic view as I belayed Micah and Erika to the final anchor spot. As I studied the surroundings, I was confused by the presence of an impressive spire of rock about a quarter mile away. I eyed it suspiciously as I belayed.

When Micah and Erika reached the summit, we all high-fived and hugged.

"I sure am glad we got to climb the Maiden," I said. "By the way, what's that one?"

I pointed to the mysterious spire.

"Well, take a look at that! It's the Maiden!" Micah managed to say before we all became incoherent with laughter.

The day was fabulous; the three of us were grateful to have met and enjoyed the wrong climb together. We didn't get lost on the hike out, and made it back to town in short order. The Southern Sun—*the* bar hangout for climbers—welcomed us with cold local microbrews. While we waited for our burgers, I went to the bathroom to wash up. I checked my phone messages and heard Heather's voice from back home: gleeful and sly.

"Amelia, call me as soon as you can. I talked to Dave."

The post-climbing beer could wait. I went outside and called Heather.

"Hang on for this one; it's pretty weird," Heather said. "There was a psychic fair here, in Woodstock, over the weekend. You know I'm not going to talk to just anyone. I walked over there on the first day and wrote down some names. I researched the psychics and found this one guy, Adam, who seemed pretty legit. He's a medium.

"So, I went back the next day and sat with him. I just requested a general reading, none of the medium stuff. I asked him about Chris.

"He was doing all right. He said some stuff that kind of related to Chris's recent doctor visit. He was in the middle of asking me if we were planning a vacation when he got real weird. This guy is far out. He started twitching and shaking his head. I thought he was gonna lose it."

Heather allowed for a dramatic pause as I heard her inhale her cigarette.

I was pacing on the sidewalk in front of the Southern Sun, aware I'd left my new friends sitting inside without an explanation.

"So, this guy, Adam, is a total character. He's super skinny with a giant feathery Afro. He closed his eyes and his crazy hair covered his face while he shook his head. I looked around to see if anyone was watching this guy. I thought he was going to pass out.

"Finally, he opened his eyes and he says, 'Dave is here.'"

I took a deep breath.

"Yeah. Crazy," Heather said. "He said Dave really needed to give me a message. Dave was saying 'thank you.' He told me Dave was holding up the cut-outs. He gestured as if he was spreading paper dolls between his fingers. You remember the cut-outs, right? The paper doll robots Shawn makes?"

"Oh, I remember," I said. "I've been imitating Shawn this entire trip. I've been leaving the 'thank you' cut-outs taped to the door of every friend I stay with!"

"Oh shit! I can't believe it!" Heather said. "Of course you were leaving cut-outs. That makes it even better!"

Heather's message from Dave perfected my happy day. I was living right, connecting with new friends and celebrating bonds with old—and even dead—friends.

The next day, I woke up in Boulder—the town that had welcomed and soothed me—feeling sad and missing Dave, and headed to my favorite coffee house on Pearl Street. I sat, thought of Dave, and felt his absence as I enjoyed coffee and pastry. I wished he was there enjoying it with me. I thought about going home to fall weather. I thought about what it would do to my broken heart. I wondered how I'd get on during the East Coast fall without my love.

Fucking James David had left me feeling empty. I kept thinking of his eyes—so vibrant. His so-full-of-life eyes had made me want him. I felt a new urgency regarding life. I yearned for it. Recognizing James as *alive* was intoxicating. I was ravenous for aliveness, and somehow this was congruous with my desperation to bring Dave back from the dead.

I remembered the sweat hut Mike built in the Adirondacks after Dave died. I remembered looking at my body and seeing emptiness. That image, and the incredible vast emptiness that Dave left when he died, made me open to the idea of having a baby. Life, life, life! Getting pregnant would feel like bringing Dave back. Fuck a stranger to make Dave's baby. This idea made it OK that James David, this stranger boy, and I had had unprotected sex.

I wondered, if I'm pregnant, will I become a mother? Is this how it's supposed to work?

Sadness and loneliness were creeping in on that morning; my thoughts were dark. I sent a text to Eve. Sweet Eve. Supportive Eve.

Loving, sentimental, weepy Eve. I wrote: "Every day I wake missing Dave urgently."

And that was when the day's healing started. Eve called minutes after I sent the text, "to hear my voice," she said.

So, that's love. So, there was no Dave for me. But Eve's call reminded me: there was still love, still friends.

Then, a little later, Dana called. More love. Unconditional and vibrant. My friends reaching out to me healed me.

One of my favorite Boulder features was the creek that meanders through town. The water beckoned me. When I wasn't climbing, I'd sit at its edge. I'd sprinkle Dave there, pray, and chant.

On my sixth morning in Boulder, I woke early and headed to the creek. For a while, I was alone. As the sky brightened with new day, the community came to the water. Old, young, dogs, hippies, squares, babies, college kids, punks came to sit by, wade in, swim in, and tube down the creek. Everyone smiled at and made eye contact with one other.

At the water, surrounded by community, I thought, "I'm staying here in Boulder—The Promised Land."

I did stay a few days longer. I watched live music, ate good food, drank local beer, and made new friends. I climbed with different people in different places. I was climbing hard and feeling strong. Of all the rock in the Boulder area, I was most intrigued by Eldorado Canyon. I was determined to climb there.

On one of my last days in Boulder, I headed to my new favorite hangout, The Southern Sun, for dinner and to find a climbing partner. I sat at the only open seat at the bar, right next to Alan, and we fell into conversation right away. I asked him if he wanted to go watch the bluegrass band I'd just read about in the local free paper.

We left to go check out the music. At the new locale, our conversation deepened. We talked about climbing as spirituality.

"So, we should climb tomorrow. I'll take the day off from work," Alan suggested.

"Uh, *yeah!*" I agreed. "Where are we going to go?"

"Eldo!" Alan announced.

We were instantly and completely psyched. Alan and I connected; it was clear we shared passions and values.

"Want to go for an adventure *right now?*" Alan asked.

We left the bar and headed to Alan's apartment in Eldorado Springs, the town on the edge of Eldorado Canyon. The tiny community is steps away from the world-class rock climbing I longed to explore.

That night, Alan led me into the canyon and up a meandering steep trail. It was dark, but the near-full moon was rising. We agreed we'd done the right thing by leaving the bar for the wilderness we both so craved and loved.

"What do you think happens when we die?" Alan asked.

We'd shared ideas about Buddhism and our faiths back at the bar. We'd talked about the connectedness of the Earth and its inhabitants.

I couldn't stop the unfolding.

"Funny you should ask," I playfully answered, between breaths. Alan was cruising up the mountain at a breakneck pace. We hopped over rocks and roots in the darkness.

I told him about Dave's illness and death, the books that helped me, and Heather's experience with the medium.

"Huh," Alan responded. "I knew you were gonna have a good answer for me."

We reached the summit and sat in the moonlight. In our silence, I had the distinct feeling that our minds were linked and our spiritual discussion continued without words.

Alan invited me to sleep on the couch in his minimalist apartment in the tiny, artsy community of Eldorado Springs. *The Tibetan Book of Living and Dying* was on his bookshelf.

My encounter with Alan was a synchronistic gift among many on my Heart Heal Trip. I left T-H-A-N-K-Y-O-U cut-outs for him.

My routine of chanting at Boulder Creek and rock climbing in a majestic-feeling land was hyper-connecting me to Dave. Instead of finding a couch to sleep on for my eleventh night in Boulder, I headed farther into the wilderness. I camped in Rocky Mountain National Park for a night.

Just after dawn, I walked down to a stream. I chanted mantras to the Buddha of Limitless Light and the Buddha of Compassion while sprinkling some of Dave's ashes. I told Dave I hoped he was around me—mixed in with the cosmic unifying force. I told him I didn't know what to think of Heather's medium, but it seemed legit.

I told him I wanted to join the light. I wanted to die and be his wife again in a new realm.

I walked out over the stream on a fallen log. As I chanted and sprinkled more ashes, I visualized Dave—as man and as ash—unified with the light above and the water and ground below. I visualized him leaving this world to eternal peace. Letting go was the best thing to do for us both. Letting go would take us both higher and, ultimately, back together as one.

I returned to the shore after sprinkling Dave's ashes. There, I hugged some trees. The third tree oozed an energy that felt like Dave. I held the tree, and it felt soft and vibrant; it *was* Dave. We rubbed noses and held each other.

It was a powerful elixir to feel Dave so strongly—in a tree, within me, behind a friend's kind eyes.

Back in Boulder on the morning of the fortieth day after Dave died, the last day the Tibetan Buddhists believe a soul exists between lives in the bardo, I woke wanting to connect my mind and body. I wanted to be conscious of sending Dave to limitless light.

I used a computer at the local library to find a yoga class and meditation session.

I went to a hot yoga class that afternoon. Immersed in steamy sweat, I remembered the sweat hut Sugar Shack Mike had built. I remembered the awareness that the universe would fill the emptiness inside and around me. I visualized filling my empty-without-Dave heart with light and filling the empty-without-Dave world with his immortal-being energy.

In the evening, I visited the Osho Meditation Center.

When I walked in, all the doors were closed and marked with "In Session" signs. I sat in the waiting area until a woman greeted me with a warm smile and handshake. Her name was Chris.

"Do you have experience with meditation?" Chris asked as she accepted my cash donation for the session.

"My husband, David, died forty days ago," I said. "I used *The Tibetan Book of Living and Dying* as a guide while he died from brain disease, and now, after his death. Together, we practiced the Phowa."

"Ahhhh," Chris smiled. "My husband, David, died last year. He had brain cancer for nineteen years. I think we're both in the right place."

I smiled too. My heart raced pleasantly. The low light in the room pulsed.

"My friend Chris is living with brain cancer. He and his wife are my spiritual guides," I said.

"Figures," Chris said with twinkly eyes. "Tonight's meditation will focus on the bardo."

The synchronicity was uncanny. I had found my way to a meditation center in Boulder, Colorado, miles away from home and worlds away from where I ever imagined life would take me. I was welcomed by a woman whose experience with love and death mirrored mine. She had the same name as my like-a-guru friend, and our late husbands shared the same name. And the focus of the night's meditation was the bardo, the topic that inspired me to seek a meditation center.

During the meditation, Chris played a video of Osho, the Indian spiritualist and guru, presenting his teachings on the bardo. He explained that it's possible for a meditative person to navigate the after-death bardo with awareness and choose his next life. Over the course of many Earth lives, a conscious person gains more awareness to choose his next life, bringing him closer to enlightenment.

So, Dave might be choosing a womb to be born into for his last life before enlightenment? My womb? Maybe having sex with a stranger named James David gave Dave's soul a place to be born?

The next thing Osho spoke about was the inability to describe or label certain human relationships. It reminded me how Ram Dass writes in *Be Here Now*, "You are the guru."

Osho said we all have a master. I am Dave's master. He is mine. He's my guru; I'm his. I'm his wife; I'm his mother. He's my husband; he's my son.

I scattered Dave's ashes as I moved across the country, letting him go bits at a time. I knew acceptance and truth like never before. I learned that everything *is* connected and spirits *are* real. A cosmic energy connects humans and Earth: it binds life and death. The gifts and messages I received by being open to this energy were undeniable.

I spent two more weeks traveling, visiting friends, and rock climbing.

When I arrived at my last stop—Portland—it felt like a homecoming. It was my first time visiting the city Dave and I had admired from across the country for over a decade. Two of Dave's closest friends and bandmates, Jay and Scott, had moved there, and talk of Portland frequently came up. The possibility of visiting or moving to this art and music driven hipster community always danced in the background of our long-term plans.

I got to Portland at the start of a three-day music festival. I parked Frank's car in front of Jay's apartment, found the key Jay had stashed for me, washed my face, and hopped into Anna's car with her and Frank.

We spent the night speeding from venue to venue to see as many bands as possible. Jay and Scott each caught up with us throughout our explorations. We took in the music, ate donuts, and drank beer.

Portland, music, and Dave's bandmates sucked me into a celebratory whirlwind. Being with Dave's brothers put a new twist on my mourning. The desire to live fully together, in honor of Dave, drove us. In each moment together, we were all aware of both missing Dave and feeling surrounded by Dave. The Mother of All Parties continued.

The next evening, Jay hosted a cook-out. We packed his back deck with Jay's eleven-year-old son, Ely, and ex-wife, Kathleen, along with Scott and his wife, Ali, and Frank and Anna. Everyone in the crew had known and loved Dave. We sat on the deck surrounded by fragrant trees decorated with creeping vines. I was in a lush new place.

After we ate, while Ely led the crew inside to play foosball in the attic, Jay and I stayed downstairs. Jay played guitar while I did yoga. When we were together, the Dave presence intensified exponentially. I lay on the floor, feeling Dave pour out from Jay's guitar. I felt Dave's hands on my open palms; we melted together. Time and space disappeared.

Later, upstairs, I played keyboard to Jay's drumming. Scott and Frank joined in, and we all alternated instruments. Playing music with Dave's bandmates, I felt Dave helping me let go. I didn't consider myself a musician. Dave erased my hesitation, embarrassment, and self-consciousness. It didn't matter. I was making music. I was connecting to my friends—on this side and across the curtain—with a universal language. It was awesome.

I left my beat-up pink Nalgene bottle, half-full of Dave's ashes, with the boys. I left Dave's soul brothers with their permanent big piece of Dave. I was sad—sad, and heavy.

Being with Dave's friends had brought me back in time—to the happiest times of my life—and made me hyper-aware of the depth of my loss. My husband was gone. No matter how close he felt when I was surrounded by our friends, he was still far away.

The Other Side

Back at home, I realized I needed balance. I needed to learn how to keep the faith and the quest for enlightenment going without Dave.

I had been keeping it together for him. Without him, I could try for a feel-better material life, where I'd go out to movies and rock shows, wear cute outfits, and meet boys and new friends. Or I could build on my new, enormous knowing about life, death, and egolessness. I could be empty and alone, and dwell there to become stronger. I could fast, abstain from drugs and sex, meditate, do yoga, pray.

What I really wanted was to balance it all. I suspected it was possible, but I was only beginning to learn the way.

In late September, I went back to work at the Ginger Man. My first night back, my ego was suddenly huge. My mourning and my needs were magnified. Before I could punch in, I turned on my heels and beelined from the restaurant. I stood just outside the kitchen door to talk with my manager and friend, Julie.

"There will be a ton of cute couples on dates. And I keep remembering you hired me on my two-year wedding anniversary," I whined to Julie. "Everything makes me think of Dave. I can't be happy now. I'm not sure I'm capable of doing a good job."

"Honey, I know you'll be OK," Julie encouraged. "We're all here for you. You can take an easy section, and everyone will back you up."

Julie's willingness to support me and ease me back into the real world, while not letting me off the hook by sending me home, gave me confidence to go back inside the restaurant.

After a smooth night that helped ease my mind, I went home with a heavy heart.

I was disappointed in myself for getting swept up in what felt like ego bullshit.

I was acting like a bratty human: me, me, me. I was perpetuating sadness to build my drama. Hadn't I learned anything from *Be Here Now?*

After some hard thinking, I let go and allowed my sadness. I did miss Dave. It was hard to be at the restaurant. I hadn't reached enlightenment yet. I had some practice to go.

The Heart Heal Trip was a great spiritual journey. I spent the time chanting mantras, scattering ashes, feeling free and Earth-connected, and meaningfully uniting with strangers and friends. Back at home, the altar felt so small.

One way I found to make my altar grow was reaching out to people with stories about Dave. Allowing the story to come out to others is as important as letting people reach out to me.

One of my favorite bands is Midlake. Their album *The Trials of Van Occupanther* was a soundtrack for me while living with dying Dave. Their meaningful and reassuring lyrics inspired me to keep trying and seeking even when life was hard and seemingly meaningless.

Eight weeks after Dave died, I was thrilled to find out that Midlake was playing close to home. I was back from my Heart Heal Trip just in time to see the show. I took a spot standing near the front of the stage for the opening band's last song or two.

When Midlake took the stage, I was enraptured. They were a powerful wall of sound. The six guys in the band were my age and totally cute. Boys with guitars always make me think of Dave. I had mixed feelings. In part, I was comforted by these musicians who embodied Dave's spirit. But I longed for Dave to be playing music on stage, and for me to help him carry gear to the car after the show. At once, I was peacefully aware of the connection between the living and dead, and the deep unification achieved through music, and I was desperately missing Dave.

I cried through most of the show.

When it was over, I wiped my tear-drenched cheeks and maneuvered to the side of the stage where the band boys were stacking gear. I approached the bass player—the cutest and dirtiest of the bunch.

"Thanks for the amazing show. That was great," I said with a smile. "Any chance I can explain what your music means to me with an inspirational story?"

"Thanks. Wow. Uh, sure," the bass player replied. "Come on upstairs after we're finished loading the van."

I met my new friend by the van and followed him upstairs to the lounge where the band and crew were eating pizza and drinking beer. The sound of live music from downstairs shook through the floor.

The bass player led me to a table on the balcony overlooking the city street and offered snacks and beer. A couple of the other band members wandered over to receive my compliments. I started my story.

"My husband, Dave—a talented indie rocker much like you guys—died in July. He was sick for a couple years, and he died in our house surrounded by friends. Your music was part of the sound-track," I began.

I quoted their songs and explained what those songs meant to me and how they comforted me while caring for Dave. I confessed how intense and emotional seeing their show had been for me.

"Yeah, I know," the bass player gently said. "I saw you crying."

I poured my heart out to these guys. I told them how they reminded me of Dave, and that I was probably similar to their wives— relishing loading music gear and watching my love shine on stage. We talked about unconditional love and marriage. We talked about the fragility of life and our lack of control.

"My story is inspirational," I said, "because it exemplifies the connectedness of all things. Your music helped me; you guys are creating powerful art that's benefiting the world. It's all meaningful. We all make an impact on each other."

I spent the months after Dave's death encountering awesome people and good-weird situations. Each of these encounters was a comfort in my time of grief. I was practicing what I learned while caring for Dave. I was letting go and allowing. I was releasing Dave to the light and feeling his spirit in me and through others.

Days after the Midlake show, I went to Woodstock to go to a message circle with Heather. Adam, the medium Heather had met with while I was in Colorado, led the circle. He would attempt to make contact with and share messages from the dead.

We were among a group of six attendees at the message circle at Sage Healing Center in Woodstock. We were all strangers. Adam knew nothing about me except my first name. To start, he led us in a meditation where we visualized being in our childhood bedroom. He suggested the bedroom door opens and in comes a dead person we know.

In my visualization, the door opened and my maternal grandfather came in, followed by my mom. After they came in, I noticed that Dave was in the background, sitting in a chair.

At Adam's suggestion, we opened our eyes. He was cross-legged on the floor, expressively using his hands and rolling his eyes as he chattered.

"There's a tall, handsome gentleman showing himself. His is tall and looming, but seems pleasant and friendly. His name is Harold. 'Hal' is OK too."

I was dumbfounded. Adam's description sounded like Grandpa! And his name *was* Harold. But I kept quiet. Except for the name, the details were general. Despite Heather's experience with Adam, I was skeptical.

"Hal is wearing a military uniform. Looks like World War II era. He has many medals," Adam continued.

I felt less skeptical. Before I left on my trip, I'd looked at my Aunt Patti's old pictures of Grandpa at Pearl Harbor in his decorated Army uniform. The most distinctive was a portrait where Grandpa powerfully and handsomely filled the page. I was struck by how tall and grand he was. Patti showed me a box of pins and medals and told me about his honors and distinctions.

"I think that might be my grandfather," I offered.

"Oh, good. He wants to give you a message," Adam said.

He started talking faster now that he was directing his words to me.

"There's a young woman with him. She's gorgeous. She's hip; she's wearing a skirt and boots. I don't think it's possible, she looks too young, but I'm getting the feeling she's your mother."

"My mom died when she was twenty-four," I said. "She was beautiful and stylish."

"Oh, good. I got the message right. They want you to know they're with you and have been with you. They've been here to help you with the hard time you've been going through," Adam announced with a nod.

That sounded nice. I was still a bit skeptical, though, and didn't acknowledge I was going through a difficult time.

Adam shook his head so that his puffy, curly hair waved wildly.

"No, no, no!" he said. "I got that wrong. You aren't just going through a hard time. No, you've been completely knocked on your back. You survived something. They know you're still reeling, and they're here for you. They need you to know that."

"Yeah," I replied quietly. Adam looked into my eyes with great sympathy.

"Others are with your mom and grandfather. There's someone else important for you to hear from."

Adam closed his eyes and pursed his lips.

"Mmm. He's young too. His name starts with a D," Adam offered.

My skepticism was gone. I felt warm and comforted. Adam was familiar and genuine, like an old friend.

"My husband, Dave, died in July," I told Adam.

"Aha. Well, he's here too. He's with your family. He's quiet; tiptoeing in the background for now."

Tiptoeing didn't sound like Dave's style. I was disappointed that Adam didn't have a message from Dave. He'd been focusing on me for half an hour, so I understood when he moved on to seek a message for someone else.

Adam sat still with his eyes closed for a few moments.

"Let's see who else I can get a message for," Adam said. He walked to the other side of the room.

Adam talked with another woman.

"Hmmm," Adam shook his head while he was trying to focus. "I'm getting something… oh, I'm sorry, I need to go back over here," Adam said, moving back to the spot where he heard from my family.

"OK," Adam continued, "Dave is impossible to ignore. I think he's getting more comfortable with me." Adam smiled big and giggled as he said, "He's *very* lively. And talkative. Pleasantly overwhelming."

"He wants me to encourage your writing. I'm not sure how serious you are about writing, but Dave thinks it's very important. Even if you're only keeping a journal, it may turn into something more," Adam instructed.

Adam's eyes were wet as he went on, "Dave wants you to know he's with you a lot. He knows you can hear him when you're quiet."

Adam went back across the room to continue the conversation Dave had interrupted. I thought about what he told me. In the car, when I was driving on the Heart Heal Trip, I'd talk out loud to Dave. Many times, I could feel him close—like when I hugged the tree in Colorado—or hear his voice. I daydreamed about these times, with a new confidence about the legitimacy of my experiences.

Adam interrupted my thoughts.

"Wow! I'm sorry everyone," he said. "Amelia's people are very distracting!"

Adam laughed and returned to his spot for communicating with my family. He turned to me.

"This may seem inappropriate. I know you said Dave just died. But he and your mom are having so much fun together, I have to assume you won't be offended." Adam took a deep breath. "They're picking out boys for you."

I smiled. I had a hilarious image of my twenty-four-year-old mother and Dave laughing together. Maybe they were inspired by my recent experience; I had been tickled by the Midlake boys. They were my age, cute, and the first interaction I'd had with a boy I could consider dating, eventually.

Adam gave me the impression this was something lighthearted for my mom and Dave to be doing together. It made sense. Dave was never jealous, and I've always been boy-crazy. I wasn't ready for a new lover, but I was glad to be reminded about the possibilities in my wide-open future.

The message circle was uncanny. I felt conflicted because I had spent the months up to and after Dave's death sending him to the light and helping him let go of his life and Planet Earth. I had confidence Dave's release from Earth was successful. Yet, here he was talking to me through a psychic in Woodstock.

I realized my understanding of what the fuck is going on—especially in terms of time and space—is minimal and unclear. Dave could be peacefully, completely gone while simultaneously being here giving messages through a medium and vibing to me through music.

After returning from my Heart Heal Trip, I took a yoga class. I was determined to stay healthy; I'd returned in the best shape of my adult life because of all the climbing and hiking I'd done out West.

Right away, what I learned in the class carried over to my yoga practice at home. I wasn't rushing or acting out of obligation to exercise. I was truly in the moment; time slipped by. I could hold poses for longer than ever because of my breathing. I learned to draw upward on the inhale and connect to limitless light, then ease deeper into the pose on the exhale and experience grounding.

The instructor, Jim, started and ended each class with meditation. The last thing he did, when his students lay flat on their backs in corpse pose, was to go to each of us and grasp our heels and "do some energy work." Jim's touch was powerful and soothing. He was a skilled and compassionate teacher.

When I showed up for class on the third week, I was the only student. Jim was happy to carry on the class despite the low attendance. He guided me through ninety minutes of meditation and postures.

After the session, Jim sat on the floor and held my feet. I zoned out and relaxed into a flush of color—blue and gold. I could feel energy moving into me from Jim's hands, so I flowed it back to Jim. I sent my energy to him with the thought: "I love you unconditionally. I'm open to receive what you have to teach me."

BAM! I could see Jim in my mind's eye. A blue wheel slowly spun from him. It had a hole in the center surrounded by square frames, like the cardboard disk in a child's View-Master toy.

Each frame contained pictures. I had a sense the wheel held all human history and truth. It spun from Jim and into me. It spun through me, moving up through my center, near my spine. As it progressed toward my head, each of my chakras was illuminated by color.

The wheel made it to my head and shot out the top of my skull. It blew my head off in the most graceful, slow, beautiful way. My chest and stomach blew apart next. I shattered into soft, electric blue shards.

Jim released my feet. We thanked one another for a productive class. We were both pleasantly dazed, with no need or desire to talk. I went home and enjoyed a euphoric evening.

The next night, I did yoga at home. I stood in tree pose and breathed deeply. On the inhale, my spine lengthened and the crown of my head reached high. On the exhale, my body grounded and connected with Earth.

For the first time, instead of my usual visualization of my legs as roots grounded in Earth, I saw my body and energy go deep into the Earth so it connected to light. I was connecting up to light and *down* to light. The light was infinite. I was part of it. I was alive on Planet Earth and figuring out I didn't have to die to stay connected to Dave and the light.

I felt strong and sane after coming home from the Heart Heal Trip. I was committed to yoga and rock climbing. I had a hit list of hard rock climbs I wanted to do before the winter arrived. I was doing the best climbing of my life. Rock climbing was filling my life with meaning. I had something to work for, something to busy my mind, and to challenge my body.

When I wasn't working, I was climbing. I was climbing differently than ever before—without fear. I was attempting routes right at my technical limit. I found a new boldness. I wasn't afraid to fall or fail. I was inspired to try, no matter the consequences.

Rock climbing with that intensity and determination was honoring Dave. That's the way Dave did things and the way he encouraged me to live. He pushed me to climb harder, higher, and farther from home. I'd always been content at my limit, never feeling compelled to push it, and Dave always questioned that and encouraged me to go beyond my comfort level.

I wasn't thinking much beyond finding climbing partners and planning excursions. I was consumed with selecting routes and pushing myself harder and harder. Climbing is meditative; it's possible to exist completely in the moment, focused only on the task at hand and survival. At those times when I was in the zone—focused and driven—Dave was with me. With my senses heightened and dulled all at once, I could feel him the best.

Climbing helped me shut off my brain and soothe my heart, but it also brought me close to Dave and relieved my loss.

The first few months after Dave's death were a difficult—sometimes agonizing—time. I was mournful. But the joy and peace I felt equaled my sorrow. In the greatest loss, I learned the greatest truth. I learned that love transcends, and love is light.

I spent time wondering why the dead can talk to the living. If they've stepped beyond, into the light, why do they bother? I felt a peace and clarity: It's because we're all connected. My human-on-Planet-Earth success can be mentored by the dead and help humanity to help the world to help the universe. We are one. We are elevating. Life and death, time and space are illusions teaching us lessons. We are evolving. God is evolving.

I gained understanding on a deep, cosmic level. On a molecular level, I felt truly connected to the universe, to God. I was on the path to healing, to taking what I learned from Dave's dying and applying it to a rich spiritual life on Earth.

So what could possibly go wrong?

Days to Darkness

In the fall, I collaged a tea canister as a gift for Sheila. I was grateful for the beautiful celebration of life ceremony she'd orchestrated for Dave. Over the pictures, I wrote:

Days to darkness
all seasons have night
and then
the morning comes

When I wrote those lines for Sheila, I thought the morning had already come. I thought I'd been through the darkness and was coming out the other side.

I underestimated my humanness. For a lesson this big, the depth of the darkness was greater than I could've imagined. Every time I thought I'd reached bottom, I was smacked with deeper pain.

Fall ended, and winter took its icy hold. Climbing season was over, and my heart froze. The days were shorter, and the lack of sunlight choked me. I was cold-blooded; my blood was congealing in my veins as the ground froze and snow piled up.

Once I stopped climbing, my fragile composure shattered. My head was too scrambled to shift my passion to one of my favorite winter sports: hiking, skiing, or ice climbing. I was done. There was nothing to distract me in the cold, dark winter.

My crew of friends and coworkers from the Ginger Man were a hard-partying bunch. We often went out after closing up, covering a circuit of downtown bars. With climbing season over and no reason to go to bed early, I accepted almost every invite to go out late. I liked drinking and I liked talking to strangers—both things distracted me from the reality of my life without Dave.

I felt as if I had nothing to lose, so talking to boys was easy. I didn't care about rejection. I wasn't looking for a heartfelt relationship; I was looking for attention and an interesting way to pass the time. Shiho's word "boyhunter" stuck. I'd chat up cute boys when I was out with my girlfriends, but my favorite partner-in-crime was my gay boyfriend, Jeff. We prided ourselves on our boyhunting skills.

Out on these quests, I'd get drunk enough and distracted enough to fall away from my day-to-day despair and into a good time. The next morning was another story, but I was getting by moment-to-moment and took whatever good feelings I could latch on to—no matter how artificial or unhealthy they were at the core. Out with my friends, I could get distracted enough to feel light.

Jeff had a long-term boyfriend, but he enjoyed the sport of the hunt and loved to encourage me. He was infinitely entertained by my antics. We'd patrol the local bars, looking for the cutest boys we could find. We'd unabashedly approach our favorites. One of my favorite lines was to talk about beer: ask a boy what he was drinking, was that his favorite, if he had visited the local brewery. Another approach I liked was marching up to a stranger and saying, "I wanted to talk to you because you're the cutest boy in this bar."

We met a lot of nice boys this way. We had a lot of fun conversations. We mingled with some duds, but generally we did pretty well.

One night we really struck out bad. We'd been at Bombers for an hour and couldn't find a single boy who piqued our interest. We had Stephanie with us, and we were questing to find her a boy. This was a particularly fun challenge for Jeff and me.

We left Bombers and wandered over to Lionheart. Right away, we felt our luck change. The place was crawling with Stephanie-style boys: big, burly, and hippieish. A group of these big teddy-bear hippies was playing pool, so we sauntered nearby, casting sideways glances, half-smiles, and the occasional eyebrow raise. We negotiated Stephanie into the pool game. She paired up with her favorite, and Jeff and I hung back to let her cozy in with her new friends.

Left to our own devices, we easily singled out our agreed-upon first choice for not just best looking, but also most intriguing, boy in the bar. This guy was hilarious: tipsy and wandering back and forth over the length of the crowded bar. He seemed to know many people and exchanged lots of smiles and words as he circumnavigated. Jeff and I fell into his pacing circuit, with me hot on his cute ass. I was following so close that when he stopped suddenly I playfully crashed into his back. He was tall and lean, a pleasure to connect with.

He turned around with big blue gorgeous eyes. "I'm so sorry!" he gasped as he touched my shoulder.

"Oh, it's OK. It's my fault; I bumped into you. How's it going?" I replied. Jeff and I introduced ourselves.

Our sexy catch was probably twenty-two. He had messy sandy-brown loose curls under a baseball hat and fuzzy scruff on his chin and cheeks. He wore jeans with a grey sweatshirt over a t-shirt. He had an endearing boy-next-door quality. He was mellow and sweet.

Occasionally one or two of his friends approached us and joined the conversation. We learned where our boy and his friends were from, what they were studying or what degree they had just graduated with, what they did for jobs and fun. We learned exactly how much each of them could drink and rough estimates of what each of them had drunk that night. They were proud of their partying abilities. We hung out long enough to share two rounds from the bar.

I looked closer at this sweet boy, and appreciated his good looks: full lips, good teeth, cute nose, long lashes. He was funny, outgoing, and personable. Jeff must have gotten a whiff of my pheromones, because he suddenly decided to go check on Stephanie's pool game.

This was my chance to break my mildly enforced no-kissing-in-the-bar rule. I was gazing up into his baby blue eyes and standing close when his romantic gaze flashed with grave concern. His eyes narrowed and his face hardened.

"Fuckin' niggers," he whispered. I couldn't believe my ears and turned to see four young black men about to start a dart game in the opposite corner. I was sick and sober all at once. There was no questioning the sincerity—he wasn't working into a bad joke or practicing sarcasm. He was angry.

"I can't believe they fucking let niggers in here. It's wrong. I can't stand this shit. Those motherfuckers need to LEAVE. I'm not staying here with niggers..." He continued. Enraged, he transformed from a cute boy-next-door to a disgusting racist fuck.

I walked away, dazed and injured. I didn't feel injured for myself, for missing the kiss, for striking out on a boyhunt. I felt injured for humanity. I felt naive and disenchanted with the world. I couldn't believe someone like that existed. He was young, privileged, and educated. He should know better; he should *be* better.

Jeff found me limping around, wounded and shocked. I explained what had happened, and he responded by getting me another beer. When our new friend tried to tag along, Jeff curtly explained he couldn't hang out with us anymore unless he apologized. The boy refused, so we went to hang out with the dart players. We watched the darts game and chatted until Stephanie found us.

She reported she was smitten with her boy. By that point, I'd had too many beers and was riled up. It didn't take much to push me over the emotional edge. I'd get snuffly and whiny if I wasn't properly distracted by a boyhunt. Racist Fuck had really set me off, and I was having a hard time recovering. Once I became emotional, I'd start down the grief road: missing, loving, aching for Dave.

We followed Stephanie back to hang out with her boy. The guy was OK. He was a musician and passionate about indie rock. So, Jeff and I found stuff to talk to him about. After a few minutes of talking, I realized my heart wasn't in it and I should head home.

Sweet Stephanie noticed my despair, put her arm around me, and asked what was wrong. Her tenderness was all I needed to open the floodgates. I hugged her and cried, and told her I was missing Dave.

Stephanie's new boy pushed his big hairy rocker face near mine and said something about how I should stop crying.

"I don't want to stop crying," I said, and I didn't. Crying meant honoring Dave, and feeling close to Dave. Being held by my loving girlfriend comforted me. And I was drunk and freaked out about my encounter with the racist. I was emotionally overloaded, and the last thing I wanted was some oaf sticking his nose in my business.

"C'mon, cheer up," he persisted. "You're fine." He started a monologue about how there was nothing that could be worth my tears and I should buck up.

I wasn't big into telling strangers my woes, and I hadn't gotten comfortable telling people about Dave. But I had to shut this guy up. "I'm sad because my husband died a couple months ago," I blurted.

The guy didn't lose stride. "So? Whatever. You gotta let stuff go. My dad died when I was a kid; you don't see me crying, do you?"

I wailed. This stranger's words really dug in deep and hurt like hell. I went from weepy to hysterical, and pushed past the oaf to rush out of the Lionheart.

Jeff and Stephanie followed me to the sidewalk and stood by as I cried inconsolably.

"What's the matter here?" a gentle voice said behind me. I turned to see a sixty-something, wizened man. "Baby, why you cryin'? Cause of some stupid guy? You don't gotta be cryin'."

The man looked at me with kind and joyful eyes. He smiled, and deep lines grooved the dark skin around his mouth and eyes. His peaceful smile was contagious. I sniffed and wiped my face.

"Now that's better," he continued. "You listen to me 'cause I have a message for you, honey. I know things. I see you, I see you are hur-tin', and I see your soul is good and strong. You're gonna make it, baby, you just gotta learn to put your shields up."

When he said "shields up," he gestured with both hands to build an invisible wall between us. "See? Like that. Shields up. You just gotta know when to do it." This man's presence soothed me. He was genuine, and he radiated compassion and empathy. He acknowledged my suffering and was there at the right time to remind me that pain could be eased. He taught me a priceless, simple lesson. He taught me I have a shield, and remembering to use it would serve me.

"You protect that beautiful spirit of yours. You're a special girl; you're good for this world. Just remember: shields up. That's my message," he concluded.

Stephanie saw my smile and wrapped her arms around me.

"Thank you," I called over Stephanie's shoulder as the cosmic messenger walked off down the sidewalk.

I was sinking deep into a lifestyle of late nights and alcohol, but cosmic messages still found their way to me. I was regularly remind-ed that everything was connected to the light. I was making the light harder to see—disconnecting myself from it—by partying instead of practicing meditation and yoga and climbing.

All summer, I'd been cruising along, releasing Dave to the light and feeling joyful. I'd been surrounding myself with goodness and maintaining my connection to the light. In the late fall, I disconnect-ed from that light, and something bad happened.

I desperately held onto Dave and wished him back to me. I felt empty, lonely, and lost without him. Grief sank in. I was consumed by ego: the Me, the It's Not Fair.

Darkness surrounded me, and I resigned myself to the notion I was meant to suffer, meant to be alone.

My spiritual practice felt meaningless. I was too miserable to maintain my meditation and yoga routine. I didn't see Donna and I stopped getting massage and acupuncture.

I thought: I am young; I feel old. I am alone. This is what it is to be thirty-three and a widow. I felt defined. In my mind, I labeled my-self: thirty-three-year-old widow.

In late November, I met Jeb. He sat at Bombers bar with three other thirty-something man-boys. They were dirty skater boys. Their skateboards were stacked against the wall in front of the bar. They wore baggy hooded sweatshirts and flannel shirts and were oblivious to the rest of the patrons at the bar.

Jeff and I exchanged wide-eyed glances after looking this sexy batch of boys up and down. We sat next to them at the slow bar.

"Who are these guys?" I asked Jeff. Why had we never seen them before? Jeff and I knew most of the bar regulars in our small town.

"Beats me," Jeff shrugged. "You better find out."

I turned to the bearded, rugged boy next to me and cleared my throat. The four guys disinterestedly raised their glances from their pints to me.

"Where did *you* come from?" I asked in a girlie voice.

The bearded redhead next to me was exhausted by my question. He looked me over and said nothing.

"Who the hell are *you?*" asked the hoodie-clad guy on the other side of the redhead.

"I asked you first."

"This is our bar."

"No, this is *our* bar."

A stalemate. These guys weren't going to be easy. I turned to Jeff, who raised his eyebrows and rolled his eyes.

"This *is* our bar," he confirmed with a nod and a sly smile.

These new boys had a punk rock edge and didn't give a fuck about making new friends. I liked them.

"Which one is your favorite?" I asked Jeff without lowering my voice.

"Easy. The redhead," Jeff answered. "You?"

"They're all adorable. But Red Flannel takes the cake," I declared.

"I knew you'd say that," Jeff said.

Over the course of a couple of rounds, Jeff and I offered a stark contrast to the punk rock skater boys. We giggled while they grumbled. I wasn't sure what kind of impression we were making on the boys until the redhead ordered his next round. When the bartender handed him two beers, he slid one over to me.

"I guess we can share the bar," he announced with a half-smile.

"Nice!" I squealed as I raised my glass to his.

"I'm Mickey," the scruffy boy said as he extended his hand to me.

The six of us introduced ourselves properly.

Red Flannel became Jeb.

We started to see Mickey and Jeb all the time. I wondered how we'd missed them in the months prior. Jeb moved in slow motion. He spoke with a Southern drawl. He had a cross-hatch pattern tattooed on his forearm and a creepy face on his shoulder. His hair and beard were dark and messy. His dark brown eyes were soft and bright; he made eye contact when he spoke and stared intently. He was sexy.

Finding Jeb was topmost on my to-do list on nights out at the bars.

Jeff was baffled.

"You're ruining our boyhunting. You're not supposed to get so focused on one boy," Jeff reminded me. "It's boring."

"But I want him. He's so hot," I whined.

"I don't know, Aim." Jeff was confused. "What exactly do you like about him?"

"His hair. His tattoos. His voice…" I rattled off the list without having to think about it. I'd been thinking about those three things a lot.

"Ah. Of course," Jeff rolled his eyes.

I was fascinated with Jeb. He was dark and dirty. He wasn't playing hard to get; he just didn't care. His apathy appealed to me.

I felt connected to Jeb. I loved all the bands in the iPod he carried with him. He was a year or two older than me, a contrast to the no-strings-attached twenty-two-year-olds I felt safe chasing. I liked that he had a history—he was from some other place and had lived what seemed like far-away past lives on Planet Earth.

I'd stay with Jeb at the after-hours bar when Jeff went home to bed. We'd stand close and stare at each other. He always made me smile.

"Your eyes are sparkly," he told me one night. "I can see myself."

I smiled big at him in answer. I didn't see myself in his eyes, bottomless in their darkness.

"Your smile," he slow-spoke, and chuckled. "You're always smiling. Why do you smile like that?"

He made me smile because he took away my thoughts. When I stared up at Jeb, everything was pushed from my head. With a light head, I had a swelling heart and an aroused body.

"Because I'm going to take you home with me," I answered with a straight face.

"When?"

"Now."

He looked at my empty beer glass and swallowed his full pint without taking his eyes off me.

At my house, Jeb sat on the sofa while I turned up the stereo to play the Black Keys. I skipped the first song on the *Brothers* album, "Everlasting Light." When the singer sings about wanting to be a shepherd, a sun, a guiding light, it made me think of Dave.

But I didn't want sun or light; I didn't want a shepherd. I wanted to dissolve into mindless darkness. I wanted to be alone and lost.

I pulled Jeb's red and black checkered flannel from his arms and swept his stained, tight-fitting thermal shirt off over his head.

With his shirt off, I saw more of Jeb's tattoos. Sloppy black outlines of naked bodies covered the left side of his torso. I leaned in close to him to make out the image in the low light.

"One of my friends drew that orgy on me. I was passed out."

Charming.

Every bad-boy detail I learned about Jeb turned me on more.

I put my mouth on the orgy. I ran my tongue over the raised lines on his soft, tight skin.

The next day, Jeb slept in my bed when I left for work. I liked leaving him there. I liked leaving my house with someone living inside. I liked it that my bed wasn't empty.

I thought about Jeb instead of Dave. I brought him home with me whenever I could find him.

Once, by the light of my altar, he showed me the scars on his hands. He told me about convulsing in the backseat of the car taking him to the ER after a viper bit him. His thumb was deformed where the skin had become necrotic after the bite. He'd sold vipers illegally, shipping them state-to-state.

His tales were far-fetched but colored with such vibrant detail I let myself be captivated with credulous awe.

Jeb oozed sex. His man smell was intoxicating—dirt and sweetness. He stood a full head over me. He was scrappy and lean without being skinny. His voice was hypnotic—a slow Southern drawl. He didn't say much, and there were long stretches of silence between his sentences.

Each bit of silence was like a vacuum, sucking me deeper into the outer space of Jeb's darkness. I never saw him in the daylight. We were always together late at night in the low light of the bar or by flickering candles at my place.

Closest to God

In late November, Susanne invited me to a ceremony. For a year, she'd been telling me about taking medicine with a bunch of spiritualists. She'd sit in a hut all night eating peyote or San Pedro cactus with a group determined to deepen their connection to spirit.

While Dave was sick, Susanne's stories of psychedelic shamanism didn't interest me. She offered to take me along, but my mind was already getting blown open without the help of medicine. I was on my own path, and I didn't feel the need to go anyplace potentially deeper or darker than I already was.

After Dave's death, after both of us dissolved into light, I was stuck swimming in the deepest, darkest abyss. When Susanne invited me to a medicine ceremony, I had nothing to lose. I was open to receive. I wasn't afraid of the drugs; I'd already figured out there was no control. I was ready to surrender to the medicine.

One Saturday afternoon, I drove east to the rural land where Susanne lived. I hadn't followed that route since Dave was sick, before we knew why his brain was going haywire. I felt relief as I glided up and down the hilly back roads. Though he was gone, I felt so much better about Dave than I had a year earlier. Dave was free. He was released from the pain and confusion of his illness. I was released from worry, from the agony of watching my strong, beautiful love's mind and body disintegrate.

The paradox of my emotions was intense. I'd been hopelessly clinging to Dave and darkly earthbound. I closed my eyes and saw light. Dave was present and surrounding me. I knew he'd support my participation in the medicine ceremony if he were still on Earth; I could feel him with me again. This was another chance for me to live fully, to exist and experience on Dave's behalf.

I met Susanne at her house, and she drove us farther into the hill towns to where the ceremony would be held. As we rolled over the backwoods roads, I rested my head against the window. I was beyond surrendering. In the preceding days, I'd been fasting, eating only fruit and water. As my stomach emptied, so did my mind. I was prepared to allow, to be open to what the medicine would show me.

The air was still, the sky clear. Most of the leaves had fallen from the large trees lining the road. The maze of branches was so deep, it seemed the trees went on forever. My eyes traveled through maze after maze as the car coasted up and down hills and around turns.

The host put us to work as soon as we arrived. We carried blankets and pillows into a circular hut behind the house. We organized firewood into stacks depending on size.

Susanne introduced me to Henry, the man who would tend the fire throughout the ceremony.

"This is Amelia. Her husband, Dave, died in July," Susanne said.

"Amelia. Thank you for sitting with us. Those in mourning are those closest to God. You'll bring gifts to our circle tonight," Henry said as he took both of my hands in his.

I was grateful for the warm and genuine welcome. I was glad to have a place: a place in the ceremony and an acknowledged place dwelling close to God in my grief. I knew I was living connected to the light, and another way of saying that was "close to God."

A couple hours after sunset, about twenty participants took places sitting around the perimeter of the hut. Thomas, a man of Native American descent, led the ceremony. Thomas sat at twelve o'clock, I was at three, and the door out at six. Susanne sat to my left. My travel bottle of Dave sat in my pocket.

Susanne had warned me that Thomas was a serious leader and would conduct a ceremony based on Native American traditions. No one could leave once the ceremony started. I'd be sitting still all night and into the morning, except for one break.

The fire tender, Henry, introduced everyone in the circle, giving each person's name and some background.

When he came to me, Henry smiled and looked in my eyes.

"Amelia's husband, David, passed away this summer. She is mourning. Those who are mourning are those closest to God. Look at Amelia, and you will see God."

I felt light and limitless. I smiled a huge, toothy grin. I was warm and saw golden light oozing from my smile. I hadn't even eaten any peyote yet, and I was giddy and hallucinating. I looked around at the surrounding faces. Many of the other people looked sad and heavy. According to Henry, many were experiencing confusion, loss, and difficult times.

Suddenly, being a thirty-three-year-old widow wasn't so bad. I had God and light pouring into, and back out of, the hole where Dave was missing. I had a role at a sacred gathering. I was there to shine a message.

The peyote was passed clockwise around the circle in two forms: tea and a sludgy goo. When each person received a bowl, he or she set it on the dirt floor and gave thanks before eating or drinking the medicine. A small drum and maraca were also passed clockwise just after the medicine. Some people—like me—passed the instruments on to the next without making a sound, but most used the instruments along with their voices to make music. The rhythmic chants gave me tingles and made me shiver. I could see the air bending and twisting with the tones.

After making music, many people talked. They confessed worries or sorrows or explain what they wanted from the medicine. Thomas sometimes commented or advised.

The fire burned bright orange in the center of the group. Henry added wood and spread the burnt timber out from the ring with a rake. He made mandala-like patterns with the embers.

"If the medicine is too strong," Thomas instructed, "open your eyes and look into the fire."

It worked. When the psychedelic patterns and images playing on the screen of my closed eyelids felt too intense, I'd stare at the fire. The fire would calm my mind, and the effects of the peyote would dwindle. As soon as I closed my eyes or looked around, the medicine would rush back in.

The medicine ceremony was a marathon. We ate and drank that stuff all night. Most everyone vomited at some point. Henry would cover the pile with dirt and rake it into the fire. It never smelled bad or made a mess. I never once felt nauseous.

I mostly felt light: weightless and glowing. I sensed my consciousness inhabiting my body. The flesh didn't feel like me, more like a spacesuit I was resting in. Much of the time, I wasn't in the suit; I was traveling, mingling with colors and lights, and melting into darkness. The darkness wasn't scary; it really didn't feel any different from the light.

At times, I heard myself laughing. The laughter brought me back into the suit and made me aware of the Cheshire grin plastered on my face.

Once, I heard my laughter choursed with Susanne's. I turned to her, and we leaned into one another.

She was laughing with tears in her eyes.

"I miss you, Davey," she said as she stared into my eyes.

I screeched a pterodactyl call and heard Dave's voice—from my mouth—say, "I know."

The tears squirted from Susanne's eyes down her cheeks.

"Davey, Davey, Davey," she cried and sobbed.
I held her. Or the spacesuit did. Or Dave did.

That night, with eyes closed, I saw the brightest, most precise colors. I moved through a seemingly infinite space with no awareness of time. I saw exploding, imploding lights and points and lines that danced into mandalas and fractals.

I didn't have many organized thoughts or words in my mind. I only remember seeking guidance from the medicine about one thing: Jeb. After Thomas announced that the medicine had answers to our most troublesome questions, I thought, "What about Jeb? What's going on with that guy? Is he important?"

The screen on my closed eyelids flashed sky blue. I saw two darker blue fish swimming in the same direction meld together. The sky blue disappeared, and the screen turned orange-red. I saw two dark red birds join together.

This joining didn't give me a love or romantic feeling. It didn't clarify anything.

After three weeks of fucking Jeb, I missed my period. My discharge was weird—a different texture and smell.

The week before Christmas, I went to the Planned Parenthood clinic. The pregnancy test was negative. I had gonorrhea. Wow. So, now I was a thirty-three-year-old widow with a sexually transmitted disease.

I got a full lesson on STDs from the business-as-usual nurse at the clinic. Gonorrhea was easily treated with an antibiotic. I tested negative for the incurable viruses—herpes and HIV—but I would have to be tested again three months from the last day I fucked Jeb.

Her words, "If he had one STD, chances are he had another," would echo in my head until my next appointment in March.

Christmas came. The New Year came. Out-of-town friends were around. The old gang was back together. We went to all the usual spots, eating and drinking, watching live music. All the while, Dave was at once totally present—his being heavy in the snow-wet air, and agonizingly gone—his absence a black hole we all struggled to avoid being sucked into.

I cried every day through the holidays. I screamed: "I want Dave Zagorski! Daaave Zaaagorski!" over and over while I walked down

Lark Street or at the bar inside Bombers. None of my friends tried to silence me.

"I miss him too, Aim," Adam would say.

One night at Bombers, while I carried on, Katie silently held on to me and cried.

I stopped wearing mascara to keep my constantly wet cheeks from being smudged with black.

I stopped doing a lot of things. No yoga. No massage. No acupuncture. No Donna. No bleeding; I hadn't menstruated since early November.

Most mornings, I woke up urgently with the thought "Dave is slipping away!" looping desperately in my head. My thoughts were washing me down a dark, sludgy tunnel.

Dave is slipping away. Dave is slipping away. Dave is slipping away. I'm stuck here.

I felt helpless.

Then, in early January, I had a dream.

In it, I woke to a hand on my back. I turned to see Dave. I was confused: knowing he wasn't supposed to be there but so glad he was. I racked my brain to figure out what was happening. I wondered, "Is he coming home late? Have we been broken up?"

I was just happy to have him there at that moment.

"Where have you been?" I asked.

"I've been crossing over," he answered.

We lay in separate beds, a few feet apart. He reached out to hold my hand. I couldn't get as close as I wanted. Dave comforted me with his words.

I woke up unable to remember what Dave had said, but with a sense of reassurance.

I woke up remembering letting go and remembering choice.

I stayed in bed.

"Let it be," I whispered. "Don't hang on."

I stayed in bed, conscious I was where Dave had laid so many times while I led us through the Phowa. I released Dave to the light. I released myself to the light. Just like that, light flooded back. The Phowa lifted us both.

"Be here now," I thought. "Be love now."

I started my day seeing light for the first time in over a month. It reminded me of the day on my Heart Heal Trip when I spread Dave's ashes in the Colorado Springs stream. That day, I had truly released him for the first time. I had focused on climbing and the landscape and stopped longing for Dave. Then I saw magnificent beauty all around: the sky, the stream, the rocks.

On this January day, when I stepped outside, the brilliant sky took my breath away. As usual, I cried. This time, instead of miserable violins screeching a soundtrack to my pathetic life, I heard the marching beat and steady chanting vocals of Modest Mouse's song "So Much Beauty in Dirt," about seeing the ever present beauty in every aspect of our lives.

I left the house remembering choice. Oh yeah. I could decide how to handle my emotions. I could choose to let go. I could choose to rejoice in the beauty of the world. I could move on.

I could make the choice to let Dave go and do what he needed to do—cross over, go to the light, whatever.

I felt reassured by seeing Dave in my dream. It reminded me I'd see him again. In a place where two beds sit side-by-side. It reminded me he's here, sometimes more than others, passing back and forth. We are separate, but we can meet up now and then.

The next day, my Dalai Lama quote Page-A-Day calendar said: "Your bad mood serves your enemy."

I read it and laughed out loud.

The universe was putting me back on track.

I knew I'd been wallowing and in a bad mood for weeks. I'd been lacking spirit, love, and forward motion. I'd been serving my enemy: negativity.

I wrote in my journal: "This is a new day. Feeling solid about losing Dave again. Knowing death is fine, a light waiting."

I played the Black Keys song I'd been skipping since Jeb came home with me. The steady, forward-driving guitars and drums filled the room. I turned the stereo up to hear the line where the singer offers to be a shepherd, to see the listener through.

I was ready to be seen through.

I thought back over the months after Dave died. I had been cruising along, releasing Dave to the light, when something happened. I crashed.

Where had I gone wrong?

The image of the dark black circle tattoo that covered Jeb's back kept flashing in my head. I had mistaken the tattoo as a moon when I first saw it. It was a coiled sleeping snake. Either way, it was dark and alluring. My weird fascination with that nondescript man-boy had started my stagnation. That, and drinking and crying in public night after night. And the peyote ceremony.

I had slipped. Many things nudged me gently over the edge I was probably bound for anyway; no one thing shoved me to it.

As I came out of the murk, I identified the things I was missing. Most of the things were missing because I choose to let them lapse—no bodywork with Ruth or Dan, no mental health check-ins with Donna. One thing I was missing wasn't a choice: my period.

I hadn't had sex since the STD all-clear. Since that visit to the clinic, I hadn't felt right. I had taken two pregnancy tests after the negative one at the clinic. I felt as if I was carrying something. If I wasn't pregnant or infected with disease, what was it?

Recognizing choice charged me. I started doing yoga and pull-ups. I made a weekends-only drinking rule. I called Donna, Dan, and Ruth.

I remembered to balance my approach to control. One thing I prided myself on having learned was that there was no control. We don't get to decide what happens while we ride this giant rock hurtling through outer space! But allowing myself to spin out of control in this dark, desperate way was ridiculous. My complete relinquishment of control was hurting my mind and body. Instead, I could honor my spiritual understanding of the chaotic nature of life on Earth without relinquishing accountability for my choices and self-control.

If I was going to honor Dave by living right, I had to get my shit together.

I went to see Ruth. She treated me with needles and started me on herbs. Two days later, I saw Dan. While he massaged my back, I visualized my bleeding and imagined a bloody, clotted mass leaving me and going to the light. I saw the linked birds and fish from my peyote trip. In my mind's eye, I broke the birds and fish apart, and felt a wash of relief as they floated off separately.

The next day, I saw Ruth again. In a needled-up near-dream state, I visualized blood flowing from me and washing over me. On the drive home, I felt my underwear soak. I didn't care about a mess or stains as I giggled down the highway. At home, I inspected my blood: perfect, red, bright. The darkness was pressed back. I was in light again. I saw Dave in light again. He was released.

In the brutal late fall and holiday season, I had been holding on to Dave, wishing him back to me. I had been lonely, lost, *empty* without him. I had been mourning my husband, my lost life, my naiveté.

Grief sank in and the ego, the me-me-me, took control. I was consumed by wanting Dave back. I wanted him so much that I wished him inside me, growing again. I manifested the darkness into a pretend baby, in a dreamed-up rebirth of Dave via my womb. And the stagnation began.

I didn't plan it or recognize it was happening. The pain that came from losing Dave kept transforming. Old pain became new pain unimaginable.

The last step out of the darkness came when I saw Donna. In her dimly lit one-room office, she taught me the Heart Breath. We sat facing each other, me in an armchair, Donna in an office chair.

Donna told me to breathe deeply and direct my breath to and from my heart. I looked into Donna's eyes, listening to her voice and letting go of my thoughts. She instructed me to visualize energy flowing into my open heart and then back out to the infinite.

With my eyes locked on Donna, the room slipped away. For a few moments, we sat completely still and quiet except for our breathing. Then, she advised me to acknowledge any negative thoughts or feelings. She told me to visualize that negative energy and allow my inhaled breath to carry it to my heart to be absorbed and then released with my exhale.

My eyelids dropped and breath deepened with the gravity of this suggestion. With eyes closed, I saw green light ripple from my chest out to infinite space. With each breath, my heart felt stronger. The green light rippled back to me, warming my chest, and washing away negativity.

The room heated up. The sensation in my chest felt like it did when Dan gave me the massage that helped start my blood flow. With Dan, my heart heated the table, so much release. With Donna, my heart heated the room.

As usual, the light after the dark was brighter. The heart heat was warmer.

The night after I saw Donna, I opened to Chapter 1 of Ram Dass's *Be Love Now*. The chapter title was "The Path of the Heart." Ah. I was traveling the path of the heart. My heart was expanding, mandala-style.

Don't Forget Dave

Dave unconditionally supported my rock climbing lifestyle. He loved it when I traveled and adventured.

Throughout our years together, he often suggested I go climbing in Yosemite. The enormity of Half Dome and El Capitan awed him.

"You need to climb El Cap!" he said more than once. "That's what it's all about."

"Nah," I'd say. "I don't need to climb anything that big."

"I'll go with you. I can belay. Or cook. Yeah, I'll cook for you when you climb. And I'll play guitar back at the campfire," Dave would muse.

"But I don't wanna climb El Cap. It's too scary, too big!" I tried to explain. "I don't need to go that high. I'm not that kind of climber!"

Dave lived a dare-to-be-great lifestyle. He always wanted to go higher, harder, faster. He was a true adventurer.

Even though he wasn't a climber, he admired rocks, climbers, and the sport. He pushed me to go to the extreme as a climber. He wanted me to give climbing—or anything else I loved doing—my all.

When we were together, I was too content to seek Yosemite-big climbing adventures. It wasn't until we split up that I really pushed my climbing limits. Without him as my mate, I had an emptiness that would partially fill when I lost myself to climbing. Even when our relationship had fallen apart, I'd think of Dave when I climbed. He'd been an inspiration and invested companion for so long he intertwined with my passion for rock climbing.

After we learned about Dave's brain disease and were back together, I used climbing to cope with the agony of watching Dave's brain disintegrate and his body die.

When I'm climbing, I'm completely in the moment. It forces meditation, complete focus. Once I decide to climb a route, nothing else matters, everything else slips away. It just happens. Climbing requires physical strength and ability along with skills to set gear placements, follow the route, and keep a calm mind. As I'm climbing, these things come together for me on a subconscious level. My brain functions differently than it does for the rest of life. Things are clear. My mind doesn't wander; my senses are keen. Touch, smell, sound, and sight all register with acute precision. My vision is fine-tuned. I see minute features and details of the rock. Climbing is liberating and exhilarating. It is so much fun. Advancing vertically is so very satisfying. I often feel playful. I always appreciate where I am and what I'm experiencing. I feel grateful for the rock and for my ability to climb it. I find special intimacy with my surroundings. I'm connected to the rock, the air, the land. The absence of thought allows for a primal connection with Earth.

After Dave died, climbing was one of the few things to which I felt committed. Climbing and adventuring in the woods were my first priorities. Nothing else felt as valuable.

Climbing healed my head and heart in ways nothing else could. The extreme mental, emotional, and spiritual elements of climbing allow a whole-being approach to a healthy grief evolution.

I didn't think twice when Sam, someone I had only climbed with twice, invited me to California for a month of climbing in Yosemite. My climbing experience and mind-blowing relationship with Dave brought me to a place where I was psyched to climb hard and big. And I was prepared to take an opportunity when the universe offered it. I was ready to drop everything to run off on a climbing trip that was sure to be one of my life's most challenging and memorable.

Dave loved Yosemite when he visited as a kid. He'd told me this, and his mother reminded me when she heard I'd be visiting this magical place.

I was eager to lay my eyes on the place that was so impressive it stuck in Dave's mind after seeing it just once as a child. I flew into Oakland airport on the first of June, bound for Yosemite on a Friday afternoon in the park's busiest month. Except for the first-come-first-served Camp 4, all park campsites and hotels had booked up months prior.

My friend Katie's sister, Evelyn, worked on the Yosemite trail crew and had welcomed me to crash with her for a night or two. I drove my rental car across the Central Valley in 100-degree heat and followed the highway until it became a windy, narrow road through the mountains. The views became more and more spectacular as I went. I let bits of Dave's ashes fly out the car windows.

Once inside the park, I followed Evelyn's directions to the trail crew cabins. I pushed through the tall wooden fence door marked "Private Residence" as inconspicuously as possible. The path ran between two rickety cabins toward the river and ended at a picnic table. Four people sat there in the sun.

The picturesque setting had me smiling so wide I could barely squeeze out an introduction.

"You must be here for Evelyn," someone said. "She's inside cooking."

One guy offered the bottle of whiskey that was being passed around.

"Welcome," he said as I took an initiation swig.

Adorable, tattooed Evelyn came bouncing out of the cabin to greet me. She introduced me to the trail crew. I went to my car to grab the load of groceries I bought in Oakland and offered snacks to go with the trail crew's beer. Evelyn shared her home-cooked Indian-spiced dinner with me and I settled in with the hard-working, dirty crew. I was right at home!

We spent the evening in the trail crew's back yard. The river rushed by hypnotically and the night sky opened to infinite stars poking through vibrant indigo. We sat around the fire and I listened to the crew's stories of living in the backcountry for weeks at a time. Tales of life with no running water or contact with the outside world started me fantasizing about my own adventures-to-come. I fell asleep fireside, looking at the California stars, listening to Evelyn play guitar and sing Gillian Welch's "Look at Miss Ohio."

I was grateful for my hosts and their warm welcome. I was content in a magic place.

I felt vastly different from how I felt the last time I traveled west after Dave died, on the Heart Heal Trip. This time, I was on a climbing trip because that's what I did. That's who I was. I was a climber, an adventurer. It was satisfying to be something, instead of trying to be different or move on from something.

I wasn't dwelling on being a thirty-something widow. Or a boy-hunter. Or homeless, or in control, or out of control, or any of the other labels I assigned myself over the years Dave was sick, dying, and dead.

Meeting new people wasn't a distraction or part of a healing prescription. I was meeting new people because I was traveling and that's what I loved to do. I was on an adventure.

I was adventuring for adventuring's sake and climbing for climbing's sake.

When Sam met me on the evening of my second day at Yosemite, we set out to climb just a couple hours before dark. We were both energized and excited by the Valley. We were ready to climb every day we had in the park as long as the weather and our bodies permitted.

I won the rock/paper/scissors shoot and set out to lead the first route. One of my climbing mentors back East had recommended it. The steep crack climbing wasn't the style I was used to. Although the grade was well within my usual ability, I struggled from the very start of the route.

I used many excuses for the difficulty I had with the climb: jet lag, laziness, improper diet, wrong pants, and the transit of Venus.

The truth was rock climbing is hard. The first day in an unfamiliar place is usually tough. The Yosemite trip was a big deal. I came to this world-famous, notoriously hard and intimidating climbing destination alone. I was a qualified, independent climber on a long, committed trip away from home. Sam was the catalyst for the Yosemite adventure, but I hardly knew him. There was a chance we wouldn't get along or share climbing goals and plans for the trip. I had to be prepared for a solo adventure, seeking partners and routes if need be.

Sam and I ended up becoming friends. We shared many climbing goals and a willingness to compromise and go along with each other's plans when we didn't see eye-to-eye.

Since guests were not allowed at the trail crew's cabin, Sam and I soon outstayed our welcome. After three nights there, we gave up a day of climbing to wait in line at the famous Camp 4.

Camp 4 is legendary among rock climbers. It was home base to the Stonemasters—the hard climbing, dirtbag Yosemite climbers of the 1970s. Because it didn't take reservations, it was the only place to sleep that wasn't booked. It operated on a first-come-first-served basis. The only way to secure a campsite was to wait in line and hope for the best. Camp 4 allowed each person only seven nights total between the months of May and September.

We went to work in Yosemite Valley: climbing like it was our job. The routes felt awkward, but I was determined to get comfortable on the foreign-feeling rock and learn the climbing style required to succeed. I started my own personal Yosemite Crack Climbing Crash Course. We fell into a schedule of early rising and bedtime. Each day, we explored the Valley seeking longer and harder routes. We aspired to climb on El Capitan—the 3,000 foot granite monolith that towered over the Valley and set the standard for big wall climbing. The tallest section of El Cap would require technical skills far beyond Sam or me, and gear neither of us owned. Our goal was to climb the shortest line, one that ascended the eastern most buttress on the magnificent formation.

We used up our seven-night allowance at Camp 4 just as the temperatures started rising. It would be too hot to climb in the Valley, so we ventured east to the high country of Tuolumne Meadows.

We set up at the campground and headed to Lembert Dome to test the Tuolumne rock. To take it easy and ensure a fun day, we opted for a five-star classic route that had a difficulty rating well within our ability.

We scrambled up forty feet of easy climbing to what we suspected was the base of the route. Sam tentatively wandered over the first pitch of slab, looking for gear and holds that didn't crumble to the touch. He stopped after sixty feet, announcing that he was already at the start of the second pitch.

The plan was for me to link the second and third moderately rated pitches and set Sam up for the final harder pitch. I plunged into my lead, stepping delicately on the sandy, rotten rock. I proceeded slowly, but surely. Route finding was next to impossible. The slab was sprawling; one feature was indistinguishable from the next when compared with the guidebook.

Our certainty about whether we were on the right route was somewhere around "hunch" level. After fifty feet, it seemed likely that I'd worked through the crux—described as a bulge and corner system in the book—of the second pitch.

For the third pitch, I was looking for a crack capped by an overhang. I got to a stance at the start of a crack and plugged in the smallest pieces of protection I had. I tried working into the crack from a few angles before deciding it felt harder than the supposed 5.8 rating.

My lack of confidence about whether I was on the correct line made me hesitant to climb higher. I added a larger, more secure piece of gear to a horizontal crack to my right to turn my marginal gear into an anchor.

Sam followed the pitch, muttering about poor guidebook instructions, crumbling slab rock, and impossible route finding. He liked the look of the crack fifteen feet to the right of where I had stopped. He traversed over to the easier-looking crack and walked up it without hesitation.

We agreed that the crack I attempted looked harder than 5.8, but we both felt that what Sam led was easier than 5.8. So, maybe we weren't on the route. That uncertainty combined with the dirty rock and the setting sun made us decide to quit for the evening.

We walked off the slab. Sam confidently—even happily—led the way. I followed reluctantly. We traversed the low angle slab at the path of least resistance, but I still felt as if I could topple head-over-heels at any moment.

"Oooh, this is scary. This is dangerous," I said, trying not to whine.

"If you fall, you aren't gonna die. You probably won't even get hurt. You'll just slide to the bottom," Sam tried to reassure me. "Anyway, you won't fall."

When Sam said I wasn't going to die, it made me realize I didn't *want* to die. It was two years after Dave's death, and I was happy to be alive. In the years following his death, I wasn't suicidal. Instead, I simply thought that dying would be OK, a release from Earth suffering and a chance to connect to the light.

We made it down and back to camp for early bed, our first-day-in-a-new-area fiascoes behind us. We settled in for a few days of climbing in Tuolumne Meadows. We enjoyed the change of scenery and lower temperatures, but we couldn't quiet the sound of El Cap calling to us.

After our last day of climbing at Tuolumne, we drove back to the Valley as it was getting dark. We knew we'd exhausted our stay at the only legal camping spot, so we waited until dark and inconspicuously wandered into the thin woods near the base of El Cap to sleep.

The next day, we woke up early and set out to climb El Capitan—the notorious landmark that Dave had always chided me for not aspiring to climb. El Cap is a qualifier among all serious climbers, but it was more important Dave thought it was the ultimate climbing achievement.

El Cap's 3,000-foot main face dwarfed the 1,200-foot route we aimed for on the monolith's lowest side. The East Buttress had an easy rating by the wall's standards. That we'd be ascending El Cap via the shortest, easiest route didn't ease my jittery anticipation. It would push my limits; it would be scary and hard.

The day before, Sam refused to rock/paper/scissors battle me to determine who would lead the first pitch. Throughout our trip, I had uncanny good luck and almost always won the shoot. Sam decided his luck might be stronger in a coin toss. We agreed the winner of the coin toss would lead the first pitch on El Cap. As fate would have it, I won.

I wasn't feeling like a winner as I stood below the chimney start of the climb. It looked burly and awkward. My chimney skills were even weaker than my crack skills. That day, my Yosemite Crack Climbing Crash Course expanded: I was to become a chimney climber, too.

I felt calm and confident as I maneuvered over and through the rock's large, ominous features. Maybe I didn't sound as good as I felt. Sam said that I made noises that sounded like I was giving birth to a whale as I wedged into and out of the most strenuous part of the chimney. Once out, I was rewarded with a super fun, steep finger crack.

Sam led the second pitch, dancing up the face and a shallow groove. He did great and should've been pleased, so I didn't understand why I heard him swearing and moaning as I followed the pitch.

When I arrived on the ledge, Sam was red-faced and scowling.

"Here! Take the gear! Go, go! We gotta get outta here!" he growled.

The sandy ledge was an anthill. Ants were waging war on Sam, covering his legs and sneaking under his clothes. They assaulted Sam with such single-mindedness they didn't bother me as I racked up for the next pitch.

I took off as quickly as I could. After the first fifty-five feet of easy scrambling, I searched for what I'd read in the guidebook description the evening before. I couldn't find the arête with pitons. The wall's many features were hard to read. I paced around the ledge looking for the best way up.

"You gotta climb!" Sam ordered when I asked for clarification about the route. "C'mon, I'm *dying* down here!"

In the interest of saving my partner's life, I plowed forward onto what looked like the cleanest line, a vertical finger and hand crack. It was safe because it took good gear, and I had Sam's life to consider, so I ignored that it felt harder than 5.6.

After the crack, some fun face-climbing led to a bolt anchor. This was the top of the pitch 3 and 4 link-up. Pitch 5 was so easy it barely qualified as technical rock climbing, so when the entire rope length stretched between us, Sam climbed too.

The simul climbing allowed me to link three easy pitches. We were on our way!

We were psyched to be speeding up the route. But we were gaining on a party of five Korean climbers in front of us.

A guide who was bringing up four amateur climbers two at a time was leading the party. Sometimes the followers were climbing, but sometimes they were using ascenders and etriers—aid gear used to ascend the rope instead of climbing on the rock—to struggle up the pitches. It was a four-rope, gear-juggling mess.

Sam and I made quick work of pitch 6. We tried waiting patiently for the party to advance so I could start my next lead: a link-up of the seventh and eighth pitches. Patience isn't one of our strong suits. Sam communicated through the language barrier, and he got a go-ahead from the party for me to lead, and try to pass the five-person crew.

The pressure to pass was too daunting for me, so I surrendered my lead to Sam.

He walked confidently through pitch 7's exposed flake and crack system and into pitch 8's thin cracks and corner. Pitch 8 was cluttered with ropes and non-English speaking novice climbers, but Sam pushed through to the belay ledge.

While Sam wrestled to establish himself at the anchor, I had time to remove my travel bottle of Dave from my chalk bag. I opened the bottle and spilled ashes onto my fingers. I raised my hand so that the wind blew the bits of Dave away.

"I'm here, Davey," I said out loud. "I'm climbing El Cap for you."

Instead of closing my eyes to chant, as was my routine when scattering Dave's ashes, I kept them open and drank in the enormity of the rock beneath me. I was high enough over the steep, featured rock that I couldn't see the ground below me. When I looked west over the expansive main wall, I couldn't see the other side. It was as if I was on an infinitely large piece of rock. Like the early world explorers, I wondered if there was an edge to the Earth, or did it go on forever?

"Amelia! You're on belay! You can climb!" Sam's shout interrupted my daydream.

As I followed the line, I went from feeling super psyched to overwhelmed by the views and exposure. I was getting more and more tired and exhilarated the higher I went.

As my fear grew, my mind wandered. Instead of staying focused on climbing, I felt a wash of sorrow. I knew I'd never have had the guts to climb El Cap when Dave was alive. If Dave was alive, if his illness hadn't derailed my life, I never would have traveled to Yosemite.

I sobbed as I climbed. The magnitude of losing Dave was as heavy as the enormous rock I was ascending. I was devastated. I felt infinitesimal.

In my raw state, Dave was suddenly present. I could see him and hear him. My spinning head slowed to a stop and I felt grounded. The paradoxical mystery of the human experience blanketed me. I felt in equal parts the agony of losing Dave and the joy of finding Yosemite. I felt surrender and power at once. The infinite emptiness I felt without Dave on Planet Earth filled with the enormity of the rock, the Earth, the universe. I saw the truly colossal energy that bound the living and dead, the earth and sky, feelings of grief and love. All those things felt interchangeable.

With my heartache eased and mind stilled, the wonder of my new life—one with opportunities to climb El Cap and travel and dwell in magical Yosemite—made me feel buoyant.

By the time I reached Sam at the hanging belay, I was still crying, but not just because of sadness and fear. I was also shedding tears of joy and peace.

At the anchor, after Sam calmed me down and got me focused on overtaking the party above, I laughed at my meltdown.

"I'm a *Gunks* climber. I never said I was a Stonemaster," I said as I sniffed away the last of my tears. "I want to start watching more TV."

The easy ninth pitch lulled me back to a state of relaxation and enjoyment.

At the belay ledge, I squeezed in among the brightly outfitted tourists.

Sam set off into the mess of ropes and climbers to lead the "mental crux" on the tenth pitch. The pitch included a wild traverse to a steep, wickedly exposed face. Sam loved the climbing. His big smile shone bright through a blue sky frame.

I linked the last two easier pitches and finally passed the leader of the party that had been in front of us. I was languid and wandering, enjoying the scenery until a boom of faraway thunder gave me a rocket boost. Afternoon storm clouds lurked in the distance.

At the top out, Sam and I enjoyed turkey jerky and chocolate before starting the descent. The climber's trail was easy to find. It wandered down third and fourth class scrambles and switchback trail for a while.

When the terrain became too steep to downclimb, we found fixed ropes to rappel. We descended 600 feet using three sets of these resident ropes. From there, a casual trail wandered to the Valley floor. We caught sight of the road just as it started to rain.

On one of our last days in Yosemite, Sam and I drove out of the Valley, to climb a granite dome across the road from the postcard-perfect bright blue Tenaya Lake. We parked next to the lake and sorted through our mess of gear and ropes. In the process of organizing, I set the bottle holding Dave's ashes on the car roof.

That bottle had been traveling with me since the Heart Heal Trip. I'd scattered Dave in places we enjoyed together (like the Adirondacks and Montreal), places I know Dave loved (like Nashville and Kansas City), and places that feel special to me (like Portland and Yosemite).

Bringing Dave's ashes with me on adventures had been a way for me to heal and to honor Dave. Two weeks after accepting Sam's invitation to Yosemite, I'd packed my camping and climbing gear along with my travel bottle of Dave, and hopped on a plane to California.

In California, the bottle was a fixture. It was sure to be in my pack along with my climbing shoes, gear, rope, and harness. So, over the weeks of climbing together in Yosemite, Sam got used to the bottle of Dave. He listened to plenty of Dave stories, probably learning more about him than about me as we got acquainted. In the parking area by Tenaya Lake, after we packed our gear, I turned from the car as I hoisted my pack on my back.

"Don't forget Dave," Sam said as he nodded to the bottle sitting on the car roof.

Sam's casual reminder was so endearing. He said Dave's name with ease and familiarity. Even for someone who didn't know him, Dave is impossible to forget.

For me, there's no doubt I will always know and remember Dave. Dave *is*, as God, Buddha, the Force is, as the universe is, as I am. As we all are.

I often think about the mystery of how Dave kept his essential Daveness right up to the end, even though the disease had destroyed most of his brain. The doctor who diagnosed him said it was a miracle he was still functioning at all—and that was a year before his death.

In that year, he didn't slow down on living. He seemed to enjoy life even more. He captivated people even more. He went on grinning his big shiny grin, and laughing his huge trademark laugh, and making us all laugh.

That's how I know we aren't just our brain. Dave was still here even when his brain was gone. We aren't just our body. We aren't even just our heart, although we feel so much through it. There's something else—something in us greater than all these things. Something shines through, keeps rocking on. Call it spirit, or a soul, or anything you like, but it's undeniable.

I'd sensed this, seen bits and pieces of the truth at the edge of my awareness, but now I know for sure. That certainty, that faith, has directed my life.

From early times in my life, like when my mom held me and fought with my dad in front of the open refrigerator door, I practiced acceptance. With Donna's influence during the last years of Dave's life, I refined this approach to life's suffering by learning to allow.

In the years since Dave died, I know this acceptance and allowance has opened me to receive all kinds of soul-level messages and cosmic truths. The Sogyal Rinpoche quote that rang true and comforted me while Dave was dying, "Death can be very inspiring," applied to the after death time, too.

The time after my mom died was one of the most profound times of my life. I inherited a wisdom about the inevitability of death. At first, I thought the sadness I was feeling would suffocate me in my sleep, and like my young mother, I would die. After months passed with nights spent lying in bed fantasizing my death, feeling my heart stopping as hers did, I understood my life was her connection to Earth and her death was my connection to the other side. We were the same; we were one.

Looking back now, I realize I've always had an innate comprehension of love in my life, and a knowledge that death and love have always existed intimately close to one another.

When I was in fourth or fifth grade, I had a dream in which I found the corpse of a beautiful young boy in my bedroom closet. In my dream, I felt the most complete, gigantic love for that dead boy. Waking up, as a kid, I felt grief.

"I'm too young to have already met and lost my greatest love," my ten-year-old self thought after waking from that profound dream. With that thought came a larger awareness. I was comforted because I had felt that true, deep love—unconditional love. I knew the love was a gift so great it transcended and overshadowed the sadness of death.

Has every moment in my life been preparing me for losing Dave? Has this brick-by-brick building of my faith brought me to a state of being that allows me to see that losing Dave to death deepened our love and brought him closer, made him a part of me?

Maybe he was a part of me before I was born. Maybe we planned this life. Maybe there was no becoming, only an unfolding.

I lost Dave so many times: to breakup, to mental illness, to brain disease, to death. Each time I lost him, my heart broke open a little wider, until it finally broke so wide open it exploded in the brightest flash of light and blinded me with love. Love taught me truth and gave me faith.

Love is why I chased after and stood by Dave, and love is why I held his head as he dissolved into light. Love blinded me to pain and doubt and ego at the times when those things almost destroyed me. Love is why I'm grateful to be on Planet Earth and why I'm connected to the light.

Acknowledgments

Thank you to my Auntie Rae Whalen, for being the single most powerful creative influence in my life. When other aunties may have been playing dolls with their six-year-old nieces, Rae was giving me writing assignments and cassette tapes of music she thought I should know about. I've admired her art and writing from the very beginning of my life. Without her, this book would not exist. She held me to it when I off-handedly suggested I should write a book about my experiences. She read my journals and helped me read my own mind to find material and create the basis for this work.

Thank you to the early readers of rough drafts and supporters of my writing, especially Tara Alcantara, Lesley Newman, Charlotte Boettcher, Andrew Chisholm, Angel Steadman, Jennifer Schittino, Diane Dumouchel, Claire Grasmeyer, James Avrill, Nick Weinberg, Lia Ditton, Renata Stirling, Liz McPherson, and Andy Gibbs.

Thank you to Teresa Hackett for her invaluable editing support and advice.

Thank you to Ambos Books for supporting my work and polishing my manuscript.

Thank you to my Launch Team for selflessly giving your time and valuable input. It was inspiring to connect with each of you.

Thank you to every single person who touched Dave's and my life. Without you, things wouldn't have happened in the perfect the way they did. Together, we all created this story. Special thanks to Frank Gutta, Eve Grasmeyer, Heather Thompson, Chris Schorb, Adam Donnelly, Michael Murphy, Dave Wahl, Dan Wahl, Jeremy Lee, Jay Alvaro, Mike Miletech, Katie Garretson, Sheila Wahl, Kathy Lemon, Donna Schoss, Jess Moriarity, Miriam Whalen, Fay Rohrer, Jennifer Whalen, Patti Leggiero, John Whalen, Mary Fitzgerald, Denise Fitzgerald, Layne Zagorski, Beverly Zagorski, Rich Zagorski, Rick Zagorski, Scott Blais, Ken Helm, Kathleen Helm, Julie Byron, Stephanie Walser, Greg Borucki, Chrissy Kennedy, Tracey Tennity, Shiho Yamamoto, Anna Koteff, Lisa Talma, Kristen Borkowski, and Dana Minuta.